THE TOKEN ECONOMY

THE CENTURY PSYCHOLOGY SERIES

Richard M. Elliott, Kenneth MacCorquodale,
Gardner Lindzey, and Kenneth E. Clark,
Editors

Teodoro Ayllon

Nathan Azrin
Anna State Hospital

THE TOKEN ECONOMY

A Motivational System for Therapy and Rehabilitation

New York

Appleton - Century - Crofts
Division of Meredith Corporation

669-2

Library of Congress Card Number: 69-12160

PRINTED IN THE UNITED STATES OF AMERICA
E 04310

Preface

This book is addressed to practitioners who deal with behavioral problems in an institutional setting, such as nurses, recreational therapists, vocational therapists, rehabilitation counselors, ward supervisors, cottage mothers, teachers of the retarded, special education teachers, psychiatrists, social workers, applied psychologists, and applied sociologists. The book assumes no background in psychology.

The names of the patients discussed in this book have been changed to conceal their identity.

There are a number of people to whom we would like to express our appreciation. First, we would like to thank Dr. P. Bailey, formerly Director of Research for the State of Illinois, Department of Mental Health, for his assistance in the conception of this work and his encouragement throughout its duration. Dr. R. C. Steck, Superintendent at Anna State Hospital, provided the administrative arrangements and the encouragement under which the program could be conducted. We were privileged to have his constant support throughout our project. We are also indebted to Dr. I. Pavkovic, who served as an interim Superintendent, during part of our project. Countless individuals at Anna State Hospital also contributed to our work. Because of space limitations we can make special mention of only a few: Mr. Isaacs, who offered expert advice on the daily administration of a hospital unit; Chaplain Otto, for his invaluable contribution to our study of religious services; Mr. Cain of the Dietary Department, who offered his cooperation and that of his staff for the conduct of studies associated with his department; Mr. Wynn, whose cooperation made possible the use of the hospital laundry.

Much of the credit for this work goes to the 45 attendants who participated at different times in the work described in this book. We are particularly grateful to Mrs. Dorothy McClelland, R.N., who gave much of her time and talent to our project. She not only instructed attendants in the conduct of each procedure but also assisted in the supervision of the procedures as conducted by the attendants. We also want to express our appreciation to Mrs. Margaret White, who started initially as an attendant, later worked as a laboratory assistant, and finally became data analyst for the project. Many were the times when she was called upon to lend a hand in one of her various roles, and she did so with great efficiency.

At different stages of the project we were fortunate to have the professional advice and suggestions of Dr. Goldiamond, Dr. Dylrud, Dr. O. Lindsley, Dr. C. Ferster, Dr. J. P. Brady, and Dr. S. Rosenzweig.

John McHale and Maurie Ayllon gave many suggestions and much needed encouragement in the initial stages and during the more difficult stages of writing. Various parts of the first draft were read by Dr. J. Henderson, Leonard Feingold, Alice Harmon, and Floyd O'Brien. Jay Powell, Ron Bittle, Judy Houseman, and Gladys Stark compiled the bibliography and assisted in the general preparation of the manuscript. Dr. Hake, Dr. Hutchinson, Dr. Miller, and Dr. Rubin of the staff of the Behavior Research Laboratory at Anna State Hospital gave advice at various stages of the research program. We also wish to thank our editor, Prof. K. MacCorquodale.

This investigation was supported by the Psychiatric Training and Research Fund of the State of Illinois, the Mental Health Fund of the State of Illinois Department of Mental Health, and NIMH Grant 4926.

T. Ayllon *
N. Azrin

* Currently Professor of Psychology, Georgia State College, Atlanta, Ga.

Contents

First they tell you you're wrong, and they can prove it. Then they tell you you're right, but it's not important. Then they tell you it's important, but they've known it for years.

Charles F. Kettering

CHAPTER 1

Introduction

THE MENTAL HOSPITAL AS AN APPLIED LABORATORY

A state mental hospital is a severe testing ground for any theory of human behavior. Almost every conceivable behavioral difficulty can be seen there, often in its most extreme form. Senile disorders, neurological disorders, adolescent problems, employment problems, sexual difficulties, addiction, alcoholism, general disculturation, intellectual retardation, and neuroticism converge and interact in one community. To gaze upon this multiplicity of disorders and problems is to be overwhelmed by a sense of hopelessness and helplessness. Any simple answer that one might consider for the problems of one patient seems irrelevant for other patients. Theories of human behavior which have seemed so relevant in treating neurotics, such as psychoanalysis and nondirective therapy, flounder when encountering the institutionalized psychotic. It seems that every type of explanation has already been proposed, applied, and found wanting in its general application, including psychotherapy, group dynamics, recreation therapy, vocational therapy, drug therapy, etc. One feels compelled to do something—anything—to assist this forsaken segment of humanity. One might feel that if only the individual could be made to "talk out" his problems, then some cure might be achieved. Yet, a large segment of the patients will not listen, much less respond, to any conversation. How can we achieve therapy by having the patient reach an insight into the meaning of his hallucination when there is not even sufficient motivation for him to listen to the therapist? How can a vocational therapist pry a patient loose from his psychosis by interesting him in learning a vocational skill when it is not even possible to interest the patient in eating to stay alive? Where does one begin in imparting a sense of personal identity and worth to a patient that has been incontinent for 10 years? How can "loss of social feeling" be responsible for the difficulties of the mongoloid girl whose gaze is continuously fastened on the attendants for some small sign of social approval and social attention; rather, her extreme social dependency appears to constitute an additional problem for her.

Various diagnostic categories have been proposed for creating some order out of this chaos, but the illustrative textbook case is rarely to be found. Who is to know whether the mental state of the young lady is that of paranoid persecution as the case history states when the young lady has not yet been heard to utter a word? Consider the gentle old motherly lady who has been classified as a schizophrenic but whose only problem seems to be her refusal to be discharged, a refusal strengthened by her family and society's unwillingness to accept a 70-year-old who has been absent from society for 20 years. Why is she in the hospital? How did she ever get here to begin with? The official records give no indication.

Psychologists and psychiatrists alike have fled from this graveyard of psychological theories, leaving only a small but extremely dedicated group of psychologists and psychiatrists to deal with these problems. The ratio of patients to psychologists or psychiatrists in a mental hospital, where the need is greatest, is often in the order of 1000 to 1. Yet the patient who is well enough to come to a psychologist's office in the middle of an urban metropolis at the appointed time surely does not suffer from the type of problem which disables the mental hospital patient for whom confinement is necessary.

Society has been influenced by the same considerations that affected the psychologists and psychiatrists and has usually placed the mental hospital in a geographically remote and inaccessible place where it need not be confronted with a problem with which it cannot cope. State mental hospitals are usually located at a great distance from any metropolitan area in much the same way, and probably for the same reason, as are prisons. The psychologist or psychiatrist who is sufficiently dedicated to attempt to deal with the disorders of mental hospital patients suffers, then, from the additional sacrifice that he must himself remain geographically and culturally isolated while doing so.

Due to the scarcity of psychologists and psychiatrists, those who are in the hospital are often unable to devote any of their time to problems of treatment. Instead, they are often caught up in the administrative urgencies of the hospitals, the discharge of which leaves little time to practice the therapeutic and research skills in which they were trained. Because the isolated clinician can devote only a small part of his time to therapeutic and research endeavors, he usually selects those problems and patients that will derive the greatest benefit. The most commonly treated and studied patients in the mental hospital are likely to be those who have already had some skill in a vocation, are educable, are under 45 years of age, have an intact family situation to which they may be returned, communicate readily and coherently, and have no obvious neurological or physical debility as a corollary of their behavioral disorder.

The great majority of patients still remain untreated. Recent statistics indicate that the median age of state mental hospital patients is approximately 65 years. This means that half of all patients in state mental hospitals are at such an advanced age that vocational opportunities are almost totally lacking and family ties have usually been broken. Even if there were nothing wrong with them, it would be difficult to discharge them into the outside world, since the outside world has no place for them. The longer these patients remain in the mental hospital, the more severe their behavioral problems seem to grow. One currently hears the phrases "hospitalism" and "institutionalization," which describe a state of apathy and lack of motivation that is acquired by a stay at a mental hospital. The hospital community is usually geared to providing the biological necessities of life, and perhaps some minimal level of recreational opportunities, but the overall relationship is a parasitic dependency in which the patient need not function in order to obtain most, if not all, of the activities or privileges that might still be of interest to him.

The large mental hospital is a testing ground for psychological practices as well as theories. Any general procedure that is found to be effective with the great range of problems encountered in a mental hospital will probably find great applicability in many different disciplines concerned with human behavior. A method of controlling the aggressive outburst of a destructive patient would seem to have great relevance for the control of criminal behavior outside of the hospital. Similarly, a procedure that could motivate a vegetative psychotic who has been hospitalized for 20 years might be appropriate for motivating a high school dropout to return to school. A procedure that motivated a withdrawn patient to seek out the company of other patients will probably have some relevance in building social habits in school children. A course of action which enabled a congenitally retarded child to function in some fashion should surely have some message for developing improved methods of teaching a normal child the multiplication table in a more efficient manner. From this point of view, the mental hospital provides a challenging opportunity to devise totally new psychological and educational procedures in spite of the adversities that such an environment seems to present.

OBJECTIVES AND SCOPE OF THE RESEARCH PROGRAM

The basic objective of the research program which this book describes was to design a motivating environment based upon reinforcement theory, specifically operant reinforcement theory. The central feature of operant reinforcement theory is that behavior is greatly influenced by the changes that the behavior produced in the environment. We can designate these environmental changes that result from a response as the consequence of the response. When a favorable consequence results from a behavior, this is called positive reinforcement. The effect of this favorable consequence is that the behavior increases. Many specific relationships have been discovered regarding the principle of positive reinforcement, including statements about the immediacy of the reinforcement, the amount of the reinforcement, the importance of the response requirement, etc. The principle of positive reinforcement tells us that if we wish to increase some desired behavior, then favorable consequences should be arranged for that behavior. Conversely, the principle states that if one does not arrange favorable consequences for a behavior, then that behavior will be relatively infrequent. If a behavior has been producing favorable consequences, and then these consequences are discontinued, the process is called extinction. The Law of Extinction states that a previously reinforced response will decrease in frequency if the reinforcer is no longer produced by the response. Studies of extinction reveal that the decrease in frequency of the response will depend on how long it has been since the behavior has been reinforced. A behavior for which a favorable consequence has only recently been discontinued will have decreased only slightly in frequency. A behavior for which the favorable consequence has been discontinued for a long period of time will have decreased greatly. Similarly, the effectiveness of a reinforcing event depends on the amount of time for which the reinforcer was used. If a reinforcer has been arranged for a response on only one or two occasions, there will be relatively little increase in the frequency of the response; but if the favorable consequence has been arranged continuously, then a substantial increase will occur in the rate of the response.

Any attempt to influence behavior can be considered as involving two aspects: one of which is to increase desired behavior; the other, to decrease undesired behavior. It can be seen that the Laws of Reinforcement and Extinction provide a method of achieving both of these objectives. Whenever one desires to increase the frequency of a desired behavior, the Law of Reinforcement provides a concrete procedure for doing so, just as the Law of Extinction provides a concrete procedure for producing a decrease in an undesired behavior. The overall objective of this program was, then, to design a motivating environment in which the two principles of reinforcement and extinction would operate at maximum effectiveness in producing the desired behaviors and eliminating the undesired ones.

The Laws of Reinforcement and Extinction have been verified in their broad outlines by almost every major learning theorist. Guthrie (1935) and Spence (1956) are two theorists that have stressed the contiguity aspect; Hull (1943) and Miller (1951), the drive reduction aspect; Mowrer (1950), contiguity as well as drive; Skinner (1938), the functional aspect of the behavior; and Thorndike (1935), the confirmatory aspect of stimulus-response relationships. In spite of these differences in emphasis, all of these theorists have confirmed the above statements regarding the behavioral effects of reinforcement and extinction. The generality of the Laws of Reinforcement and Extinction has been shown with many different types of animals, with different types of animal behavior, and with simple human behavior, for example, the verbal learning of Thorndike (1931) and Greenspoon (1955), as well as the nonverbal learning of simple motor responses by investigators such as Lindsley (1956), Bijou and Orlando (1961), and Long et al. (1958).

The knowledge that the theory of reinforcement has extensive experimental support is in itself of little value in suggesting specific means of designing a complex motivating environment that will achieve treatment and education. Virtually all studies of reinforcement theory have used very simple responses, such as having a person press a button or call out a word. Even clinical applications have selected responses that are simple ones, such as thumbsucking or a nervous tic. How can the theory of reinforcement be used to modify the complex varieties of behavior that one desires in a therapeutic or educational program? The same problem exists in regard to the use of reinforcers in designing a motivating environment. The reinforcers used in past reinforcement studies of humans have been extremely simple and usually tangible items such as cigarettes or candy. A motivating environment that intends using many of the complex human motivations can scarcely restrict itself to such simple tangible items. The previous research also provides little information on how to use reinforcement theory in a complex and fairly naturalistic environment. Most of the studies of reinforcement theory have taken place in laboratory situations or in a room where the individual has been isolated from others. Also, how should the responses be recorded and how should the reinforcers be delivered? In previous applications of reinforcement theory the simplicity of the response has permitted the use of automatic recording devices to record the frequency of the behavior. Yet, the complexity of the behavior being studied in a total motivating environment such as a hospital ward would seem to preclude the use of many automatic recording devices. Similarly, even though previous studies have used automatic devices to deliver the reinforcers, the complexity of reinforcers in a total motivating environment precludes the use of automatic devices for delivering the reinforcers. It is small wonder that reinforcement theory has not previously been applied to the design of complex human motivating environments.

Reinforcement theory uses terms such as response, behavior, reinforcer, and extinction which seem to have obvious theoretical relevance to problems of human behavior. But how does one translate each of these terms in such a way that the reinforcement procedure can be applied to complex human behaviors and complex human reinforcers? The reader will understand the lack of assurance that the authors felt when we initially embarked on our objective of designing a motivating environment that had therapeutic objectives and would be capable of dealing with the myriad aspects of behavior disorder encountered in a mental hospital.

The explanations of behavior provided by Freud in terms of the ego, superego, and id are familiar to all of us, as are the more specific explanations regarding the defense mechanisms of identification, sublimation, projection, and reaction-formation. Reinforcement is conspicuously absent as a central concept. Nor is the principle of reinforcement given any great weight in the self-actualization explanation of Rogers (1951), the cognitive dissonance explanations by Festinger (1957), the need-for-achievement motives of McClelland et al. (1953), the positive and negative valences of Lewin's (1935) field theory, or the many other explanations in terms of personality traits, attitudes, values, and social status. It seems, then, that most psychological theories of human behavior attach little importance to reinforcement as a major cause of complex behavior. Rewards, to be sure, are recognized in most of these theories as a possible factor, but they are not entitled to the importance attributed to the other factors listed above. A reasonable conclusion might be that a motivating environment based on reinforcement would exert little or no effect on complex human behavior.

The only conclusive way of determining whether the Laws of Reinforcement and Extinction can be used as the basis of designing a complex motivating environment is, of course, to try it. Before we could attempt it, however, procedures had to be developed to answer such questions as the following:

How does one go about selecting and specifying the behaviors that are to be dealt with in a motivating environment? What behaviors should one deal with? Is it possible to simultaneously deal with complex behaviors and yet have some objective and standardized way of measuring them? How should the choice of the behavior that one elects to deal with in the motivating environment be governed by factors outside of the motivating environment?

How does one go about discovering what is reinforcing for a large group of people, knowing in advance that every individual differs in his preferences from every other individual and differs with respect to his own preferences at different times? Also, how can one discover reinforcers for individuals who are nonverbal or who will not for some other reason verbalize their preferences?

Given that one has discovered some reinforcers, how can one maximize the effectiveness of the reinforcer? How does one avoid problems of satiation? How does one avoid problems of reinforcers competing with each other? How does the individual know that the reinforcer is available?

How can one arrange for reinforcers to follow a response when immediacy of the reinforcer delivery is impracticable in an overall behavioral program?

How can one record whether a behavior has been performed properly without going through the impracticable procedure of continuously observing the patient? How should the responsibilities be divided up for the staff as well as for the patients? What kinds of procedures can be developed to assure the delivery of reinforcers without using automatic devices?

How does one teach a new behavior that was not previously in existence?

Reinforcement theory has one great advantage over other types of theories of human behavior as a model for answering the above questions. The very definition of a reinforcer involves environmental change. It follows, therefore, that an application of reinforcement theory will stress environmental events that can be directly measured and controlled. In contrast, other theories of behavior which rely on perceptions and cognitions as the primary explanations must attempt to control these perceptions and cognitions if they wish to modify behavior. The emphasis on these inner mental states does not readily suggest what types of environmental changes should be made.

The authors' combined experience imparted a feeling of general competence in applying the principles of reinforcement to new problems but certainly not to this global task of creating a total environment that would be conducive to rehabilitation and treatment. We had conducted many experiments with lower animals and, more to the point, with humans (see "References"). Our human work had included artificial laboratory types of situation in which we studied children, adults, normals, and psychotics, but usually under laboratory situations. One of us (T.A.) had successfully developed a means of using reinforcement principles to eliminate specific symptomatic behaviors of individual psychotics, such as compulsive behaviors and anorexia. In all of these past endeavors, however, problems that seemed to lend themselves easily to the influence of reinforcement procedures had generally been sought out. Other investigators had used reinforcement procedures to eliminate specific symptoms of psychotics, also; but none of us had yet attempted to design a total environment that would deal with all of the behavioral problems in a mental hospital. The writings of several learning theorists in psychology stated confidently that general reinforcement principles might solve the problems of mental patients, but the specific details as to how these principles would operate were almost totally absent. For the most part, these statements "explained" after the fact why a behavior arose, rather than spelling out in advance what specific procedures one could follow to modify the behavior.

REWARDS IN MENTAL HOSPITALS

What is new about using incentives? The use of incentives in any applied setting is by no means novel. Most educators will state without reservation that they use rewards for appropriate performance wherever and whenever possible. Similarly, in criminology, one can point to the use of paroles as examples of the general philosophy of rewarding appropriate performance. It would be very rare to find a mother who would not declare enthusiastically that she relies on rewards. So, too, industry provides many incentives for employees. There seems, then, to be agreement that rewards are desirable and are an effective method of modifying human behavior.

Yet, we shall see that in spite of this agreement that rewards are desirable and effective, in practice rewards are usually intuitive, incidental, infrequent, often trivial, unstandardized, and given with little regard to their relationship to the rewarded performance.

Gross miscalculations are often made regarding what it is that is rewarding for mental patients. It is commonly assumed, for example, that mental patients are unhappy about being shut off from the world and would be delighted if only some rational representative from the outside would come in and talk to them. One recent expression of this philosophy has been the intensive and conscious effort to encourage volunteers to visit mental hospitals. Yet, the reaction of patients to a visitor is often one of avoidance, escape, or utter indifference. The patients will often hide, turn away, or move to another part of the ward. Another common conception of what is rewarding for mental patients is the assumption that patients are delighted to have visits from their old friends and relatives. Common observation of hospital patients reveals, however, that the converse is more likely to be true. Frequently a patient will refuse to accept a visit from a member of his immediate family, even a husband or wife who has made a special trip of several hundred miles for the express purpose of that visit. Several days or even weeks of coaxing and persuasion are often necessary to convince the patient that the visit should be permitted to occur without "a scene."

Another example is that patients would prefer to be outside the ward or hospital if only regulations would permit them to be so. In particular, the so-called "locked-ward" is looked upon with extreme disfavor as preventing patients from leaving the hospital or even the ward. Many hospitals, indeed, have prided themselves on the fact that the gates surrounding the hospital have been left open, resulting in no mass exit by patients. The failure of the patients to leave the hospital suggests that it was a misconception to believe that exit from it was desired. Similarly, when locked wards are suddenly unlocked, the general experience is that few patients avail themselves of the opportunity to visit other parts of the hospital. Indeed, many patients refuse to leave even when the attendants insist upon their doing so.

Still another manifestation of the common failure to ascertain correctly what is rewarding for the patient is the compulsory attendance at recreational functions. Mental hospitals commonly schedule dances, plays, group dances, etc. under the assumption that these are rewarding. Instead, it is often necessary to employ recreational therapists whose time is chiefly spent in persuading patients to participate.

Does the attendant's personality influence unduly? In spite of the occasional success in the use of the above rewards with some patients, several factors seem to be operating that make the delivery of these rewards at best a casual enterprise. One factor is the personality of the attendant, who is usually the central mediator of rewards in a mental hospital ward. Some attendants seem to be intrinsically more disposed to reward. For example, one attendant will spend most of her time, almost to the exclusion of other activities, walking about and talking to the patients, noting improvement or changes in their behavior and commenting on them enthusiastically. Other attendants are concerned almost entirely with the custodial aspects of the ward and attend to a patient only when his behavior disrupts the ward. The same types of problems seem to occur with respect to transient changes in the attendants' behavior, or one might say, their moods. Even an attendant who customarily is friendly, attentive, and continually interacting with patients will, at times, act quite the opposite. Fellow employees are heard to comment on such an occasion, "She's in a bad mood today," or "She's had trouble at home." Whatever the reason might be, it is not possible to solve the problem of inconsistency of reinforcement by pre-selection of certain personality types as attendants. The normally reticent attendant will sometimes be observed to be enthusiastic, just as the normally friendly attendant is found to be sometimes reticent.

The way an attendant feels about a given patient will determine the likelihood of his rewarding the patient. Patients who are verbal or who are the same age, of the same religious background, or from the same town as the attendant are often selected as favorites. Conversely, a patient who is reticent, who speaks poorly or with an accent, who is of an unusual or unpopular race or religion, who dresses poorly, who is untidy with respect to toilet habits, who occasionally assaults an attendant, who complains a good deal, who curses frequently, etc. is often disliked by the majority of attendants or by a particular attendant.

The factors of personality difference, mood, like and dislike of specific patients are not unique to attendants, of course. One can easily excuse any laxity in administering rewards due to these factors by stating that the attendants are, after all, "only human." But that is just the point: One cannot rely upon the attendant's intentions as a measure of what she is doing. The attendant is too much influenced by predispositions, external events, and behaviors of the patient to be expected to administer rewards in an impartial, objective, and standardized manner. Nor would we expect anyone else to be capable of doing so without some special method of implementation. They, too, would be "only human."

To what extent can a mental hospital permit the adequate supervision of a reward system? The first problem that becomes evident in watching attendants carry out the instructions of a supervisor is that of scheduling their time. An attendant is usually responsible for several dozen patients. In a state mental hospital, this responsibility often means a ratio of 100 or more patients to one attendant. This ratio precludes an adequate reward procedure in the usual mental hospital situation. For example, suppose the following type of instruction was given to an attendant, "Whenever one of your patients talks normally, that is, not in a psychotic or silly way, praise her, pay attention to her, and be nice to her in every way that you can." To accomplish this objective even with as few as 10 patients, the attendant would have to be capable of being in 10 different places at once. Even if all other aspects of her reward procedure were satisfactory at any given time, she would be performing one-tenth of her designated responsibility. But attendants have considerably more to do than just walk around rewarding and being nice to patients. Their duties involve speaking to the medical staff, speaking to the R.N., answering telephones, supervising clothing, maintaining the sanitary condition of the ward, writing ward reports, escorting patients, attending committee meetings, communicating with the supervisor, informing fellow employees of changes in ward procedure, reporting accidents, talking to relatives, running errands, performing custodial activities, ascertaining the whereabouts of a patient, grooming, bathing, and shaving patients, supervising eating, and myriad other activities that more than occupy a 40-hour week. If, at a given moment, an attendant is asked why she did not attend to a given patient, the most frequent and justified response is "I didn't have time," followed perhaps by an explanatory statement such as "The phone was ringing," or "I heard someone hollering at the other end of the ward," or "I was helping Sally make her bed," or "I was busy talking to the nurse about the missing ash trays," etc.

Is the lack of personnel responsible for the inadequate reward system? The point being made here is not that attendants are remiss in their duty to implement a reward procedure, but rather that even under ideal conditions, the current system of rewarding patients is inadequate. One apparent solution to this problem of competing activities would be to assign one full-time employee to each patient and to relieve that one employee of all responsibility for any administrative and custodial activities on the ward. This is indeed the direction that some mental institutions seem to have taken. The constant cry is for more personnel, the assumption being that the problem will be solved by numbers alone, with no account of what the employees are doing. This rationale is mistaken. Even if one employee were assigned to each patient, the procedure would be inadequate if performed in the usual manner.

What is wrong with the system of rewards in mental hospitals? Assume now that all the factors affecting the reward procedure are ideal: The attendants have been specially selected because they have outgoing personalities; they have a stability of mood that is unaffected by any outside events, have no special likes or dislikes of particular patients, and have been assigned exclusively to work with a given patient. Could a satisfactory reward system then be implemented? The answer is "no." The reason for this categorically negative answer is that rewards in mental hospitals are inherently difficult to implement and next to impossible to record and supervise. These difficulties arise with different types of rewards, whether they be social in nature—such as verbal approval—or material in kind—such as cigarettes.

Verbal types of rewards have special problems of supervision and recording. Consider the specific example in which an attendant stated that she had been giving verbal approval to a patient assigned to her. The attendant was asked, "How often did you reward her this afternoon?" She stated, "Oh, about five times." When asked for how long, she answered with great difficulty, "Oh, for about two minutes, I think; I can't remember exactly." When asked, "How many times did you reward her on Monday?" she answered, "I can't remember, but I think that it was about the same, about a dozen times a day is the way it's been running." The records, however, showed that Monday was that attendant's day off; she wasn't even on the ward. Retrospective reports have little value in recording a reward procedure.

Verbal rewards are obviously difficult to implement or supervise in a standard manner, but what about more tangible rewards? Consider, for example, a case in which an attendant states that she has been allowing patients to go out on a walk whenever they are adequately groomed. An attendant is usually assigned to go out with patients when they do not have an officially approved grounds pass. It would seem, then, that one could obtain some record of whether the patients were indeed given the reward of a walk, considering the ease with which exit from the ward could be recorded. But the memory of the attendant who took the patients out on the walk has, in practice, been found to be extremely deficient in showing which patient went out and which did not, even after a lapse of only a few hours.

The problem also occurs with respect to giving out candy and cigarettes. In spite of the attendant's avowal that the procedure is being followed consistently, the availability of the candy or cigarettes as well as her subjective interpretation of whether it should be handed out at a given time will determine whether the patient actually is offered the item.

It is not sufficient for the attendant to state that she did or did not reward the patient. What is also needed is a record of the type, amount, and duration of the reward. For example, did the attendant give the patient one cigarette or an entire package? Was the verbal approval given for 2 minutes or 30 minutes? Was the extra food a dessert or a steak? Did the movie used as a reward last for 10 minutes or 2 hours? What happened to the use of a walk as the reward when it was raining? Did the patient go out to the hospital dance alone or in the company of other patients?

The general problem here is that there are no schedules set up in advance that specify the amount, duration, number, place, and manner in which the reward is to be given. In addition, there is no record made of the delivery of the reward that would permit the supervisor to determine whether the procedure took place. The reliance is almost totally upon the memory of the attendant with, at most, very infrequent direct observation of the interaction by the supervisor.

A paradox exists, then, with regard to the use of rewards in the mental hospital. The hospital staff will state, without equivocation, that rewards are being continually given for desired behavior and that no problems have occurred in doing so. Yet, observation of the manner in which rewards are dispensed reveals that not only do problems occur but implementation as described is administratively, logically, and temporally impossible. In the absence of any clearly defined schedule of reward and record of its occurrence, no problem in administration will ever be brought to one's attention, since the problem is not subject to scrutiny. There can be no statement of what went wrong when there is no possibility of recording under the usual procedures whether it ever went right.

As a beginning it may be stated that the usual procedure of administering rewards in a mental hospital constitutes a very severe problem.

CHAPTER 2

General Procedure

CHRONOLOGY

We first conceived of the token economy and its use as a motivational system for therapy during the early part of 1961. We formally submitted a proposal to the Illinois Psychiatric Training and Research Fund on June 6, 1961, to determine the feasibility and effectiveness of this hitherto unexplored and untried approach to treatment. We initiated the program in November, 1961, and it has continued up to the time of this writing, a period of about six years. The broad outlines of the method described in the remainder of this book were not developed until the end of 1962. The remaining time was spent in continuously modifying, revising, abandoning, and developing particular portions of the procedure. The problems of psychotics are so serious and pressing that one is very much tempted to publish immediately the results of a procedure that seems to be beneficial. We resisted this temptation for about four years before publishing our first report (Ayllon and Azrin, 1965) in order to develop the procedure and to assure ourselves that it was not of transient effectiveness. This extended period of application prior to publication of the procedure also enabled us to ascertain whether the procedure produced undesirable side effects that might override the benefits obtained. The Appendix of this book contains the experimental report which was published in 1965 in the *Journal of the Experimental Analysis of Behavior*. This report is a highly condensed summary of the motivating environment and is concerned primarily with the experimental evaluation of its overall effectiveness. The report can be read after reading this book, since reference will be made to the relevant sections as necessary.

INTERACTION OF THEORY AND PRACTICE

Organization of this book reflects the general manner in which we developed the motivating environment. Whenever a specific procedure was found to be effective in practice, we attempted to formulate a "general rule" on the basis of previous psychological evidence that would explain why that procedure was effective. The formulation of a general rule usually led to several more procedures that probably never would have occurred to us otherwise. If we were unable to formulate any general rule as to why a specific procedure was effective, then many variations of that procedure were used to determine which aspect of the procedure was continuous. Every rule led to direct application to determine its practical usefulness. Conversely, for every procedure that was found to be useful, we tried to formulate a rule and then to use that rule to generate other procedures that could be evaluated in practice.

It was our objective in devising this motivating environment that it be applicable to other mental hospitals, as well as to other settings that have some rehabilitative or educational objective; a "cookbook" type of description of the specific procedures used in the motivating environment would have little value in environments that differ in the type of individuals and administrative structure encountered. The statement in terms of general rules enabled us, and hopefully will enable our readers, to adapt the general rules to other treatment and learning environments. The amount of attention paid to each of these general rules will not be in agreement with the degree of importance that is often attached to these rules in reinforcement theory. An example of the discrepancy between this applied endeavor and basic reinforcement theory is the small amount of attention given here to intermittent reinforcement or to schedules of reinforcement. Although much is known about schedules of intermittent reinforcement, most of this information appeared to be irrelevant to the practical objective of providing maximum motivation, since nonintermittent reinforcement was found in practice to be most effective. On the other hand, the rules regarding the discovery of reinforcers for a particular population are central to any practical application of reinforcement theory. Consequently, the section on discovery of reinforcers constitutes a major section in this book, reflecting the practical importance of the problem.

PATIENT SELECTION

The patients selected for inclusion in the special ward environment were those who were most resistant to the currently used procedures. Newly admitted patients were deliberately avoided, although one or two were included in order to ascertain the effectiveness of the procedure for such patients. The procedure followed in obtaining all of the patients was to ask the supervisors of the other wards in the hospital what patients they would like to have transferred out of their ward. This simple question resulted in the referral of patients who were often very old or those who were not performing any useful work on their own ward, who were causing problems for the previous ward staff, or who often were not verbal, or if verbal were annoyingly so. The transferred patients were rarely engaged in any type of psychotherapy at the time of transfer, reflecting the staffs' apparent conviction that little more could be done. By almost any standard the patients taken as a group would probably be categorized as least likely to benefit from any type of treatment or to be discharged. The median age was about 50 years or more at different stages of the program; the median number of years of known hospitalization in a mental hospital was about 16. In addition, most had not completed high school and many had not completed grade school; most were from rural communities in which few vocational opportunities were present; some were incontinent, some were assaultive, some were described as vegetative; almost none had any history of performing ward assignments; almost none expressed any desire to leave the hospital; very few had any visitors from either family or friends. The mean number of visits per year per patient was less than two; for most patients the number of visits per year was zero. The appearance of most of the patients was disheveled and unkempt with little regard for personal habits of cleanliness or appearance. Some of the patients had never been heard to utter an intelligible word or sentence and were initially regarded by the attendants as mute. These are the patients that are most often overlooked in any treatment or care procedure and would seem to present the most severe test for any new treatment procedure. In general, the range of behavioral disorders suffered by these patients was so severe that they might well be designated as "back ward" patients. The only reason for excluding patients from the therapeutic ward was if they had some kind of medical disorder that required their periodic confinement in the medical treatment ward of the hospital. We could not bring a total environment to bear on such patients for an extended period of time without fear of interruption by transfer to the hospital medical ward.

Safeguards for the Rights of Patients

A source of serious concern to an investigator of human behavior is the proper respect for the rights, dignity, and health of the individuals who are being studied. This concern is necessarily very great when one studies mental patients in a state hospital, since such patients have usually been committed to the institution by court order. Several procedures were adopted in the motivating environment to guarantee that the dignity of the patients was respected in every way and that there was no infringement of their rights. At the same time equally intensive efforts were made to assure that the patients received the most intensive and effective therapy available. Hospital regulations currently guarantee that all patients are informed of their civil rights. This procedure was followed for the patients studied here.

In addition to formally notifying the patients of their legal rights, the ward procedure incorporated certain practices to guarantee that there would be no inadvertent infringement of these rights, no disrespect to the patients as human beings, and no interference with the therapeutic objectives. First, visits to the ward by outsiders were encouraged so that all of the treatment methods used would be under public scrutiny. Second, the tour of the ward was conducted, as will be described in detail later in this book, by patients themselves, thus guaranteeing that any abridgments of the rights or dignity of the patients could be voiced directly by the patients to a member of the public. Third, referrals to the ward were based on the recommendation by the hospital staff on the previous ward that the new ward treatment would be beneficial for that particular patient. Fourth, all patients had the opportunity to transfer to another ward (some did so), governed by the limitation that the probable therapeutic effect of the transfer would be beneficial to the patient in terms of her treatment objectives. Fifth, all patients were encouraged not only to leave the ward but to be discharged from the hospital. Some of the new procedures developed for producing these discharges are described in the chapter on the prompting-shaping rule. Sixth, the attendants were periodically and formally instructed to report to the supervisor any unintended or accidental infringements of the patients' rights as individuals.

Experimental Design and Individual Treatment

In evaluating the effectiveness of different therapeutic procedures, an experimental design was deliberately chosen that would guarantee that all patients who could benefit from the new procedure would be given it. The present experimental design considered the effect of a given treatment procedure on each patient. This is in contrast with the experimental group versus control group type of experimental design in which those patients in the control group would have been deliberately denied the benefit of a therapeutic procedure because of research considerations. All patients were given the new procedures if they appeared likely on therapeutic grounds to benefit from that procedure. Therefore, it will be seen that for some of the experiments reported in this book only some of the patients were given the treatment procedure. Once a treatment procedure was found to be effective for a given patient, that procedure was maintained for that patient for as long as there were clinical reasons to believe it was effective. It was possible to follow this design since the overall objective of the motivating environment was to produce constructive and useful behaviors.

SELECTION OF WARD STAFF

The method of selecting attendants for the special ward environment was governed by the desire that any method developed should not be dependent upon the unique skills of a particular staff member. To the extent that the motivating environment produced beneficial effects because of the procedures used, then such an environment should be capable of functioning adequately somewhat independently of the specific interests, skills, or attitudes of the ward attendants. A therapeutic environment that required a high level of formal education of the ward staff would necessarily be prohibitive and impractical since such staff does not exist in sufficient numbers at this time. To emphasize the ward procedures rather than highly individualized skills, we required only that the prospective attendants pass the usual examination given by the State of Illinois Personnel Department for mental hospital attendants. The qualifications for this position are the receipt of a high school diploma or its "equivalent," plus a passing score on an examination that consists primarily of verbal and quantitative material such as is usually seen in a general aptitude test. None of the attendants selected had any college training; many did not have a high school diploma. Forty-five different attendants were employed at different times during the six-year period. The standardized nature of the ward procedures was evidenced by the ready adjustment of new attendants when they replaced those who had left. Similarly, one can see that the motivating environment did not depend on the unique personality attributes of the registered nurse who functioned as the ward supervisor, since three different registered nurses served as supervisors at different times. Similarly, the medical supervision of the ward did not seem to require distinctive personality attributes in that 12 different physicians had medical responsibility for the ward at different times. The only personnel that remained constant in the motivating environment were the supervising psychologists. Even they could be absent for periods of a month or more without disruption of the motivating environment once the program had been established. The easy interchangeability of the various personnel allowed a constant check on whether the procedure was indeed standardized.

THE MOTIVATING ENVIRONMENT AS PART OF ANNA STATE HOSPITAL

A major problem in developing new procedures in a large mental hospital is the administrative difficulty in making changes in the established work patterns of the attendant staff. Several features of the total environment at Anna State Hospital enabled us to make these changes readily. Anna State Hospital is the second smallest state mental hospital in Illinois, having a capacity of about 2,000 patients. The hospital has had a tradition of separate departments, with department heads having the authority and responsibility for making innovations, a system strongly approved of by the Superintendent. This innovative spirit in the hospital permitted changes to be made within the specific ward used for the motivating environment without requiring concurrent institution-wide changes. The tradition of individual responsibility also allowed for changes within the specific ward environment without having an institution-wide committee give approval to every detail of the proposed change. The small size of the hospital, the innovative spirit of the hospital, as well as the specific objectives of the therapeutic ward contributed to this ease in making changes. The therapeutic ward was deliberately limited to a maximum of 46 patients, which is a fairly small ward relative to some other wards in this and other state mental hospitals. The small size of the ward and the small number of attendants employed on it administratively simplified the problem of instituting new procedures.

SYMPTOMATIC VERSUS CONSTRUCTIVE BEHAVIORS

We have previously noted the extreme types of symptoms that are seen in some mental hospital patients. One approach in dealing with patients has been to apply special treatment to these symptoms.

The general philosophy that emerged from our efforts, however, was to emphasize the positive aspect of the patient's behavior. Every attempt was made to bring the total environment to bear on building constructive and functional patterns of behavior on the part of the patients, leaving until a later date the problem of eliminating symptoms. Surprisingly, it was found that once the procedures were effective in establishing functional behaviors, many of the symptomatic behaviors were no longer present and could not be studied. One can only speculate, of course, but it appears that the symptomatic behaviors by their very disruptive nature were reduced or eliminated because they could not exist side by side with the functional behaviors. In a sense, they were incompatible. In some instances, such as aggressive behavior or stealing, where a symptomatic behavior persisted, the treatment for such symptoms was made possible only after the constructive behaviors were established. The general procedure was to provide the patient with additional opportunities for engaging in constructive behavior and obtaining extra privileges at those times when she was most symptom-free. Such a procedure was, of course, impossible until the patient was actively engaging in these functional activities and availing herself of the many privileges. The general philosophy here may be summarized as eliminating the negative aspects of behavior by emphasizing the positive.

On an intuitive level this emphasis seemed to make sense in terms of the ultimate objectives desired for the patient. Symptoms such as fantasy or paranoia may be annoying; but if the rest of the behavioral repertoire of the individual is functional and adaptive, these symptoms are often overlooked in normals as idiosyncratic character traits. When the individual is not functioning properly, it is very tempting to attribute the disability to some symptomatic behaviors. In the case of the non-functioning patient, the elimination of the symptom alone would not restore his functioning. One is all too familiar with the tendency of "sophomore psychologists" to describe the symptomatic behaviors of normal non-institutionalized individuals. Society appears, nevertheless, to be willing to tolerate these so-called symptoms so long as the individual is a self-sustaining functional member of the society. The corporation president that mumbles to himself may be characterized as an eccentric genius. The unemployed individual that mumbles to himself is more likely to find himself recommended for institutionalization.

MAXIMIZING MOTIVATIONAL FACTORS

The seriousness of the behavioral problems of the patients made it clear in the very beginning of the program that no single source of motivation would be effective for even a small proportion of the patients. The general approach developed was to bring every conceivable source of motivation to bear upon the patients in an effort to provide incentives for engaging in functional, useful behavior. The opportunity for privacy was used as a motivator, as was the opposite desire to have social contact. As simple a motivator as extra snacks was used, but also as complex a motivator as religious participation. Once a means of motivation was discovered, then almost unlimited opportunity to gain access to that event was provided to the patient. The opportunity to engage in a particular activity within the ward, to speak to any staff member of the ward or in the hospital, to have any physical item on the ward, to wear some particular type of clothing, to eat a meal at a particular time, to have a particular type of reading material and so forth were all brought to bear in providing incentives to the patients. This large variety of motivational events was maintained throughout each 24-hour day, all seven days of each week. It is in this sense that the program can be described as a total motivational environment.

Just as the program attempted to bring the whole environment to bear on the individual in providing motivation, so did the program attempt to involve the whole person, and not merely isolated behaviors. Every behavior of which the individual was capable and which served some useful function in the ward or hospital environment was encouraged. The behaviors were as simple as personal care or housekeeping, or as complex as those normally conducted by paid hospital employees. To the extent that any behavioral pattern could be identified as useful and functional, to that extent was an effort made to establish the behavior for each of the patients. Where factors mitigated against the establishment of complex behaviors, efforts were devoted to establishing the simpler ones as a stepping stone. Full-time and active involvement of the patients in many varied and useful activities was the objective of the program.

Absence of Coercive Procedures

Just as the behavioral procedure emphasized the establishment of positive functional behavior rather than the elimination of eccentric or symptomatic behavior, so, also, did the program emphasize the use of positive rewards rather than coercion or negative events. Neither verbal nor physical coercion was used at any time. Neither hydrotherapy procedures nor electroconvulsive shock procedures were ever programmed in the semipunitive fashion that one occasionally encounters in state mental hospitals. Nor were threats by the ward staff tolerated. The rationale for avoiding these noxious events was perhaps based more on ethical and moral considerations than on considerations of probable efficacy. The ethical issues involved in imposing aversive stimulation on an institutionalized patient seemed sufficiently complex that the authors felt strongly about avoiding the use of such coercive procedures until more justification had been established regarding their necessity. Rather than introduce any punitive measures for disruptive or symptomatic behavior, the motivating environment established as many positive reinforcers as possible and discouraged disruptive behaviors by causing the disruptive behaviors to delay slightly the availability of the positive reinforcers.

STANDARDIZATION OF PROCEDURES AND QUANTIFICATION OF BEHAVIOR

The motivating environment was developed with the objective of providing a treatment procedure that could be widely used. Extensive usage obviously could not come from a system that required considerable evaluative judgment as to the specification of the treatment procedures or to the nature of the behavior. For this reason, considerable care was taken to ensure that all of the methods used could be specified in simple, everyday language requiring no formal education or special instruction. Similarly, the attempt was made to categorize the behaviors in everyday terms, yet in language that allowed for a minimum of conflicting interpretations. As noted previously, a deliberate effort was made to avoid giving the attendants any formal instruction in learning theory. In this way we could be assured that the attendants' successful execution of the procedure was not based on their having a particular bias, philosophy, or theory about mental illness.

Efforts were made, also, to express behavioral changes in quantitative terms. The advantages of such an expression are that the behavioral changes can be readily evaluated by other practitioners with a minimum of interpretation. Such quantification is also highly desirable for providing a means of evaluating this research endeavor. From a clinical point of view the quantification of behavior provided a valuable means of describing the state of progress of a given patient at a given time, as well as changes in that patient's progress.

Administrative Feasibility

The desire to develop a procedure that would have wide applicability also required that the procedure be administratively and economically feasible. For this reason special devices and recording equipment were minimized. Also, the procedure was developed in such a manner that minimum ward personnel would be required, especially professional members of the staff. Wherever possible, services ordinarily performed by off-ward staff members were performed by the on-ward staff, thereby reducing the demands on the off-ward staff.

Treatment Evaluation

The method of evaluating the effectiveness of the motivating environment was to measure the extent to which the individual was engaging in useful and functional behaviors. This criterion is analogous to the criterion used in formal education and in medicine: The effectiveness of an educational procedure is evaluated by the degree of proficiency that the student has attained; the efficacy of the medical procedure, such as a splint or a cast for treating a fractured bone, is measured by whether the bone has grown together properly. In neither case is the simple termination of treatment used as the criterion. One would be very reluctant to state that an educational technique was effective because the student could be dropped from the school system. Nor would medical treatment for the bone, or for cancer, be considered effective because the physician felt that the patient could be discharged from the hospital. The bone might very well have been set improperly and the student might very well have learned nothing, but outside somehow circumstances permitted both to manage. It may come as some surprise, therefore, to learn that the criterion of discharge (termination) rather than the effectiveness of treatment is often used in evaluating treatment procedures for mental patients. In developing the motivating environment we preferred to directly measure the relevant behaviors that were being treated.

CHAPTER 3

Selection and Definition of Behavior

DIMENSIONS OF BEHAVIOR

A first step in any behavioral program is to decide how to describe the behavior. Since the English vocabulary already contains so many words for describing people, one would not anticipate any problem as to which words to use. People or their activities can be labeled *wealthy*, *honest*, or *intelligent;* and these labels seem satisfactory for communicating the desired information in everyday conversation. An alternative method is to use terms that are more quantitatively descriptive, substituting *annual income* for *wealth*, *IQ score* for *intelligence*, *school grades* for *academic inclination.* The term *intelligence* has the advantage of dealing with a wide variety of behavior in a wide variety of situations and seems to be more meanfully related to complex human performance than does the more restricted term *IQ*. On the other hand, terms like *IQ* and *annual income* are more specific. Two separate philosophies have arisen corresponding to these two types of descriptions. The important difference is the extent to which each depends on the personal interpretation or judgment of the observer. The subjective measures of wealth and intelligence are greatly influenced by the observer's interpretation, whereas the objective terms *annual income* and *IQ score* have a standard meaning that is not greatly affected by the momentary mood of the observer.

What grounds might be used to choose between more objective as opposed to more interpretive terms in a behavioral program? The answer generally agreed upon would be to use whichever works the best. The ultimate criteria, if one is interested in function, is, of course, whichever are more useful in arriving at generalizations that work. Stated otherwise, the objective of behavioral research is to discover generalizations and procedures that can be used by other scientists or practitioners. It is this necessity for use by others that constitutes the concept of replication. A generalization or technique must be capable of being repeated by other psychologists if it is to have any value in a science of behavior. If the terms that are used in a generalization depend greatly on personal interpretation or judgment, then other individuals will have difficulty in replicating the relationship. For example, if one investigator says that he has discovered that wealth is related to happiness in marriage, then another investigator will have some difficulty in replicating this relationship since his own ideas of wealth and of happiness in marriage are likely to differ greatly from those of the original discoverer. On the other hand, if the relationship is stated in terms of annual dollar income and number of years of marriage, then less interpretation is needed.

Similarly, a generalization which states that family structure is related to sociability is more difficult to replicate than a generalization which states that the older of two children in a family will write more words per communication in some standardized test situation. A later investigator can be reasonably sure that he is doing the same thing as the first investigator in deciding which child is older and how many words there are in each written communication, whereas the concepts of sociability and family structure depend greatly on the personal interpretations given to these terms by the two investigators. The point is not that these concepts are equivalent: Wealth is not the same as annual dollar income; number of years of marriage is not equivalent to happiness in marriage; family structure is not the same as relative age; and sociability is certainly not the same as number of words per written communication. The central point here is that the need for replication seems to require that the terms used in a generalization be relatively free of personal interpretations and evaluations. As a consequence of this desire for replication, the decision to use descriptive rather than interpretive terms seems to have occurred in many and very different areas of psychology.

We shall first examine several types of psychological investigations to determine how psychologists have developed concepts that are relatively free of interpretations so as to permit easy replication by other investigators. To the extent that this attempt at descriptive concepts seems to be general, a rule will be formulated concerning the choice of these two types of terms. Detailed examples will then be given about the usefulness of descriptive versus interpretive concepts in developing the motivating environment.

Animal Behavior

Upon examining studies of animal behavior, especially those that have been done in the laboratory, one finds that psychologists have usually specified the responses of the animal in descriptive rather than interpretive terms. Consider, for example, a problem that seems to be inherently interpretive or subjective; that is, the topic of how an animal learns to anticipate an event or how he comes to use an event as a signal or a symbol.

One possibility is to subjectively categorize the animal's appearance in terms of whether it looks as if he is expecting an event to occur. Pavlov (1927), while studying intestinal secretions, noticed that his dogs began to salivate in anticipation of his arrival in the room with some dog food. Rather than rely on an interpretive or subjective estimate of whether the animal was expecting the arrival of the experimenter, Pavlov decided to use salivation as his measure. He specified the dimensions of his response even further by measuring this behavior in terms of the number of drops of saliva. By showing how the number of drops of saliva varied in time and in amount, he objectively studied this complex process of subjective anticipation in a manner that has permitted replication by later scientists. Pavlov's findings are considered by many to constitute the beginning of the science of associative learning. The significance of his contributions is probably not that he discovered subjective anticipation, but rather that he developed techniques for quantifying it in descriptive units of measurement.

Similarly, psychologists have tended to rely on descriptive units of behavior when studying such diverse processes as learning, motivation, discrimination, psychophysics, and perception. The interpretive philosophy of measurement would categorize the animal in each of these subject matters as being motivated or bored, as having learned or being naive, as having perceived an object or being unaware of it, etc. Although it would be simple enough for a human observer to observe an animal and obtain a subjective estimate of whether the animal has learned, whether he "really" understands, or whether he has formed a concept, investigators have sought physical means that permit the behavior to be measured. As a consequence, many types of physical apparatus have been developed, such as the runway, the T-maze, the jumping stand, the lever-pressing situation, shuttle-boxes, and activity wheels.

Rather than designating the activity of an animal in judgmental terms, as would be required by the interpretive philosophy, the psychologist places the animal in a device such as an activity wheel and deals thereafter with the number of revolutions of the wheel as his descriptive unit of measurement. Similarly, instead of categorizing an animal as motivated, which would be the method used by the interpretive philosophy, the psychologist places the rat in a runway and measures the speed of the rat in traversing the runway. Discrimination, instead of being categorized as the animal's understanding of a stimulus difference, is described as the number of lever-presses that the animal made when one stimulus was on, compared to the number that it made when a different stimulus was on. The response used may be based on the movements of only a few muscles, for example, as measured by an electromyograph, or it may involve the movement of the entire animal through space. The descriptive units of measurement are, therefore, appropriate to the study of very complex phenomena, such as learning and discrimination, as well as to the study of the whole animal. Further, all of these techniques using descriptive measures have resulted in extensive replication.

Automatic measuring devices

The use of descriptive measures of behavior should not be confused with the use of automatic recording apparatus. The number of lever-presses of a rat in an operant conditioning situation is a descriptive unit of measurement. It may or may not be recorded by counters that are attached to the lever; it is possible for a human to simply count the number of times that the animal presses the lever. Similarly, the speed with which an animal runs down a runway may be recorded by an automatic apparatus such as a photocell arrangement. But, alternatively, the observer could record the time with a stopwatch, or even a simple clock. In both instances, lever-pressing and running speed, some error might be introduced by not using an automatic apparatus; but the basic nature of the measurement is descriptive rather than interpretive. Pavlov (1927), for example, simply counted the number of drops of saliva without benefit of an automatic recording procedure, but the number of drops of saliva was a descriptive unit of measurement. O'Kelly and Steckle (1939), Daniel (1943), and Ulrich and Azrin (1962) measured aggressive behavior between rats in terms of specific postures and movements of the rats; no automatic apparatus was used. Yet, these measures qualify as descriptive units since they refer to some specifiable physical aspect of the behavior, rather than to some evaluative judgment of whether the animals were aggressive.

Previously the statement was made that automatic recording is not the same as a descriptive statement. This distinction can be made clear by giving an example in which automatic recording was used, but unsuccessfully because of the failure to give sufficient descriptive specification of the behavior. Ferster and Skinner (1957) had discovered that a uniform rate of key-pecking resulted when the key-pecking response of pigeons was rewarded intermittently. Ferster and Skinner had used an automatic recording apparatus for measuring each key-peck. This recording apparatus not only specified when a pecking response occurred but also specified the durational aspects of the response. Bullock (1960) observed that the pecking responses that he obtained under a similar reward procedure did not follow the same degree of uniformity as had been reported. By examining the procedure used by Ferster and Skinner (1957) for defining their response, he noted that his physical specification did not take account of the duration. Bullock (1960) had inadvertently allowed the duration of the key-peck to be a factor in his recording and reward procedure. When he changed the specification of the response to make it identical to that of Ferster and Skinner, the pattern in turn became identical. This example illustrates how important it is to specify the response in descriptive terms, even when an automatic apparatus is used. This example further illustrates how descriptive units of measurement provide for replication of previous findings.

Animal psychologists are not the only ones who have selected descriptive units of measurement. Psychologists of human behavior also have preferred the descriptive units. When a psychologist is concerned with applied or basic problems of human behavior, he is in effect concerned with the change in some behavior, be it verbal or nonverbal. The same advantage of replication exists for the psychologist of human behavior as for the psychologist of animal behavior. From a practical point of view, of course, this advantage of descriptive units is even more important for applied problems, since it enables the reader to decide more definitively whether a given procedure will work in an area of human concern.

Human Behavior

Measures of intelligence

In the study of intelligence, for example, subjective techniques were in existence long before intelligence tests were devised. The subject was placed in a situation where he was permitted to discuss topics provided by the interviewer or chosen at random. The nature of the conversation was completely free, and the categorization of the subject's behavior by the interviewer was subjective. An applicant, then, could be categorized as very promising, very bright, intellectually curious, highly knowledgeable in mathematics, verbally facile, etc.

An alternative has been the development of more descriptive measures of behavior. The Wechsler-Bellevue Intelligence Test and the Stanford-Binet Test allow free responding on the part of the testee, but the tester has before him fairly specific instructions on how to categorize the responses. In some items only one word can be called a correct answer. In other items there may be a choice of two or three words, with some allowance being made for grammatical variations.

The most complete specification of the response in physical terms has been the use of multiple-choice items in intelligence tests such as the Otis and the short form of the Wechsler-Bellevue and the Stanford-Binet. In these multiple-choice tests the response is limited to checking or circling one of several alternatives. No scoring interpretation is necessary; the specification of the response is so complete that the recording procedure can be performed via automatic scoring machines such as computers. The intelligence test as a tool for predicting scholastic and other behavior has been one of the most conspicuous successes in the field of psychology and educational testing. This success has been achieved because of the power that comes from precise specification of the response in question.

Measures of personality

Clinical psychology has demonstrated a similar concern for specifying the response in more precise terms. Advances in clinical diagnosis were introduced by the use of tests such as the TAT, in which the response categories were designated in advance and an approximation toward descriptive specification was made. In the TAT, for example, the patient is given a score for homosexuality, depending on whether the response he makes in looking at a picture involves mentioning people of the same sex or of a different sex. Another approximate specification of the behavior to be used for diagnosis is that provided by tests such as the Rorschach. When using the Rorschach test, the clinician has before him a manual which delimits gross categories of responses in which he is to place a response. A statement that mentions color, for example, is to be scored under the category of "a color response." Similarly, a statement that indicates movement falls under the category of "a movement response." Considerable room for interpretation and subjectivity exists, of course, but the direction is toward a more strict definition of the response categories than in the TAT.

The ultimate in specification of the response in personality tests is the use of the multiple-choice diagnostic test, best illustrated by the MMPI. The MMPI test consists of several alternative responses which the subject simply checks. As there is no need for interpretation by the clinician, automatic scoring devices are commonly used for recording the responses of the subject. Precise specification of the response in the study of personality can also be seen in the development of tests such as the Allport-Vernon test, another multiple-choice form in which all subjectivity of the tester about the personality of the subject is eliminated.

Measures in industrial and social psychology

An example from industrial psychology concerning response specification is the well-known Hawthorne study, conducted at the Western Electric Co. by Roethlisberger and Dickson (1939), in which the productivity of the workers was not left to gross subjective interpretation but was measured directly as the number of units manufactured per day. Similarly, in the area of group dynamics a study in communication by Leavitt (1951) used physically defined response measures by counting the number of notes passed by each individual, and by defining the activity of the group as the completion of all the required symbols. The sociometric tests of Moreno and Jennings (1945) advanced the study of friendship patterns, which would seem to be an intrinsically subjective affair, using response categories that consisted only of the names or the rank ordering of names of individuals. The interaction chronograph procedure of Chapple (1949) was an excellent illustration of the use of physically defined response measures. In that procedure the interaction between individuals was measured in terms of the initiation of an interaction, its duration, its termination, plus derived measures such as the ratio of initiations to terminations.

Modification of Behavior

Operant conditioning and behavior modification studies in humans have shown the same concern for physical specification of the response. Greenspoon (1955), in studying the effect of reinforcement on speech, delimited the response categories to plural nouns versus all other types of words. Lindsley (1956), in studying the changes in the learned performance of an arbitrary response, specified precisely the force and distance necessary to achieve the knob-pulling behavior that he was measuring. Similarly, Bijou and Orlando (1961); Long, Hammack, May, and Campbell (1958); Holland (1957); Weiner (1962) etc. used a button-pushing or panel-pushing response that activated an electrical switch as a means of specifying the response being studied in as exact terms as possible.

In more applied studies, Baer (1962), in his study of thumb-sucking, specified the response as the child having his thumb in his mouth versus not having it in his mouth. Mowrer (1938) measured the presence or absence of urine in the child's bed in his study of enuresis by arranging for an electrical circuit to close when moisture was present. Bandura (1965), in his study of aggression, defined the aggressive response as striking a doll with a force exceeding a specified minimum. Lovaas, Freitag, Gold, and Kassorla (1965), in their study of self-destructive behavior, used the response category of the child physically striking part of his body against some other object. In their attempt via conditioning to maintain the behavior of wearing glasses, Wolf, Risley, and Mees (1964) measured the frequency and duration of occasions during which a child kept his glasses on. Wolpe (1958) had the patients raise their fingers when they did not feel anxiety in his reciprocal inhibition therapy. Salzinger and Pisoni (1958), in their study of affect in schizophrenics, similarly delimited the response category by including as information only those statements preceded by the personal pronoun "I" or "we." Barrett (1962), in her successful elimination of tics, measured the tics in terms of movements of the patient's chair produced by the tics. These and similar studies suggest the following rule.

Dimensions of Behavior Rule: Describe the behavior in specific terms that require a minimum of interpretation.

A psychological relationship is that between two responses or that between a response and some other event. Reliable replication of measures of this relationship requires that the subjective interpretation of the experimenter or observer not be a factor. When the response is measured in subjective terms, there is no assurance that any other investigator with quite different expectations, biases, and predispositions will obtain the same result. For this reason, the Dimensions of Behavior Rule may be considered the paramount rule of psychology. To the extent that a psychological investigation does not follow the Dimensions of Behavior Rule, its worth is slight for psychologists who wish to use the results and to build upon them.

An investigator has no way of knowing whether he has produced the same or different behavior with respect to intelligence, verbal communication, friendship pattern, degree of communication, choice of friends, degree of neuroticism, social interactions, or industrial productivity unless he has specific information about what the behavior was. The Dimensions of Behavior Rule places the burden of description on the physical aspects of the response, thereby removing the necessity for subjective interpretation.

Reliability coefficients

Agreement between observers is often used as a substitute for physical measurement of a response. This is evidenced by the extensive use of reliability coefficients. Yet, these reliability measures may say nothing about the physical basis of the response; they may only indicate social agreement which might very well have occurred entirely on the basis of shared subjective interpretations. For example, consider a study in which all nouns that are spoken by a subject are followed by a reinforcer. The subject lists the following words in sequence: drama, theater, play, act, house. The word *play* would undoubtedly be categorized as a noun. Consider now an alternative sequence: run, jump, play, hop, skip. In this sequence the word *play* is designated as a verb. The experimenter in this instance has engaged in interpretation of the response, possibly in terms of his conception of the intent of the individual, rather than on the basis of the physical properties of the response which allows no possible categorization as to whether it is a verb or a noun. It is very likely that perfect reliability would have been obtained had several observers been used to score this behavior. The consistency would in no way have demonstrated the reality of the response as being a noun. Rather, it would have been testimony to the temptation to introduce interpretive factors, and one's own susceptibility to them.

Observer's expectations

Probably no experiment has ever been conducted in which the experimenter or the observers have had no expectations about what the results might be. The Dimensions of Behavior Rule makes it easier for the experimenters to avoid reading their interpretations into the data by forcing them to attend to, or record only in terms of, some physical aspect of the response. In many instances the degree of bias of the observer is considerable, especially when he is engaged in an applied endeavor, as is especially true in a therapeutic enterprise in which a "cure" is fervently desired. Several studies have been conducted which show similarity of response measurement in scoring Rorschach tests among those individuals trained in the same way, as compared with individuals trained differently. Even in basic research the identification of the experimenter with a particular theory or point of view, which he always has to some extent, will cause him to record the data in a manner that reflects something other than the behavior itself (Rosenthal and Lawson, 1964).

Other applied areas

The distortion and error that result from interpretive characterization of performance have led to the adoption of physical measures of performance in many applied fields of human endeavor not considered psychological studies. Consider the question of promptness of an employee. Rather than have a supervisor provide a rating once a year to determine an individual's promptness in reporting to work, many employers have adopted a time clock or some other method that directly registers the time of arrival of the employees. Another example is the use of such interpretive designations as accuracy. In the case of a bookkeeper or cashier, it is certain that no two supervisors will ever agree about the accuracy of a given employee. The substitute used by many employers is to check the correspondence between the obtained and the desired performances as physical measures of accuracy. In the case of the bookkeeper, an audit of the books constitutes a physical measure of the performance. In the case of the cashier, the correspondence between the sales slips and the money at hand constitutes a physical measure of the performance. In either case, the interpretive designation of accuracy has been eliminated and a statement of the frequency of correspondence in figures has been substituted. A common method of evaluating salesmen illustrates the present distinction. One can characterize a salesman as being efficient and conscientious, or apply a seven-point rating scale in terms of his productivity. Alternatively, one can measure the effectiveness of the individual in terms of the dollar amount of his sales, thereby substituting a descriptive dimension of the response for an interpretive one.

Specification of the physical dimensions of the response is so critical that one might say that no behavior should be designated as a target unless this rule can be met.

The Dimensions of Behavior Rule and Its Application in the Motivating Environment

The Dimensions of Behavior Rule was used as a general guideline in categorizing the behavior of the patients in the motivating environment. The objective of the ward was to restore functional behavior to the patients. Obviously, a rating of whether a patient was behaving functionally would constitute an evaluative rather than a descriptive designation of behavior. Consequently, as seen in Table A-6 of the Appendix, the behaviors were described more specifically as dietary assistant, waitress, sales clerk assistant, secretarial, assistant, cleaning assistant, assistant janitor, laundry assistant, etc. Even these designations were too gross, however. If these descriptions had been used alone, it would have been necessary to evaluate a given patient's overall performance, say as a salesclerk assistant. In accord with the Dimensions of Behavior Rule, the salesclerk assistant's behavior was specified in more detail as: "Assembles commissary items; displays candy, cigarettes, tobacco, cosmetics, dresses, and other variety store items so they can be seen by all. Prepares ice, glasses, and cups for hot and cold beverages. Asks patient what she wishes to buy. Collects the tokens from patient and tells the secretary the name of the patient and the amount spent. Puts commissary supplies away."

Another example of this attempt to use descriptive terms was the specific description given of the dishwasher's duties. Rather than evaluating a patient's overall performance as a dishwasher in terms of whether she exhibited cleanliness, the description on Table A-6 of the Appendix reads: "Patient prepares dishwater; fills an automatic dishwasher; washes dishes, silver, and glasses. Operates automatic dishwasher; washes cabinets, sinks, and tables and puts everything away. Patient counts silver (knives, forks, and spoons) for all patients and places them in containers ready for next meal." By specifying these behaviors in detailed and descriptive terms, one increased the likelihood that future practitioners would be able to replicate the results obtained in this motivating environment and to build upon these results using procedures that are known to differ in some specifiable way. An overall rating of dishwashing performance would provide no such basis for knowing whether the results obtained by another clinician were in agreement with the results reported here.

Obviously, the behaviors given in Table A-6 are not completely specific, but still allow some interpretation. For example, under the dishwasher's responsibility, it was stated as one of the specific duties that the patient should prepare the dishwashing machine. This description still leaves a wide margin for interpretation as to what constitutes preparation of the machine. The general rule of thumb that was followed in deciding whether a behavior was sufficiently described was to observe closely whether any disagreement or differences in evaluation resulted between the attendants who otherwise did not communicate extensively about the specific nature of the job. This general rule of thumb was in a sense a miniature type of replication. To the extent that a new attendant categorized behavior in the same way as an older attendant, the recording procedure could be replicated. It was noted earlier that agreement between observers did not necessarily mean that the behavioral measures were valid, since such agreement could have been based upon some type of social influence or common bias. By making the job description very specific, however, as in the example of the dishwasher, it was hoped that such biases would be minimized. The disagreement or confusion between attendants as to what was meant by a behavioral description was used as a warning that the job description had to be specified in more detail. The following examples or incidents in the motivating ward environment illustrate specific instances in which such disagreements or confusion led to refinement and greater specification of the behavior.

Grooming assistant

Wilma M. had been signing up regularly for the position of grooming assistant. Her job record showed that even though she had been performing the job regularly, several occasions occurred in which the attendant in charge noted that the duties were not being properly carried out. On the face of it, then, it appeared that Wilma's adequacy in performing the duties was varying from day-to-day. Closer analysis of the work record indicated that it was one particular attendant who was observing Wilma on those days on which she was judged not to have fulfilled her duties satisfactorily. On the other days, when she did seem to be satisfactory, a different attendant was the observer. What superficially was a variation in performance of Wilma seemed rather to be a variation in the observational criteria of the attendants. This assumption was confirmed by close observation of the patient's work by the supervisor, since this observation revealed little difference in the day-to-day performance. Yet the differences in evaluation persisted. The attendants involved were individually questioned regarding the basis of their evaluations. The result was that one of the attendants had assumed that since Wilma was a grooming assistant, she should also help to clean the tubs after each bath. Since Wilma had not been doing so, this attendant had regarded her performance as deficient. The other attendant did not consider cleaning the bath tub a part of Wilma's responsibility. The disagreement between the attendants turned out to be a failure of the job description to provide enough behavioral detail. The solution as dictated by the Dimensions of Behavior Rule was to specify the grooming assistant's duties more completely. The duties were changed to include a specific statement that the job of grooming assistant should include the cleaning of the tub after each bath. The different evaluation by the two attendants then disappeared. What originally had appeared to be a problem of evaluation of how well a job was done turned out to be a conflict of agreement on job duties. Following this increased specification of the job requirements, there was complete agreement among the five attendants in charge of that activity during the next 10 occasions that Wilma held the grooming assistant position.

Excessive clothing

Rita O. was a patient who wore an excessive amount of clothing. She often wore several dresses, several pairs of stockings, several sets of underwear, and even several coats at one time, indoors as well as outdoors. An attempt was made to reduce the extent to which Rita wore this extra clothing. As a first step, a measure of the amount of excessive clothing was necessary in order to evaluate the effectiveness of the proposed therapeutic procedures. Measurement of the extent of excessive clothing would seem to be a fairly straightforward procedure. It was decided to have Rita weigh herself first with her clothing on and then without the clothing; the difference between the two measurements would give the weight of the clothing. The difficulties encountered in the measurement of pounds of clothing, a measurement which seems to have obvious validity as a physical unit of measurement, illustrate the importance of specifying the behavior in as much detail as possible. Rita was weighed fully clothed three times a day (just before breakfast, lunch, and supper), and the average daily weight was obtained. These measurements revealed that Rita wore about 45 pounds of clothing, with very little variation in this amount over a period of 30 days. Sudden and strange variations in the amount of clothing began appearing, however. Within 60 days the amount of clothing had increased to 75 pounds; then one day the weight showed a sharp drop to 45 pounds, a decrease in 30 pounds of clothing. This 30-pound decrease was difficult to account for because gross observation indicated that Rita was still wearing approximately the same number of garments. In attempting to account for some variables that might have produced this drastic change in weight, the scales were checked but found to be operating satisfactorily. Then the supervisor directly observed the weighing procedure on three successive occasions, but this direct supervision revealed nothing unusual. A more detailed examination by the attendants of the patient's clothing, conducted while the patient was taking a bath, revealed that she had sewn large pockets in the lining of her dresses in which she stored a large collection of small heavy objects. On the next occasion when Rita was weighed, she was asked to put these miscellaneous objects aside. Without these objects, the weight of her clothing was again 45 pounds, as it had been initially. This example illustrates how continuous attention was needed to specify in detail a response, even though the response initially appeared to be more than adequately specified. In this instance even so straightforward a measurement as weight of clothing was found to be too gross a specification.

An uncooperative patient

Patsy J. was a patient who produced different types of reactions from different attendants. Some of the attendants spontaneously evaluated her as cooperative, whereas other rated her, equally strongly as uncooperative. As a special project an attempt was made to determine the basis for this differential rating of Patsy. The attendants were asked to give examples of cooperative and uncooperative behavior by Patsy. After much discussion, it seemed that the rating of Patsy's cooperativeness was based primarily on her willingness to take tranquilizing drugs three times a day as prescribed, whereas the ratings of Patsy's uncooperativeness were based primarily on her refusal to take half of her scheduled baths. We have here an example of an overall rating that appeared to be a categorization of Patsy's general behavior, but was, in fact, based only on a small part of her activities. Instances of this sort regularly occurred in the motivating environment. Time and again specific behavioral deficits or anomalies were found to constitute the sole basis for gross characterizations of inadequacy. As an incidental by-product of the experience with Patsy, a special project was undertaken to increase the regularity with which she took her baths.

Readiness for discharge

Donna V. had been performing many jobs in the motivating environment. The high level of her performance led to considering her for transfer from the ward to a "half-way house" outside of the hospital. The question to be decided was whether Donna was capable of functioning in this half-way house; could she care for her own needs and perform whatever work might be required in her new location? An interview by a social worker with Donna resulted in the social worker's conclusion that Donna was not capable of independent functioning. Yet the behavioral records from the motivating ward environment showed that Donna had been regularly bathing herself, brushing her teeth, dressing independently, making her bed, grooming for each meal, and most importantly, working six hours each day with only one absence during a period of 15 months. Her performance in her job led to no disruption of her co-workers, and her activities were sufficiently integrated with those of her co-workers that she was able to get her job done. Further, the record showed that she had obtained a grounds pass during off-duty hours for 90 out of the previous 120 days. When Donna had the grounds pass, she was outside of the ward without direct supervision by any staff member. No reports by any hospital member had occurred that indicated she engaged in any undesirable behavior during these unsupervised periods. In spite of the rating of the social worker, the patient was ultimately placed in the half-way house. She has been functioning there adequately during the last six months. This example is provided to illustrate the two methods of categorizing behavior; one in terms of an overall evaluative rating, the other in terms of specific behavioral patterns. In the case of Donna V., it is not possible to say that the rating of Donna's incompetence was right or wrong. Nor would even a longer period of functioning in the half-way house provide a completely conclusive answer to the correctness of diagnosis. The point to be seen in Donna's case is rather that descriptive units of behavior make it possible to rationally analyze the basis for a recommendation without complete reliance on an intuitive rating.

Clerical helper

Pamela B. held the position of clerical helper. Initially the duties of this position were not specified in detail; the only specification was that the clerical helper assist the regular secretary with her clerical duties. Serious conflict arose between the regular secretary and Pamela. Pamela spent much of her time sitting idly by, awaiting some specific instructions from the secretary. Pamela also began bringing in material to crochet with during the intervals in which she had no specific assignment. The regular secretary began rating the patient's performance as unsatisfactory. Direct questioning of the secretary and direct observation of the patient indicated that the job was not sufficiently specified. Specific duties were, therefore, outlined after long consultation with the secretary. The specifics of the duties were continuously modified as a result of the application over a period of several weeks. The final description used was as follows: "Types forms, answers the telephone, uses the intercom to page hospital personnel, takes telephone messages, and runs errands to other offices throughout the hospital when requested by any member of the staff." With this more detailed specification of the job, the regular secretary was able to evaluate Pamela's performance more consistently. Pamela still spent part of her time reading and crocheting when she did not have specific duties to attend to, but there was a common understanding between her and the regular secretary as to what constituted free time when these personal activities could be performed. From a subjective point of view, the secretary no longer was upset about Pamela's failure to perform her duties; and Pamela no longer felt guilty about crocheting or reading. This example illustrates a detail about the Dimensions of Response Rule: The specification of the job duties should be continually communicated to both the employee and the supervisor, and in each other's presence, so that any misunderstandings in phraseology can be easily resolved.

TARGET BEHAVIOR

Adherence to the Dimensions of Behavior Rule does not seem difficult when a specific part of a training program is being described. One does not feel uncomfortable about describing the activities on a given day in a specific classroom as being instruction on how to avoid a split infinitive. It seems much more difficult, however, to apply the Dimensions of Behavior Rule in describing the objectives for the entire year. The inclination, then, is to define the objective as teaching the individual to be a good writer. Yet the advantages of the Dimensions of Behavior Rule apply as well to specification of the overall objectives of a training program as much as it does to the specific activities within that program. The problem of selecting objectives for an overall program and not merely a specific activity will be dealt with next.

Every training procedure is faced with the problem of deciding what skills or behaviors to train. Assume that an investigator wishes to train a pigeon to peck an illuminated key when it is green and to refrain from pecking when it is red. The experimenter might state that his objective is to teach a discrimination or the concept of color. Similarly, if an experimenter puts a rat in a maze, the objective might be described as an attempt to teach the rat direction. Or the objectives might be described in even more general terms, as for example, teaching the rat discrimination, persistence, accuracy, perceptiveness, or self-control. It might be assumed that these traits once learned would have a general application. But this is very rarely the case. The laboratory investigator may very well teach a discrimination between red and blue that will have no relevance to the desired performance in a discrimination between red and green. Yet both performances involve color discrimination. Similarly, if the trait of accuracy was what the rat learned when he had been trained to turn left as opposed to right, then the rat should also be accurate in a new situation that required responding to a green stimulus and not responding to a red. If what is learned are traits such as discrimination, accuracy, attentiveness, and persistence, effective functioning should result in all new situations that required the traits. Yet the extensive psychological studies on response generalization indicate that such traits do not generalize.

The same problem exists for the applied educator. Assume that one wishes to teach typing. If this objective is defined as teaching motor coordination, one could presumably teach this trait by training the individual to insert pieces of odd-shaped blocks into similarly shaped holes. Although some of the components of this skill might be involved in typing, the training of a typist that had been instructed only in that manner would seem to be deficient. Similarly, if the objective in educating a judge is to teach him wisdom and justice, presumably this trait might be taught through such tasks as refereeing at a baseball game. Yet there is little assurance that the individual would render a verdict in accordance with established legal precedents unless instruction had been given regarding them. Again, if one had designated the objective in educating army officers as being able to create a disciplined mind, aggressiveness, courage, resourcefulness, etc., such traits could just as easily have been taught by using the game of chess, which is an activity that could be equally characterized by these general designations. Yet, it seems clear that the desired objective of creating an effective officer would hardly have been realized.

Target Behavior Rule: Describe the desired performance in behavioral terms.

The Target Behavior Rule has been followed in some form by many disciplines concerned with applied education. For example, vocational schools do not merely give courses in some general area of secretarial duties; rather they teach specific skills such as typing and filing, operating duplicating machines, using office calculators, answering the telephone, addressing letters, completing business forms, and taking dictation.

A rather vivid example of the importance of specifying the objective of an education program in behavioral terms is seen in a study of combat effectiveness of fliers in Korea. Pilot candidates had been selected during training on the basis of the degree of "normality" on projective test scores, the assumption being that effective combat performance could be characterized as exhibiting the general trait of emotional stability and maturity. Direct measurement of combat effectiveness of fliers (Sparks and Niess, 1956) revealed a negative correlation between scores of emotional maturity and combat effectiveness. To the degree that the program was selecting fliers of differential effectiveness, it was in the direction of selecting those who were least effective. The error in this case, also, was to define the behavioral objective in general trait designations rather than in behavioral terms.

Applications of Target Behavior Rule in the Motivating Environment

Treatment of mental patients is basically an applied educational endeavor, and the mental health educator is faced with the problem of deciding what behaviors the patients should display. The objectives of mental hospital treatment have usually been phrased in general terms utilizing trait designations. The objective is often stated in terms of teaching the individual to be normal, to recognize the difference between fantasy and reality, to control his urges, to engage in reality testing, to exercise self-control, to resist frustration, to tolerate ambiguity, to be able to discriminate, etc. Such objectives provide little information for the applied educator as to what specific behaviors he should be teaching. For example, a mental health educator would find it very difficult to know how he should teach reality testing, especially since many aspects of the patients' behavior demonstrate that this general trait already exists, and in as high strength as in nonhospitalized patients. The patients can be seen to walk around chairs rather than through them, pass through open doors rather than collide with them, walk rather than fall down a stairway. Nor can it be said that the social discriminations of mental patients are completely lacking. They often show a highly developed ability to report abusive behavior on the part of the attendants, to specify in great detail aspects of other patients' behavior that they dislike, etc. Similarly, a patient shows discrimination in his verbal hallucinations. A patient may talk to himself while watching television and when by himself, and not on other occasions.

The Target Behavior Rule requires that the mental health educator specify the objectives of the patient's treatment not in terms of traits and abstract concepts such as "adjustment," but rather in behavioral terms. In the motivating environment, the specific behaviors designated as the target were that the patients dress themselves; make their beds; go to the dining room unassisted; eat without assistance; sweep, mop, and wax the floors; serve meals; wash the dishes, arrange the cutlery; answer the phone; escort and inform visitors; help keep records of the ward procedure; assist in scheduling activities; work in the ward cafeteria; work on other wards as attendants' assistants when needed; count; make change; empty trash; read; write notes and letters; etc. A fairly complete description of most of the behaviors designated as targets on the ward are given in Table A-6, which is accompanied by a specific description of the dimensions of these behaviors. These behaviors were trained in the motivating ward environment. Because there were not enough jobs on the ward for everyone interested in working, other jobs were made available outside the ward but within the hospital grounds. The performances outside the ward designated as the target behaviors were (1) dietary worker, (2) clerical worker, (3) laboratory worker, (4) laundry worker. The specific behaviors included within a job classification varied widely, from answering the phone to folding linen in the hospital laundry. Table A-3 in the Appendix includes a fairly complete description of these behaviors, and it is these behaviors that were selected as the targets, rather than general trait designations such as "being helpful," or "cooperative."

RELEVANCE OF BEHAVIOR

Another factor that governs the decision to select a particular response is whether the response can be expected to be maintained outside the training situation. One of the fundamental laws of conditioning is the Law of Extinction, which states that when reinforcement of a response is no longer forthcoming, then the rate of the response will decrease, possibly to zero. This Law of Extinction tells us that no matter how objectively defined the behavior is and how clearly specified as a target, that behavior cannot be expected to be maintained outside the training situation unless there is some reinforcement for it there. The Law of Extinction suggests, then, the following rule for selecting a response for training.

Relevance of Behavior Rule: Teach only those behaviors that will continue to be reinforced after training.

The selection of an irrelevant response for training is unlikely in a practical training situation. Apprenticeship programs, in particular, seem to be relatively free of this possibility. The plumber's apprentice has very little occasion to be trained in behaviors that are not intimately involved in the behaviors required of plumbers. Similarly, a baseball player is unlikely to be given training in skills other than those required or intimately related to those needed in playing baseball. It appears, however, that once formal educational systems are established which are remote from the final situation in which the skill is to be utilized, irrelevant responses may be taught. The reason appears to be that at one time the response in question was necessary, but the changing outside environment no longer reinforces or maintains that behavior. The separation between the formal educational system and the outside environment, however, seems to have resulted in a failure to identify this discrepancy. In such cases, the teaching of a skill is often continued. The reason for its instruction is no longer given in terms of the value of the skill *per se*, but in terms of some dimension that has not been evaluated and, in many cases, is incapable of evaluation.

The older and more detached the educational system is from the post-training environment, the more likely one is to find violations of the Relevance of Behavior Rule. Liberal arts colleges seem to be a prime example of a training environment that is divorced from a post-training environment. Liberal arts curricula include many courses that are not applicable to the existing problems of man. Receiving the Ph.D. degree requires a knowledge of foreign languages that will probably never be used; Latin and Greek are taught to "train the mind," even though they have no functional value in any linguistic community. Of course, the claim of "general value" derived from teaching certain courses may be justified. The Relevance of Behavior Rule requires that the value of the training be definitively established. *The rule makes no judgment that these behaviors have no value;* rather it states that unless they have value in the real world, i.e., are going to be reinforced, they will be abandoned or forgotten. It may be true that the skills have some intrinsic value that will not be manifested by any concrete change in an individual's behavior or reinforcement after training. If the value of the training cannot be submitted to empirical test, i.e., that behavior is not maintained in the real world, then the objective of the training rests on intuitive grounds. Since intuitions differ, the training may be equally intuited to be useless. A recent example illustrates this point. At the time of the establishment of the Peace Corps, a large number of universities were asked for help with the training of Peace Corps members. The Peace Corps found that the training offered by universities was largely irrelevant to the applied nature of the Peace Corps objectives. The solution arrived at by the Peace Corps was simply to develop their own training program.

A similar example is illustrated by the development of institutes for teaching English to foreign students. Typically, these institutes do not employ faculty members from the English department, since the objective is to develop verbal facility in the student quickly, without concerning him with the subtle aspects of English composition, literature, and rhetoric. The highly applied objectives of the institutes could not be satisfied by the college English curriculum, which is largely irrelevant to initial language acquisition. A simple question that can be raised regarding a training objective is: Will the trained behavior be maintained by the post-training environment? If not, the training will have no enduring effect, and its existence must be justified on some nonempirical basis.

The applicability of the Relevance of Behavior Rule seems fairly obvious as a means of eliminating training in vocations that have become almost entirely obsolescent. The rule seems equally valuable in identifying specific aspects of a vocational training program which have become nonfunctional. Colleges of pharmacy continue to teach students to combine ingredients in preparing prescriptions, even though pharmaceutical houses now generally supply the desired compound or mixture in final form. Radio "ham" operators must pass an examination in telegraphy, even though modern radio communication rarely requires this skill and automatic devices are available when telegraphy is needed. Secretarial schools teach shorthand, even after the dictating machine makes this skill almost unnecessary.

The criterion of usefulness of the trained response may be difficult to ascertain for some types of behavior. Swimming may be a useful (reinforced) response only once in a lifetime, when the individual capsizes in a boat; but the degree of its usefulness at that time justifies its training. Similarly, use of the proper exits during a fire is a rarely reinforced response, as is movement to an air raid shelter or application of first aid. Yet intuitively the importance of these infrequent responses justifies the training. The Relevance of Behavior Rule dictates that one ascertain the frequency or likelihood with which such behaviors will be required so that this frequency can be used as a basis for including, or excluding, them in training. It does not seem possible to formulate any strict guidelines as to precisely how useful a behavior must be or how frequently it occurs before one adopts some training for the behavior. However, in the absence of any empirically derived information about the frequency or usefulness of the behavior, no empirical basis exists for its inclusion in a training program.

A response may be useful after training in situations other than the original training situation. A child is taught to copy numbers not because it will be maintained outside of school, but because it is a response that later facilitates teaching the child to write a number without copying. Similarly, teaching a particular sound may not be justified by the use of that sound in isolation, but rather because the sound is a component of many words that will be useful. Therefore a response must be evaluated in terms of its utility *per se* and its usefulness as a component or prerequisite for other meaningful behaviors. Subjects such as Latin, philosophy, manual arts, and remotivation therapy may well have utility because they facilitate the acquisition of other, more obviously useful behaviors. Indeed, it is probable that the acquisition of any performance will have a facilitative effect for some others. Harlow (1949) has shown with monkeys that the acquisition of one discrimination in a conditioning situation results in more rapid learning of successive discriminations in that situation. This facilitative effect has been described as "learning-to-learn." Apparently competing responses and emotional factors adapt out during the several learning problems. Also, the form of the response and the general situation are similar in each problem, which probably contributes to the facilitative effect. This general phenomenon has also been studied with nonsense syllables and motor skills and has been alternatively designated as "positive transfer." Because of the facilitative effect of one skill on another, it may well be that learning such subjects as philosophy will improve all other skills that require logical thought, or that learning cabinet making will improve all other skills that require manual dexterity. Considering the large number of skills in philosophy and cabinet making, it seems certain that the acquisition of all these skills will facilitate some other skills in some way. The Relevance of Behavior Rule requires that usefulness for the final behavior be demonstrated, not assumed.

Suppose that the study of philosophy facilitates the learning of some other skills. Is this a sufficient basis for studying it? A practical question may be raised as to whether this same degree of facilitation could result from instruction in another subject, such as chemistry. Perhaps the study of chemistry teaches one to think as well as does the study of philosophy. The Relevance of Behavior Rule dictates that chemistry rather than philosophy be studied if performance in chemistry is also known to be reinforced in its own right, in addition to serving as a vehicle for the component skills of thinking. In more abstract terms, the rule suggests that of several types of skills available for producing a generalized ability, the skill that will also be reinforced in its own right should be trained.

Application of the Relevance of Behavior Rule to the Motivating Environment

In the field of mental health, violations of the Relevance of Behavior Rule are found whenever the training procedure is divorced from the target environment. Patients in mental hospitals are often instructed in arts and crafts, group singing, child-like games, musical activities, and group discussions on arbitrary topics. These activities are often included under formal programs designated as recreational therapy, music therapy, play therapy, vocational therapy, group therapy, remotivation therapy, etc. Many hospitals have departments that dedicate a great deal of time and energy to teaching the patient to finger paint, to learn basket weaving, or to do ceramic work. In some instances, embroidering or folk dancing are taught to the patient with the hope that such activities will keep the patient interested in people and things. Admittedly, activities of this kind may well provide the patient with greater self-control, awareness of others, and self-confidence. On the other hand, the Relevance of Behavior Rule would suggest that until there is evidence that such activities do develop self-confidence and other traits, it would seem prudent to teach the patient behaviors that are relevant in the community—for example, to hold down a job, follow instructions, ask questions, complete the job, be prompt on the job, and refrain from distracting others on the job. These and other behaviors associated with the performance of work are particularly important when the patient under consideration has to return to an environment in which he makes his living by holding down a job. Again, before deciding what response to train, careful consideration must be given to determining the type of environment in which the response will be displayed. Certainly, except for individuals too young or too advanced in age, the training of behaviors directly relevant to work is of utmost importance. Yet the work skills are not the only ones that a patient would learn in such training. Since most jobs require some social interaction, the patient would also learn how to get along with others under conditions where the presence or absence of social skills is meaningful to the successful completion of the job.

The behaviors developed by musical, recreational, and play therapies are not typically justified by their usefulness outside of the training environment, since the usual noninstitutional environment of adults rarely maintains such behaviors. Mastery of the above skills or activities will in no way ensure the patient's return to, or acceptance by, the community outside the hospital. Again, no judgment is being made regarding the value of such activities. The Law of Extinction warns us that whether or not these activities have intrinsic value, they will be abandoned in the absence of reinforcement in the natural environment.

In applying the Relevance of Behavior Rule to the selection of behaviors to be trained, it was necessary to ask what behaviors the patients could be trained for that would be maintained by their post-training environment. What kinds of behaviors would be required of the patients in their new environment should they be discharged from the hospital? The type of environment to which the patients would return seemed somewhat predictable, given the general economic and social backgrounds of the patients. Almost all of the patients in the programmed environment were from rural or lower-class communities. They were all females. Most were housewives prior to admission and presumably would continue to be so after discharge. Their advanced age and their limited formal education indicated that if they were to be employed, they could hold only non-skilled positions. The target behaviors for these individuals seemed, therefore, to be the various performances involved in housekeeping and in unskilled employment. Common observation of the activities of housewives indicated that such household chores as making beds, dusting, mopping, cleaning, serving meals, etc. were being maintained at a high level by housewives. Similarly, common observation of unskilled employment activities indicated that such behaviors as arriving at work on time, remaining for the entire period, following instructions of a supervisor, interacting with fellow employees when necessary, and other such minimal behaviors were maintained by some reinforcement in such unskilled positions.

Most of the patients over 65 years of age would almost certainly spend the rest of their lives being cared for by a state hospital, since vocational opportunities were almost nonexistent for them and most of these patients no longer had friends or relatives who were willing to care for them. Even for these patients, the types of activities listed above were such that common observation indicated that most of them would be encouraged or reinforced by the staff members of a mental patient hospital should the patient not be discharged. Therefore, reinforcement could be expected to be maintained at a high level in the general hospital community, also.

A detailed list of the activities for which the patients were reinforced is given in Table A-1 of the Appendix. Each of these behaviors was included only if it satisfied the Relevance of Behavior Rule as determined by observation of what behaviors were being maintained in relevant target environments. A total of 65 patients were cared for in the motivating environment at different times. The maximum number at any one time was 45. Of these 65 patients, 58 performed some duties related to the functioning of the ward environment. They performed at least one hour's work per day for a minimum of 40 days. Only seven of the patients failed to perform this amount of work. Thirty of the patients held one or more of the positions described in Table A-6 for over one year; ten of them held various positions for as long as three years. Thus, the motivating environment was successful in motivating the patients to perform these relevant responses, some of them for very long periods of time.

Four of the positions listed in Table A-3 are similar to nonskilled jobs outside the hospital; these are the dietary worker, clerical worker, laboratory helper, and laundry worker. Twenty of the 65 patients held one or more of these positions for a period of one year or more. Six hours per day were spent in each of these positions, being fairly comparable, then, to a full-time job outside the hospital. The degree of useful employment of a large number of patients over such an extended period of time is significant because all of the patients selected for study in the motivating environment had a long history of idleness. The behaviors needed to perform each of these four positions for extended periods of time are the same as those needed to hold a position outside the hospital. In addition, the consequences that maintain this work are also fundamentally similar. The patients in these four positions worked to obtain tokens that enabled them to secure greater comfort, better living accommodations, and a wide range of privileges. Outside the hospital discharged patients would work to obtain money for the same type of benefits.

CHAPTER 4

Discovering Reinforcers

PROBABILITY OF BEHAVIOR RULE

What Is a Reward?

A reward is typically considered in terms of the subjective reaction that it produces. It is something that makes you feel happy, contented, satisfied, pleased, or glad. One asks, in an attempt to specify what is rewarding, "What is it that the individual really wants?" "What is its symbolic significance for him?" "What aspect of the individual's personality does it express?" "What attitude does it embody?" "What needs are being fulfilled by it?" "What is its unconscious meaning?" The attempt in this subjective endeavor is to specify the phenomenological or subjective world of the individual. Carried to its extreme, this mentalistic philosophy minimizes the necessity for obtaining measures of behavior upon which to base one's estimate of subjective likes or dislikes.

Rewards or Reinforcers?

The distinction between rewards and reinforcers reflects the difference between a mentalistic and a behavioristic approach to human behavior. The terms *reward* and *reinforcement* have been used fairly interchangeably, yet a difference between them exists which is crucial for success in discovering effective human motivators. A reinforcing stimulus is defined as an event or consummatory behavior that leads to an increased probability of a response. The definition of reinforcer has its basis in its effect upon behavior. In using a reinforcer one asks, "Has the rate of the behavior increased?" "Is it occurring more frequently than before?" A reward, on the other hand, is often used to indicate a subjective state leading to pleasant or satisfying sensations. In using a reward, one usually asks, "Does he like it?" "Is he happy with it?" The definition of *reinforcer* is always in terms of some measurable stimulus or measurable behavior of the individual; the definition of *reward* is not.

Discovering reinforcers in the animal laboratory

Studies in conditioning and learning very frequently use food or water as reinforcers, and many studies have been conducted to determine what aspect of food accounts for its effectiveness. For example, the sucrose concentration (Collier and Willis, 1961) or the number of calories in the food has been established as important in determining whether a given type of food will be reinforcing. One attempt to determine the underlying reason for the effectiveness of a reinforcer was made by Hull (1943). Hull postulated that reduction in physiological need was the determining factor. Hull's principle suggests that food, water, sex, and various types of physiological comfort could be used as reinforcers. This generalization has received considerable support from other studies of animal learning. In working with humans, however, it is considered quite undesirable to utilize these various types of physiological needs and physical comfort.

A general rule has emerged from operant conditioning studies for discovering effective reinforcers without determining the underlying reason for their effectiveness. The general rule is to observe the natural frequency or probability of the event. It is unnecessary to know, for example, how many calories or how much sucrose concentration there is in a given food. Instead one might ask how probable it is that the animal will eat that type of food, or how frequently he will eat it.

Probability of occurrence seems to be the more important consideration, as seen by the fact that some types of activities, such as sex, may occur for no more than a few minutes a day, yet are highly probable when the opportunity exists. Similarly, eating may occur for only a few minutes a day and not have a high continuous frequency but will still be categorized as a highly probable event when the availability of food makes the opportunity to eat possible.

This general principle has received extensive experimental verification in operant conditioning studies, especially those involving "chain" schedules (Kelleher and Gollub, 1962). Premack made novel use of this principle in an extensive series of experiments. A common procedure in studies of conditioning has been to use drinking or eating as a reinforcer for running. Premack (1962), in an ingenious experiment, first found the probability of running when the opportunity was freely available. He then determined the probability of drinking when water was freely available. In the specific circumstances of his experiment, the probability of running was greater than the probability of drinking. When running was then arranged as a reinforcer for drinking, he found that drinking behavior increased. This arrangement of consequences is a reversal of the typical situation in which drinking serves as a reinforcer for running.

Another example of finding the reinforcing properties of an event exclusively on the basis of its probability is that of Butler (1957). Monkeys frequently peer through the openings of their cage at nearby animals or people. Consequently Butler used the opportunity of one monkey to view another as a reinforcer for bar-pressing. Viewing a nearby monkey proved to be a reinforcer, as evidenced by the increase in the bar-pressing response.

Reinforcers in human studies

The probability of occurrence of a given behavior should also serve as a basis for discovering reinforcers for humans. Common observation indicates that many parents intuitively use this principle in encouraging children to eat their entire meal. Parents frequently tell the child that he will be allowed to go out and play, which is a behavior with a high probability of occurrence, if and when he finishes eating, which is a behavior with a lower than desirable probability of occurrence.

As another example, one of the most probable activities of normal adult humans in a work situation is to avoid work. It should follow, therefore, that the opportunity to rest would be a reinforcer. This is what was found in a study (Azrin, 1960) that used rest periods as a reinforcer with normal human subjects who were in a simulated work situation. The work output increased when the rest period was arranged as a reinforcer for working. A third example is found in child psychology. Observing a cartoon movie is a highly probable event with children when the opportunity permits. It should follow that a behavior could be strengthened by using the opportunity to observe the cartoon. Baer (1962) used this activity as a means of reinforcing children for not thumbsucking. Similarly, Nathan, Schneller, and Lindsley (1964), in a psychotherapeutic situation, used the opportunity to see or hear the therapist on a TV screen as a reinforcer. Yet another example of this principle has been the use of cigarettes with psychotic patients. Lindsley (1956); Ayllon, Haughton, and Hughes (1965); and Hutchinson and Azrin (1961) made effective use of this principle by using cigarettes to reinforce various behaviors of patients who had a high probability of smoking. This background in animal and human experimentation leads to a general statement which specifies one way to discover reinforcers.

Probability of Behavior Rule: Observe what the individual does when the opportunity exists. Those activities that are very probable at a given time will serve as reinforcers.

As applied to the discovery of motivating events in human behavior, this rule states that the first step is *to observe what the individual is actually doing.* Those events that are very probable on a given occasion should, then, be effective reinforcers. This principle of identifying reinforcers on the basis of the probability of occurrence has special applicability to human behavior. Most events that are reinforcing for humans do not seem to be capable of analysis on a simple physical or chemical basis. Humans are reinforced by engaging in activities that are indeed fairly difficult to specify in a simple physical or physiological way, such as watching cartoons, listening to music, attending church, talking to other people, dancing, etc. A special advantage of this Probability Rule for humans is that it does not require knowledge of why such activities are reinforcing, nor does it attempt to measure an individual's mental state.

Applications of the Probability Rule in the Motivating Environment

Reliance was placed upon the patients' behavior itself to discover reinforcers. The staff was instructed to observe closely what the patients did or tried to do at any time during the day when no pressures were being put upon them to do anything in particular. These observations were transmitted either verbally or in writing to the ward supervisor. It was noted that certain patients often hoarded various items under their mattresses. The activity in this case, in a general sense, consisted of concealing private property in such a manner that it would be inaccessible to other patients and the staff. Since this event seemed to be highly probable, it was formally scheduled as a reinforcer. Keys to a locked cabinet in which they could conceal their private possessions just as they had been doing with the mattresses were made available to patients.

Another activity that was observed to be highly probable was the attempt of patients to conceal themselves in several locations on the ward in an effort to enjoy some degree of privacy. A procedure was therefore instituted whereby a patient could obtain a portable screen to put in front of her bed or access to a bedroom with a door. Another event that had a high probability of occurrence for some patients was a visit with the social worker or psychologist. This was used as a reinforcer by arranging appointments with either of these staff members. An activity that was fairly subtle but which could be identified in terms of probability or frequency of occurrence was the choice of particular patients to sit with at mealtime. The critical aspect of this activity seemed to be the opportunity to be with some patients rather than with others while eating. This was used as a reinforcer by scheduling the patients to eat in different groups. The patient could then select that group in which her friends ate. An activity that is easily overlooked as a reinforcer is the choice of one chair over another. Particular patients were seen to consistently preempt a given chair for their own use. This activity was, therefore, scheduled as a reinforcer, rather than being freely available.

One of the experiments conducted in the motivating environment to determine empirically the validity of the Probability of Behavior Rule involved religious services. This activity was selected because of the high probability of attendance at religious services by some patients.

Experiment 1: Attendance at religious services as a reinforcer

Procedure. Twenty-nine patients served as subjects. The other patients were not available at the time of this experiment. The religious service consisted of a period of prayer, songs, and a sermon conducted by the hospital chaplains in a room especially designated for this purpose. The room was decorated with typical religious ornaments such as a cross, candles, and a podium. A piano was also available. At the time for the scheduled religious service, everyone was notified by an attendant. The chaplain, in addition, went through the ward greeting everyone and inviting them to join him at the service. Admission was free. No other activities were scheduled on the ward that might compete with the religious services. This procedure was followed for a period of five religious services. The next five service periods had a turnstile requirement for admission to the religious service. The patient operated it with one token, which allowed her access to the room where the service was conducted. The final period of five services reinstated free admission to religious service. (The rationale for using tokens will be discussed in Chapter 5.)

Table 4–1

Religious Services as a Reinforcer

	Free	1 Token	Free
Mean attendance	10.2	8.6	10.0

Each phase based on five service periods for 29 patients.

Results. Table 4–1 shows that when admission to religious services was freely available, there was an attendance of 10.2 patients per service. When admission to the religious service was one token, the attendance was slightly less: 8.6 patients per service. When the token requirement was terminated, there was a slight increase in the average number of patients attending religious services.

Discussion. The high probability of attendance at religious services for some patients led to its use as an additional source of reinforcement in the motivating environment. The findings indicate that the religious services were in fact a powerful reinforcer for some patients. Only a slight difference in attendance occurred when the religious services were available for tokens. When access to religious services was made free again, a few more patients attended, indicating that the slight difference in attendance previously noted was related to the token requirement, and not to simple passage of time.

By selecting those behaviors that have a natural high frequency or high probability of occurrence, the behavioral engineer has a useful technique for discovering reinforcers that are peculiarly human.

Probability of Behavior Rule Applied to Recreational Activities

Additional evidence of the effectiveness of the Probability of Behavior Rule is seen in the following experiments. Activities frequently attended by the patients were the commissary, going outdoors, musical activities, and movies. Therefore, applying the Probability of Behavior Rule, admission to each of these activities required payment of one token. Next, the token requirement was discontinued for a period of time. A final period during which the token requirement was reinstated was put into effect to determine whether attendance at these activities was related to the token requirement.

Experiment 2: Commissary as a reinforcer

Procedure. Thirty-seven patients participated. A commissary, held three times a day, was set up in the dining room directly on the ward. Sales items and their prices were displayed in everyone's view on the counter where food trays were picked up at meals. The experiment was run in three phases, each consisting of 45 commissaries. In the first phase, a one-token admission was charged. In the second, admission was free; and in the third, a one-token admission was again charged. Just before each commissary, an attendant announced clearly throughout the ward, "Commissary time, Ladies. Come to the dining room for commissary."

Table 4–2

Commissary as a Reinforcer

	1 Token	Free	1 Token
Mean attendance	16.5	21.0	17.3

Each phase based on 45 occasions for 37 patients.

Results. As Table 4–2 indicates, initially an average of 16.5, or 45 per cent, of the 37 patients attended each commissary. In the second phase, the mean attendance rose to 21 (57 per cent); and in the third phase, it went back down to 17.3 (47 per cent).

Experiment 3: Going outdoors as a reinforcer

Procedure. Thirty-seven patients participated. A supervised walk with an attendant was scheduled daily. The procedure was divided into three 12-day periods. In the first period, going outdoors for a walk cost one token; in the second, it was free; and in the third, it again cost one token. At a specified time each afternoon an attendant called loudly throughout the ward, "Time for a walk, Ladies."

Table 4–3

Going Outdoors as a Reinforcer

	1 Token	Free	1 Token
Mean attendance	5.5	5.5	5.8

Each phase based on 12 occasions for 37 patients.

Results. As Table 4–3 shows, the mean number of walks in the first 12-day period was 5.5 patients. In the following free period this remained constant, and in the third period the change was less than one per cent. A mean attendance of about 15 per cent was maintained throughout the experiment.

Experiment 4: Musical activities as a reinforcer

Procedure. Forty-five patients participated. Music provided by phonograph records was scheduled to be held in the patients' day room directly on the ward. The experiment was conducted in three stages. In the first stage, admission was one token; in the second, it was free; and in the third it again cost one token. Prior to the activity, an attendant announced loudly throughout the ward, "Come to the musical activity in the day room, Ladies."

Table 4–4

Musical Activities as a Reinforcer

	1 Token	Free	1 Token
Mean attendance	10	14	12

Each phase based on two occasions for 45 patients.

Results. As Table 4–4 shows, an average of 10, or 22 per cent, of the patients attended each musical activity in the first stage of the experiment, when admission was one token. The mean attendance changed little in the second, free stage, or in the final stage.

Experiment 5: Movies as a reinforcer

Procedure. Movies were scheduled to be shown in the patients' day room on the ward. The procedure was divided into three periods of two showings apiece. In the first period a one-token admission was charged at each film. Films were free in the second period, and a one-token charge was reinstated in the third period. Prior to each showing, an attendant announced loudly throughout the ward, "Movie time, Ladies. Movie in the day room." She then stated the title and duration of the film.

Table 4–5

Movies as a Reinforcer

	1 Token	Free	1 Token
Mean attendance	8	13	10

Each phase based on two occasions for 45 patients.

Results. Table 4–5 shows that an average of eight, or 17 per cent of the patients attended each film in the first period, with a one-token admission. The mean attendance increased in the second, free period to 29 per cent. In the third period, this value went down to 22 per cent.

Discussion. The results of these experiments indicate that the activities attended by many of the patients could be used as effective sources of reinforcement. These activities did not cease to be valuable to the patient when admission to them required payment of a token. Whether the admission was free or not, there was relatively slight difference in attendance at each of these activities. Again, the evidence indicates that the slight increase in attendance when the activity was free was not due to simple passage of time but rather to the relationship of the activity to the token requirement. When the token was required for admission again, there was a level of attendance similar to that obtained during the initial period of token requirement. These five experiments show that behaviors that have a high natural probability of occurrence can be used as reinforcers.

Psychotherapy as a Reinforcer

What happens when the Probability of Behavior Rule is not followed is illustrated by the following experience. Psychotherapy for patients is commonly assumed to be something that patients would like, and which in any case, they would profit from. The reasons for believing this are not difficult to identify; one need only examine the environment outside the hospital to see that patients pay substantial amounts of money to psychologists, psychiatrists, and counselors in order to obtain private psychotherapy. In a mental hospital the main obstacle to providing psychotherapy for every patient would seem to be the lack of availability of qualified professional personnel. It is assumed that the patients would engage in psychotherapy if only the opportunity were available. In the motivating environment patients were given the opportunity to attend psychotherapy sessions, and formal arrangements were made with full-time psychotherapists for this purpose. All patients were asked and actively encouraged to attend the psychotherapy sessions. Only two patients out of 45 attended, and then only for two sessions. The token cost was eliminated in order to increase attendance, but without effect.

The unnecessary effort and expense engendered by failure to follow the rule can be seen in another example. It was felt that certain foods appropriate to the dietary laws of the Jewish religion would be effective reinforcers for Wendy S., who was of Jewish faith. Great expense and effort was expended to obtain Kosher foods for Wendy, only to find that they were ineffective as reinforcers for her. On the other hand, extra portions of the usual foods and desserts were effective reinforcers for her.

VERBAL BEHAVIOR IN THE DISCOVERY OF REINFORCERS

In addition to the Probability of Behavior Rule there are other procedures useful in discovering new reinforcers and expanding known ones: The verbal behavior of patients is one means. It is commonly assumed that a behavioral approach necessarily minimizes verbal factors and considers behaving organisms only as mechanical and nonverbal. Yet the patients' verbal responses in the motivating environment were recognized as important, and standardized formal procedures were used to increase the frequency of requests as a means of discovering more and better motivators for individual patients. The Probability of Behavior Rule made it possible to discover what events on the ward environment were reinforcing; the main advantage of the verbal requests was that they specified events outside the immediate environment.

To increase their frequency, the requests were considered to be a specific type of response. One factor known to affect responses is the immediacy of reinforcement for them. The longer the reinforcement is delayed after the response occurs, the less likely one is to obtain the response. Another factor is the frequency of reinforcement. The more frequently the reinforcer is delivered for the response, the more likely the response is to occur. These two principles state that the response will be more likely to occur if the reinforcer is delivered for every response without exception and without delay. It follows that verbal requests should be reinforced immediately each time they occur if one wishes to maintain the verbal requests at a high level.

Verbal Request Rule: Act immediately upon every verbal request for a reinforcer.

When a patient stated that she wanted a particular object or activity, the attendant told the patient that she would see what could be done about it. This request was then immediately conveyed to the ward supervisor, who made a decision about the desirability of granting it, and the patient was notified. An example of how this procedure was put into effect follows. Helen G. asked if she could have her breakfast eggs served soft-boiled rather than hard-boiled as was the usual practice in the hospital. The attendant told Helen, "I'll tell the nurse about it right now." She then contacted the supervisor. Within two hours of the request, the supervisor notified Helen that soft-boiled eggs would be available next breakfast. Next breakfast Helen asked for soft-boiled eggs and received them. She remarked, "This is the first time in 12 years that I've eaten soft-boiled eggs."

The following is an example of a failure to reinforce a verbal request, and the later solution to this problem. Donna V. had been receiving tranquilizer pills in the amount prescribed by the ward physician. When Donna asked for more tranquilizing pills, her request was viewed by the attendants in a purely medical context.

Later it was realized that this was just as much a request for a reinforcer as others that patients had been making. As a consequence, placebos were made available to Donna on a regularly scheduled basis in exchange for tokens. The effectiveness of the placebo as a reinforcer was shown by the fact that in a period of six months Donna obtained a total of 648 placebos. The initial failure to view the patient's statement as a request for a reinforcer delayed the use of this substantial source of motivation.

Because of the great importance of verbal requests in the discovery of reinforcers, a formal procedure was established for prompting such requests. On a regular schedule, an attendant was assigned to ask each patient on the ward whether there was anything she would like to have. The request was always repeated to minimize possibilities of misunderstanding. This formal procedure was designed to obtain more requests than would have resulted had only the spontaneous request been made. It was especially useful in eliciting requests from those patients who were fairly reticent or who communicated very little with the ward staff. Immediate attention was given to these prompted requests, just as it was to the spontaneous requests.

This procedure was especially important for many of the patients who had a low frequency of requesting special events. The reason for this low frequency of request can only be guessed at, but probably it stemmed from a history of indifference to their requests during their long period of hospitalization. With mental patients, in particular, it is extremely easy for the staff to view requests for special events as expressions of the mental disorder and to ignore them if their implementation involves any inconvenience. It is only by establishing a formal procedure and enforcing adherence to it that verbal requests can be encouraged. Sometimes in the course of identifying specific reinforcers, a patient's answer led to a general use of the item or event identified as a reinforcer. For example, when patients were asked if there was anything in particular they wanted on the ward, one patient, Janet E., answered that she wanted some shoes but that the ward didn't have the kind she wanted. To insure correct information on the desired item, Janet was given a mail order catalog from which to choose the particular type of shoes she wanted. Although originally this was used as an aid to specifying certain types of items, it became evident that Janet preferred to go over the catalog and do her "shopping" by reading and selecting the items she wanted in this fashion. Therefore several catalogs were made available on the ward. The patients could select any item in the catalog and have it scheduled by the ward as a reinforcer. This allowed patients to obtain items that were idiosyncratic to their own interests and which administrative expedience did not allow to be routinely stocked on the ward. Another variation on the same theme of encouraging patients to identify the items or events they wanted was the procedure which allowed the patients to visit the shops in the nearby town. There the patients could select any item they wished and have it made available to them by the ward as a reinforcer.

Limitations of the Verbal Request Procedure

The verbal request procedure was extremely useful, as indicated above, in discovering new reinforcers for the patients, especially those reinforcers that were not immediately avaliable in the ward environment. It was not, however, possible to assume that the verbal statement by the patient was an adequate description of what events were reinforcing. One major problem was that patients often indicated that they desired nothing, yet actual observation of their behavior indicated that there were many events that were reinforcing for them. The danger here is that the verbal statement of the patient may be regarded as reflecting the "true" nature of her desires, and that nothing is desired by her unless she has stated that it is desirable. As an example, Harriet C., when asked during the formal prompting procedure what it was that she would like, almost invariably said, "Nothing, I've got everything that I want." Even after repeated questioning and urging she repeated that there was nothing she wanted or enjoyed doing. From a mentalistic viewpoint, the proper interpretation of Harriet's statement was that nothing was reinforcing for her; yet observation of Harriet on the ward revealed that she frequently stole cigarettes from other patients when the opportunity arose. Another patient, Emily, refused even to answer the same question beyond stating, "No, no, I want nothing." Yet it was found that Emily occasionally wrote letters home requesting clothing items and magazines. These examples illustrate the frequent finding that patients will not request an item, although evidence strongly indicates that the item is reinforcing for them. In subsequent sections of this book we describe various procedures that attempted to develop utilization of reinforcers even when there seemed to be no initial predisposition of the patient to request them.

A second problem in implementing the verbal request procedure was that patients frequently requested items but would not use them when they were made available. Sometimes a patient would request a special dress that was expensive and time consuming to obtain; and when it was made available, she would refuse it. Often a patient requested a special interview with a social worker. Yet, after an appointment had been made with the social worker, the patient refused to keep the appointment. From a mentalistic point of view, this poses a paradox: If the request reflected the fact that something was desired, then why was it not used? This paradox is resolved when the patient's verbal request is regarded not as a mental revelation, but rather as verbal behavior which, like other types of behavior, is influenced by such factors as immediacy of reinforcement, frequency of reinforcement, stimulus control, punishment, etc. If one wants to reduce the frequency of requests for things that are later rejected, some cost for the rejection should be considered.

Attach cost to rejections of previously requested reinforcers

For events that were not regularly scheduled, the patient was asked to make a partial payment for the requested item or activity *at the time* that the request was made. This procedure guaranteed that the patient would utilize the activity or item once it was made available; otherwise, the number of tokens given as initial payment would be forfeited. Thus a cost was attached to a rejection of a previously requested item. Prior to introducing this cost procedure, considerable administrative chaos resulted with very little apparent gain in the discovery of new reinforcers. For example, Agnes I. consistently ordered sewing material. When the material was made available a day later, she didn't remember ordering it and stated that she didn't want it. After the cost requirement was attached to the request, Agnes' rejections were eliminated. Rather, after ordering the material, she inquired frequently about its probable date of arrival and purchased it immediately upon delivery. This pattern of behavior was characteristic of all patients after the cost requirement was instituted. Having made the initial payment on a specially requested reinforcer, the patient usually asked the attendants each day, and often repeatedly within a day, whether the item had arrived and when they could obtain it.

These procedures enabled the staff to do something about verbal requests rather than simply interpreting them. Ward attendants often are imbued with the mentalistic philosophy. They have been told in their orientation courses and in their casual readings that the important thing is to give understanding and love to the patients. Under the present procedures the attendants did no less. They encouraged verbal statements, but in a more standardized fashion than they would have had they followed their introspective philosophy. In addition, however, they acted upon these requests. In a sense, the formal method of dealing with verbal behavior provided not only a way of assessing the patients' motivation but a means of satisfying it as well. The staff in the motivating environment, just as in other wards, praised, complimented, congratulated, attended to, smiled at, caressed, and gave other demonstrations of affection to the patients.

The motivating environment cannot, therefore, be viewed as an automatic mechanical system in which reinforcers are delivered according to standardized regulations that permit no other social interaction. The point is, rather, that all of these social interactions occur *in addition to* the formal scheduling of the reinforcers.

VARIATION OF REINFORCER

Variation of Reinforcement Rule: Use many variations of a known reinforcer to discover new ones.

This procedure provides a standard and objective basis for discovering reinforcers in those instances in which the Probability of

Behavior Rule and the procedures based on verbal behavior are not feasible. The Probability of Behavior Rule is useful when the opportunity to engage in the activity exists in the individual's current situation. The procedures that use verbal behavior to discover reinforcers are not useful when the subject does not know if an event would be reinforcing if available and is, therefore, unlikely to request it. The variation of reinforcement procedure does not require that the investigator be able to specify what will be reinforcing. Loosely speaking, this procedure assumes that if an event is reinforcing, then minor variations of it are also likely to be reinforcing. What follows are some examples.

Cigarettes were a popular reinforcer for many patients. Initially the patients had used only bulk tobacco, rolling the cigarettes themselves. Following the minor variation of reinforcement procedure, several different types and brands of cigarettes were made available. Some patients selected filter cigarettes to the exclusion of other types, while others chose mentholated cigarettes. Even more unexpected was the discovery that chewing tobacco was highly reinforcing for one of the patients! Similarly, soda drinks were available in a wide range of flavors. Bedspreads, floor mats, and throw cushions were items that were offered in several attractive colors. In addition, walks were scheduled so that their route varied. Low and high beds were available, as well as a variety of different types of chairs—rocking chairs, straight chairs, metal or wooden chairs. Cabinets also were offered in two different styles with one or two drawers, with or without locks.

Adhering to the Probability of Behavior Rule, it was observed that for some patients, church attendance was a highly probable event. The opportunity to attend services was, therefore, made available. Following the variation of reinforcement procedure, each service was ended with the chaplain asking for contributions and passing a collection plate. Surprisingly, it was found that the opportunity to give was a reinforcer for the patients! The total given to the collection plate for a period of two months was 49 tokens, or seven tokens per service. An average of seven patients had attended each service. Thus, an additional source of reinforcement was discovered by providing a variation in the manner in which the religious service was conducted. Sometimes minor variations of a known reinforcer resulted in the discovery of additional reinforcing events. For example, it appeared that 18 patients chose the opportunity to eat with a particular group because it had been given more time within which to eat the meal than the other groups had. When the time was reduced to only five minutes for that group, eight of the 18 patients continued to select it although the time allowed to eat in that group was now less than for the other groups. It had been assumed that the selection of the group was due to the longer time allowed for eating. Thus, an additional source of reinforcement for choosing a given eating group was discovered: namely, the company with which one eats.

In any institution or natural setting the number of reinforcers available in the immediate environment of the individual will be restricted either by custom or by imagined administrative regulations. Yet the range of experience for most humans is such that it cuts across specific environments. Regardless of the specific situation in which one is attempting to modify human behavior, one can be almost certain that the individuals in that situation have engaged in a wide range of activities outside that context. Many of these activities or objects on the outside undoubtedly were reinforcing. No single situation with which one is likely to be working can be expected to incorporate all of these potential sources of reinforcement. It is essential, therefore, to recognize that sources of reinforcement will always go beyond those available in the immediate environment. Simple recognition, however, is insufficient. If this assumption is correct, then formal procedures should be instituted to make use of these untapped sources of reinforcement, rather than excusing their absence because of administrative or situational happenstance.

CHAPTER 5

Maximizing the Effectiveness of the Reinforcer

A. CONDITIONED REINFORCEMENT

One of the major problems in using reinforcing stimuli such as bedrooms, access to church, interviews with the nurse, and similar reinforcers employed in the motivating environment is that they cannot easily be arranged to follow the patient's behavior. For example, a patient may do breakfast dishes, but the reinforcer, such as a movie, may only be available in the evening. This delay between the behavior and reinforcer delivery works against any attempt to strengthen dishwashing behavior. An additional problem raised by the type of reinforcing stimuli used here is that immediate reinforcement would often require numerous interruptions of the patient's ongoing behavior if reinforcement were delivered upon the occurrence of the response. The impracticability of such a procedure led us to examine animal conditioning studies for a solution to this problem.

Laboratory Studies

Laboratory studies with animals have demonstrated that the effectiveness of a reinforcer depends greatly on the immediacy with which it follows the desired response. A response is strengthened when reinforcement is delivered immediately. Any delay between the response and the receipt of the reinforcer weakens the response. For recent reviews of studies of delayed reinforcement see Kelleher and Gollub (1962), Bolles (1967), and Kimble (1961). An example of the importance of immediate reinforcement can be seen in

Grice's (1948) experiment with rats. Grice found that a discrimination required about 10 times as many conditioning trials when the reinforcer was delayed for only two seconds. Similarly, Skinner (1938) found that the rate of bar-presses of rats was reduced to a small fraction of its usual rate when the food reinforcer was delayed for six seconds. This reduction in response rate under delayed reinforcement has been obtained only when the delay interval contains no stimuli that are distinctively associated with the reinforcer.

When a given stimulus follows the response immediately and is associated with a later delivery of reinforcement, the response can be maintained in strength in spite of very long delays. Watson (1917) found that the performance of rats that were conditioned to dig through a layer of sawdust to reach a cup in which food was later placed was not reduced by a delay between finding the cup and getting the food. During the 30-second delay, the rats were in the immediate presence of the food cup which, although empty, still constituted a stimulus that was distinctively associated with the later delivery of food. Azzi et al. (1953) introduced delays between a rat's lever press and the delivery of a pellet. The lever press was followed immediately by a reduction of illumination at the termination of which the pellet was delivered. The reduced illumination served as an immediate stimulus change that was associated with the food delivery. The lever presses were maintained at high levels even with long delays.

The chain schedule described by Ferster and Skinner (1957) constitutes a method of studying the effects of delayed reinforcement. In the chain schedule the animal produces a stimulus change which is followed some time later by the reinforcer. In both procedures, the delivery of reinforcement occurs at some period of time after a distinctive stimulus has followed the response. The results obtained with chain schedules by Ferster and Skinner (1957) and others demonstrate that substantial amounts of behavior can be maintained by delayed reinforcement.

Tokens

Kelleher (1957) and, earlier, Wolfe (1936) and Cowles (1937), used a tangible type of conditioned stimulus to bridge the delay between response and reinforcer. In Kelleher's procedure, a chimp pressed a lever to produce tokens which could be exchanged for food only at a much later time, sometimes as long as three hours later. Wolfe and Cowles and Kelleher all found that the tokens were effective in maintaining behavior despite the long delay. In addition, Wolfe and Cowles found that the tokens were about as effective as was immediate food reinforcement.

Tokens have several valuable features as conditioned reinforcers: (1) The number of tokens can bear a simple quantitative relation to the amount of reinforcement; (2) the tokens are portable and can be in the subject's possession even when he is in a situation far removed from that in which the tokens were earned; (3) no maximum exists in the number of tokens a subject may possess, whereas dimensions such as intensity, as with volume of music, have practical maximum reinforcing value; (4) tokens can be used directly to operate devices for the automatic delivery of reinforcers; (5) tokens are durable and can be continuously present during the delay, in contrast, say, with a brief flash of light or sound; (6) the physical characteristics of the tokens can be easily standardized; (7) the tokens can be made fairly indestructible so they will not deteriorate during the delay; (8) the tokens can be made unique and nonduplicable so that the experimenter can be assured that they are received only in the authorized manner. In addition, the token has the usual advantages of other conditioned reinforcers: (1) It bridges the delay between the desired response and the delivery of reinforcement, thereby maintaining the response in strength; (2) it allows the response to be reinforced any time, whereas primary reinforcement is typically restricted as to time and place; (3) it allows sequences of responses to be reinforced without interruption due to delivery of the reinforcer. These advantages form the theoretical background of the rule that follows.

Conditioned Reinforcement Rule: Provide a distinctive and tangible stimulus event to bridge any delay between the desired response and the delivery of the reinforcer.

Social Approval

The most obvious type of conditioned reinforcement is some statement of verbal approval such as "That's good," or "You've done a good job." Verbal approval has the advantage of all conditioned reinforcers in that it provides the immediate distinctive stimulus following the desired response. Also, it does not disrupt the continuity of the desired behavior, as would the actual delivery of the reinforcing events. Finally, it allows the response to be strengthened at any time that the conditioned reinforcer can be delivered, even when the primary reinforcer is restricted as to time and place.

One disadvantage of verbal approval as a conditioned reinforcer is that it is momentary and, therefore, does not provide continued exposure during the delay interval. Perhaps most important in terms of ease of recording is that verbal approval is not standardized. That is, the qualitative dimensions (kind or type) of verbal approval do not allow for a simple quantitative measure of conditioned reinforcement. Also, its transient nature does not permit it to be transferred from one individual to another and thereby used to control the behavior of others. Further, its transient nature does not permit an accurate record of its delivery or the degree to which it was followed by actual primary reinforcement. Finally, it cannot be used to operate automatic reinforcement devices.

Another type of conditioned reinforcement is that of facial expressions such as smiles and frowns. This type of conditioned reinforcement has all the disadvantages of verbal approval, in addition to being more difficult to specify in physical terms and to record.

Points or Credits

Another method of implementing conditioned reinforcement is to make some written record, for example, with points or credits. These have the distinct advantage over verbal approval in that they last longer and leave an enduring record. As a consequence, a method is available for recording the amount of conditioned reinforcement given to the individual and the number expended. In addition, the points are standardized, have a simple quantitative dimension, and are not easily altered or destroyed since the record of the points or credits can be safeguarded. The disadvantages of points and credits are that they are intangible and hence are not in the individual's possession during the delay interval. Their intangibility also limits them as a medium of exchange and prevents their use for operation of automatic reinforcing devices.

Application of the Conditioned Reinforcement Rule in the Motivating Environment

A tangible conditioned reinforcer, consisting of a metal token, was used in the motivating environment. The token was specially manufactured so that it could not be duplicated. It was made of metal and, therefore, could not be easily mutilated or destroyed. Because of its unique markings, the token could not be obtained easily in an unauthorized manner from some source outside the motivating environment. Because of its similarity to money, it proved to be a particularly easy type of conditioned reinforcer to use since almost all of the patients had at one time had some experience with money. Without exception all reinforcing events in the motivating environment were obtainable with tokens.

B. MULTIPLE REINFORCERS

Everyone is probably familiar with the enthusiasm and appetite with which Thanksgiving turkey is greeted for several days after Thanksgiving. By the third day of eating leftover turkey, the enthusiasm often changes to indifference and then to active dislike. This annual cycle illustrates a problem generally encountered when reinforcers are used to excess with animals and humans. The problem is that of satiation. It would seem that as a reinforcer is used in excess, its reinforcing properties diminish to the point where it no longer functions as a reinforcer. Several procedures have been developed in the laboratory to cope with the problems brought about by satiation.

Laboratory Studies of Animal Behavior

In studies of animal behavior, the problem of satiation has occurred whenever a single event has been used as a reinforcer. For example, when food is used to reinforce the lever press of a rat, the lever presses occur very frequently at the start of a session but decline rapidly as the rat becomes satiated. One solution has been to restrict the duration of the session. The disadvantage of this procedure is that behavioral control is possible only during the restricted period. A second solution is to reinforce the behavior only intermittently. Intermittent reinforcement allows behavior to be maintained over longer periods of time by postponing the satiation process. The disadvantage of intermittent reinforcement is that it avoids satiation only at some cost in behavioral control, since it is well known that the more intermittently the reinforcer is delivered, the lower the frequency of the reinforced response.

Laboratory Studies with Humans

Studies of reinforcement with humans have usually used a single reinforcer; for example, cigarettes, candy, or trinkets. The likelihood of satiating the subject with one of these reinforcers is high. As was seen in the studies of animal behavior, one solution to the problem of satiation is to limit the duration of the experimental sessions. The typical duration of a session in human studies using a single reinforcer is less than 30 minutes and is scheduled only once a day. The use of intermittent reinforcement has the same disadvantage seen for animals.

Previous applications of operant conditioning to problems of human behavior have often used a single reinforcer or at most a few reinforcers (Bijou and Sturges, 1959; Lovaas et al., 1966a; Orlando and Bijou, 1960; Ayllon and Michael, 1959; Isaacs, Thomas and Goldiamond, 1960; Lindsley, 1956). No implication existed in these later studies, however, that the types of reinforcers used—M & M's food, or social attention—were the dominant motivators of human behavior. Rather they were selected for experimental convenience, and with much care to avoid reaching satiation too soon.

An alternative solution was that of Ferster and DeMyer (1962), who used multiple reinforcers. They made different types of reinforcing objects and events available to autistic children at one time. The children could select among drinking a cold beverage, playing a pinball machine, playing a phonograph record, running an electric train, etc. Staats, Staats, Schutz, and Wolf (1962) attempted to solve the problem of satiation in the same manner. They used many types of trinkets in combination with different types of candies in an experiment with children on the control of reading. Results such as the above form the theoretical basis for the following rule:

Multiple Reinforcer Rule: Use many different types of reinforcing stimuli with a given individual.

Stated conversely, the above rule dictates that one should never use a single event as a reinforcer. The reason for this, as stated above, is that there seems to be no single reinforcing event for which some type of satiation or, in the case of aversive stimuli, adaptation does not occur. Certainly, most of the biologically based reinforcers are subject to satiation, including food, water, and sex. Other types of reinforcers specifically human, such as reading a book, listening to music, watching a movie, or visiting a friend, appear intuitively to be at least as susceptible to satiation as the biologically based reinforcers. Having recognized this principle of satiation for any given type of reinforcer, it is only a partial solution to use two or three different events as reinforcers. Instead, every attempt should be made to use as wide a variety of reinforcers as is available, in spite of any inconvenience or administrative difficulty that might result from so doing.

Application of the Multiple Reinforcer Rule in the Motivating Environment

The Multiple Reinforcer Rule also eliminates the behavioral engineer's concern as to why the satiation effect should occur for a given event or a particular patient. For example, for a period of time a patient, Lisa C., was regularly paying tokens to talk with various staff members. She spent 185 tokens in a period of a month to talk to the chaplain, nurse, social worker, physician, and psychologist. During this time she also spent 812 tokens for other reinforcers on the ward. Then, without any apparent explanation, she no longer chose private talks with the staff members. Had there been no other events to serve as reinforcers, there would have been no source of motivation for Lisa. In practice, however, she availed herself continuously and freely of many of the other reinforcing events that were available to her. In fact, Lisa spent 1,122 tokens in other reinforcers during that period. The overall power of the reinforcement procedure was thereby maintained without any undue concern as to why the effectiveness of a particular reinforcer increased or decreased. The spending pattern for almost all patients was similar to that described for Lisa, in that each patient spent tokens for many types of reinforcers. Table A-4 in the Appendix shows the great diversity of reinforcers obtained for eight of the patients during a six-week period. No patient ever restricted herself to only one reinforcing event.

Failure to observe the Multiple Reinforcer Rule would have produced satiation. This phenomenon was observed and will be described later in the chapter in several experiments in which the satiation resulted for the reinforcers of popcorn and soda and attendance at movies.

Reinforcers and the Uniqueness of Individuals

One of the greatest advantages of the Multiple Reinforcer Rule is the opportunity it provides for suiting the reinforcement procedure to given individuals. It is axiomatic in studying adult humans that there will be large individual differences as to what is reinforcing. We are referring to differences in reinforcing effectiveness among individuals in contrast to fluctuations in the effectiveness of a reinforcer for one individual. This rule makes it possible to utilize the entire range of interests, likes, preferences, and motivations of that individual. There is no need to discover the one dominant motivator or reinforcer for him. Instead, all sources of reinforcement or motivation can be given full expression. Further, there is no need to decide beforehand that for Individual A the dominant reinforcer is that of social interaction, whereas for Individual B the dominant motivator is that of social isolation, as would be implied in a method based on a typology such as extraversion-introversion.

One of the misconceptions about a behaviorist approach is that it deals only with a narrow aspect of an individual's potentialities. The Multiple Reinforcer Rule gives explicit recognition to the variety of motivating factors that exist for humans and provides a standardized procedure for guaranteeing that these manifold interests will be satisfied.

Most types of psychological theory make some assumptions about the prime source of motivation for an individual and base the therapeutic procedure primarily or solely on utilization of that source of motivation. For example, in psychoanalytic theory the sexual urges are considered the dominant motivators. In the Rogerian, nondirective therapies "self-actualization" is considered the sole source of motivation. Horney considers security to be the important thing; Adler, the concept of inferiority-superiority; and Harry Stack Sullivan, interpersonal relationships (see overview by Cofer and Appley, 1964). On the other hand, statements about human behavior by ethnologists (Lorenz, 1965) stress the purely biological instincts such as aggression, self-preservation, and reproduction.

There is no need to decide which of the varying philosophies of behavior noted above is the correct one since all possible reinforcers may be made available under the present procedure. For example, some patients obtained a grounds pass in order to be alone; others, to socialize with other female patients; others, with male patients. Some received grounds passes to obtain whatever other source of motivation existed outside the ward. To the extent that any of the sources of motivation indicated by the different theories is a valid or effective one, the present procedure will allow that source of motivation to be expressed and utilized.

C. COMPATIBILITY OF REINFORCERS

In view of the aim of the motivating environment to maximize the sources of reinforcement, it was particularly important to determine the effectiveness of making many sources of reinforcement available at the same time. The question, stated loosely, was this, "Is it more effective to present the patient with a wide range of opportunities for reinforcement from which she can choose at one time, or is it better to stagger the opportunities for reinforcement in order to avoid there being too many at one time?"

This basic question is one that has also been raised by experimenters in the context of the animal laboratory, and their answer to the question is particularly relevant to human behavior.

Laboratory Studies of Animal Behavior

Animal studies of reinforcement have revealed several problems of behavioral control when more than one reinforcing stimulus is delivered at the same time, or when two different responses are available for producing different amounts of the same reinforcement. Consider the simplest example in which a rat is reinforced in the presence of a white stimulus in one arm of a T-maze, but not reinforced in the black arm of that T-maze. In one study, Krechevsky (1932) found that a given rat adopted a position preference, continuously going only to one arm of the maze and ignoring the other arm, regardless of whether food was absent or present in that other arm. Only after extended training was this position preference overcome, and the behavior put under the control of the black and white stimuli.

It has been the general experience of investigators of animal behavior in the laboratory that the same type of preference exists when two response levers are used. The animal often responds to one of the levers to the exclusion of the other. This position preference is so strong after a history of reinforcement on one of the levers that standard types of precautions have been adopted to eliminate the development of position preferences. One type of solution is to alternate the presence or absence of the reinforcer between the two levers or arms of the T-maze. Another is to have forced trials into both arms of the T-maze. In the forced trial method, one of the arms is physically blocked, and the experimenter terminates the trial only after the animal has entered the other arm.

This problem of position preferences exists not only in studies of reinforcement versus extinction but also when reinforcers of different types are available. Thus, for example, many studies have been done on the differential effectiveness of varying degrees of sucrose concentration. To avoid response preference, a two-bottle method is often used in which the low and high sucrose concentrations are assigned on a systematic basis first to one bottle, then to the other.

Laboratory Studies of Human Behavior

Studies of human behavior have revealed this same problem of response preference. For example, in three studies of the effects of an aversive stimulus, a situation was used in which two knobs were available to a patient; pulling either of the knobs resulted in the same delivery of reinforcement. The results in these three studies (Holz, Azrin, and Ayllon, 1963; Herman and Azrin, 1964; Ayllon and Azrin, 1966) was that all of the patients selected one of the knobs and responded almost exclusively to that knob.

These and similar results suggest a general rule for avoiding the problem of incompatibility between reinforcers and the associated problem of response preference.

Compatibility of Reinforcers Rule: Schedule reinforcing activities so that they occur at different times.

This rule is very easily violated in an attempt to program as many reinforcers as possible, as is dictated by the Multiple Reinforcer Rule. It might be assumed that if two different reinforcers are scheduled at the same time, the individual will select one of the reinforcers at one time and the other at another time. In practice this did not happen. Rather, the behavior of the patients very closely paralleled the behavior in the previously discussed experiments. When two or more reinforcers were scheduled simultaneously, the patients often selected one of the reinforcers to the exclusion of the others, either accidentally or because of actual preference. Once the pattern of selection was established, the other reinforcers seemed not to exist for them.

Application in the Motivating Environment

Failure to follow the Compatibility of Reinforcement Rule can lead to a waste of one or more sources of reinforcement, as shown in the following experiment.

Experiment 6: The effects of scheduling competing reinforcers on attendance at religious services

The question this experiment attempted to answer was, what is the most effective way of scheduling reinforcers—concurrently or separately? To answer this question one reinforcer, religious service, was first scheduled separately from a second reinforcer, commissary period, and later concurrently with it. The measure of effectiveness of the reinforcer was the number of patients attending the religious service.

Method. Thirty-six patients participated. First, a religious service was held only once weekly for six weeks with no other reinforcing activity scheduled at the same time. Each time the religious service was held, patients could attend by depositing a token in a turnstile, which could be done any time during the service. An attendant announced the religious service five minutes before it started. Next she took a record of all those patients who attended the service. After six weeks, the procedure was changed so that the religious service was scheduled concurrently with the commissary period for a total of six services. To control for the effects of fatigue or simple passage of time, the concurrent scheduling of reinforcing activities was followed by another period of six weeks during which religious services were once again held separately from the commissary period.

Table 5–1

Effects of Scheduling Competing Reinforcers on Attendance at Religious Services

Service scheduled separately from another reinforcing activity	Service scheduled *concurrently* with another reinforcing activity	Service scheduled separately from another reinforcing activity
7.8	2.8	8.3

Mean number of patients attending each religious service. Each period is based on six opportunities for 36 patients.

Results. Table 5–1 shows that when the religious services were held separately from commissary, about eight patients attended religious services. However, when the religious services were scheduled simultaneously with the commissary period, the average number of patients attending religious services decreased to about three patients. When the religious services were once again rescheduled separately from commissary, the average number of patients attending the services returned to about eight per service.

Discussion. The results demonstrate that when reinforcers are scheduled concurrently, their effectiveness is weakened. Stated otherwise, these results show that when the reinforcing activities are scheduled so they will not be in competition with each other, their effectiveness is maximized.

Other Applications

Admittedly, there are so many possible events that are reinforcing to the individual it is difficult to schedule each of them in a sequential manner. Still, there is little doubt that the administrative trouble caused by appropriate rescheduling of the reinforcers is more than offset by the gains in patient's participation and total amount of tokens spent on these reinforcers. Another example involving the commissary period will illustrate this point. In this example, participation in the reinforcer was already very high. Almost all of the patients were obtaining items at the commissary period in contrast with the small number that had been attending religious services. Nevertheless, a slight increase in the use of the commissary items resulted when a competing reinforcer was eliminated.

The customary procedure for commissary was to hold it at the same time that another room was made available in which there were vending machines for sodas and cigarettes, as well as a radio, a television set, and an electric cigarette lighter. This procedure was modified in accordance with the Compatibility of Reinforcer Rule such that the other room was not available until after the commissary period had terminated. The duration of the commissary period was held constant at 20 minutes. The results showed that when the reinforcing activities in the second room were in competition with the commissary period, an average of 38 patients out of 43 purchased items during the commissary. These 38 patients spent a total of 2,009 tokens in a period of seven days. When the reinforcing activities were available in succession, and were therefore compatible, three more patients, or a total of 41 out of 43 patients, spent tokens at commissary. The total number of tokens rose from 2,009 to 2,121 for the same period. In this instance motivational sources from many different types of reinforcers were left untapped because of competing response preference. Failure to abide by this rule seems to occur very easily, perhaps because of the irrationality of this tendency for response preference.

Of course, not all reinforcers are incompatible with each other. Cigarettes, popcorn, soda, etc. can be used while on a walk, watching a movie, or at a dance. The same is true for clothing and other durables that require no absorbing activity once the item is obtained. Most of these items could be obtained at the commissary periods, which were accordingly scheduled very frequently (several times each day) since use of the items obtained at commissary were generally quite compatible with other activities. This compatibility also permitted the vending machines to be continuously available without concern for interference. The Compatibility of Reinforcer Rule applies, therefore, only to those reinforcing events or activities that by their very nature cannot be conducted simultaneously, such as religious services, movies, going for walks, talks with the staff, dances, etc., none of which can be easily performed at the same moment.

D. PRIMING THE USE OF A REINFORCER

1. Reinforcer Sampling

Intuitively, it would seem that once an event is identified as a reinforcer, it should apply in different situations and for different responses. Yet there is considerable evidence to indicate that when a reinforcing event is presented in a new situation, emotional reactions will be produced that interfere with the reinforcing properties of the stimulus. Consider, for example, a series of observations conducted by O. L. Tinklepaugh (1928). A monkey was trained to pick up a particular cup after having seen the experimenter place a banana under that cup. Once trained, the animal was required to wait several seconds between the time the banana was placed under the cup and the time he was given access to it. Next the experimenter repeated the same procedure using lettuce instead of a banana. After the monkey saw the experimenter place lettuce under a particular cup, the monkey correctly identified the appropriate cup after an enforced delay and ate the lettuce. Finally, the experimenter "tricked" the monkey. He allowed the monkey to see him put a banana under the cup and then as usual imposed a delay interval. During that interval, the experimenter removed the banana and placed lettuce there instead. The monkey then picked up the cup but upon viewing the lettuce, he did not eat it. Instead he engaged in a number of auxiliary emotional behaviors and ultimately discarded the lettuce completely. The same type of food, a piece of lettuce, it should be recalled, was immediately eaten when the monkey had seen that food and was "expecting" it. In this case it appears that there was a response chain involved in obtaining the lettuce; and unless that response chain occurred in a particular context, the lettuce would not serve as a reinforcer.

In using a reinforcer, therefore, it is desirable to eliminate those aspects of the presentation of the reinforcer that are likely to interfere with its effectiveness. The results of R. C. Davis' (1934) study of high intensity noise with humans illustrate one means whereby these emotional effects can be made to adapt out. Davis presented intense noise to humans while simultaneously recording several autonomic or emotional reactions. He found considerable autonomic reaction at the onset of the initial presentation of the noise. During continued exposure to the noise, these emotional reactions were considerably reduced. Successive presentations of the noise resulted in renewed emotional reactions but at a progressively lower level until finally the noise could be presented and eliminated with no discernible autonomic reactions resulting.

These results suggest a means of eliminating the emotional reactions that surround the presentation of an old event in a new context. The event should be presented repeatedly to the individual. If necessary, the individual should be put into forced contact with the stimulus and be made to sample it. This type of procedure, designated as magazine training, was used by Ferster and Skinner (1957) to eliminate emotional reactions to a food reinforcer for pigeons. It has been observed that birds will not readily eat food in the experimental chamber, even though it is the same type of food that is available in their home cage. In the experimental chamber the food is made available by raising a tray by an electrical device. The standard procedure adopted by Ferster and Skinner was to present the tray full of food repeatedly and for as long a duration as was necessary until the pigeon sampled the food in the new context. In the discussion provided by Holland and Skinner (1961) this process is interpreted as emotional adaptation. The procedure is designed to allow the bird to adapt to the noise and visual changes associated with the food delivery. It is only after these emotional reactions have disappeared that the bird can be seen to eat immediately upon the presentation of the tray.

Nor is this process restricted to pigeons. The same procedure has been found necessary before using pellets to condition rats to bar-press (Ferster and Skinner, 1957). The standard magazine training procedure involves delivering a small pellet of food to the animal in a tray that is located in the experimental chamber. Often the first few deliveries of the pellets do not result in immediate eating by the rat. Instead, the rat, like the pigeons, sometimes shows much emotional behavior, exhibiting startle responses and withdrawal from the area where the food is delivered. Eventually the rat does not withdraw upon the sound of the pellet dispenser being activated, but rather, immediately runs toward the food and samples it. Then, and only then, can the pellet be used as a reinforcing event in the experimental chamber.

This behavioral rigidity in refusing reinforcers that are given in an unfamiliar context is not peculiar to animals, although intuitively, it might be assumed that humans would be more flexible and would allow the reinforcing properties of an event to apply from one situation to another. In one study (Sommer and Ayllon, 1956) conducted with college girls, money was given as the reinforcer upon completion of each session. It was found that after the first session, several of the girls refused to accept the money, often making comments such as "Oh, keep it, I don't really need it." "You can have it." "Give it to someone else." Similarly, an experiment by Hutchinson and Azrin (1961) with mental patients revealed this same necessity for sampling of the reinforcer in the new context. The experimenters deliberately selected for study those patients on their ward who smoked heavily. These subjects were brought into a testing room where cigarettes were to be used as a reinforcer for knob-pulling. On the first day of the study all patients showed considerable reluctance to take the cigarettes. Many of them left most, if not all, of the cigarettes in the experimental room when they departed, in spite of the instruction given to them that the cigarettes were theirs to keep. Only after consecutive sessions did the subjects readily accept all of the cigarettes and smoke them. A later study by Holz, Azrin, and Ayllon (1963) with mental patients revealed the same process. During the initial sessions of conditioning, the cigarettes and candy being delivered as reinforcers were rejected by the subjects. Similar problems occurred in an experiment with mental hospital patients who were being given tokens for pulling a knob. Although these patients had been regularly earning tokens in their ward environment, they initially refused to take all the tokens when they were delivered to them through an automatic token dispenser in the experimental room. Instead, at the end of the session they often commented "I really don't need it." "It really didn't involve that much work." "Why don't you save it for the next patient." Yet, when they were persuaded to take them, it was found that on successive sessions the tokens were quickly collected by them. Only after this sampling of the token reinforcer in the new context of the special experimental room could the token be used as an effective reinforcer. The above experimental background provides the theoretical basis for the following rule.

Reinforcer Sampling Rule: Before using an event or stimulus as a reinforcer, require sampling of the reinforcer in the situation in which it is to be used.

The Reinforcer Sampling Rule is particularly useful when the individual has had no history for using the reinforcer and is, therefore, unfamiliar with it. No consumption or use of a potentially reinforcing stimulus is likely in the absence of familiarity with it. Active sampling will provide the necessary familiarity. For example, when trying to teach a child to eat a new food, say artichokes, verbal descriptions alone will not ensure familiarity; familiarity can be ensured only by somehow arranging for the child to taste a small sample of the artichoke. The same may be said for swimming. Some type of direct contact with water may be necessary before the individual will begin to seek out the opportunity to swim. The following report in *Newsweek*, June 19, 1967, illustrates this need for active sampling rather than verbal description.

> Familiarity may breed contempt, but the Harvard business school is betting the other way. It plans to take a group of undergraduates who have expressed contempt for business as a career and expose them to a summer of familiarity with the business world . . . the students will make $110 a week and will be given "meaningful" assignments, like researching a market or joining a task force studying a specific problem . . . (p. 76).

As implied by the above quotation, the sampling of the event does not guarantee that the event will, in fact, be reinforcing to the individual; rather, the sampling allows any reinforcing properties to be exhibited if the event has any potential reinforcing properties. If the individual does not seek the event after it has been sampled, it will not be because of a lack of familiarity with it.

Even if the individual has had a history of using a particular reinforcer, it does not follow that he will use the reinforcer in the future. As pointed out above, oftentimes a change in the situation in which the reinforcer is available or a difference in the stimulus configuration associated with the reinforcement delivery will decrease use of the reinforcing stimulus. In such instances, continued sampling of the reinforcing stimulus in the new or different context should maintain the event as a reinforcer.

The usefulness of the sampling rule appears to have been recognized in some practical business situations. For example, sales organizations often give a potential customer the use of an item without cost and often under some protestation by him. A car salesman will sometimes insist on the potential customer's "taking the car for a spin," suggesting perhaps, "Why don't you try it out over the weekend; there's no obligation. Just bring it back on Monday." Similarly, book companies and record companies, unsolicited, often send merchandise to potential customers and allow a period of time during which the individual may sample the books or records. The financial solvency of these companies may attest to the usefulness of the Reinforcer Sampling Rule. A third example is a concession salesman who forces free samples on the noninterested passerby. The reader will be able to think of many similar examples. An event cannot be expected to be effective as a reinforcer until there has been familiarity with it in a given stimulus context. A simple verbal description of the characteristic of the event is often not sufficient.

Active sampling of the reinforcer may do much more than establish familiarity in a given context. It is possible that sampling will also increase utilization of a reinforcer even when context or familiarity is not a factor.

A series of experiments attempted to determine whether the Reinforcer Sampling Rule would increase the effectiveness of various reinforcers in the motivating environment. An attempt was made in these experiments to determine whether the sampling procedure would increase reinforcer utilization even when the patients were already familiar with the reinforcer in the specific context in which it was given. Three experiments concerned with this question are presented here, and three additional ones have been described in detail elsewhere (Ayllon and Azrin, 1968).

Experiment 7: Fair attendance and reinforcer sampling

The present experiment attempted to determine whether attendance at a small-town fair could be increased by means of a reinforcer sampling procedure. The fair was held on a site one mile away from the mental hospital. The available activities included rides on a ferris wheel and a merry-go-round, playing games such as bingo, buying consumables from refreshment stands, and being involved in various other types of general entertainment which are typical of small-town fairs.

Procedure. Sixteen patients participated in this experiment. During the first day, posters were conspicuously displayed on the ward announcing the opportunity to attend the fair. At approximately 9 A.M., 1:00 P.M., and 4:00 P.M. the ward attendant loudly announced that a trip to the fair was being scheduled and that all those who desired to attend should assemble at the ward exit. Those patients who assembled at the exit paid one token for the opportunity to attend, whereupon they were taken to the fair for approximately two hours. Each patient was given 50 cents to spend at the fair. The decision to attend was made while the patient was on the ward.

On the second day, all patients were required to accompany the attendant to the fairgrounds. They made their decision at the fair instead of exercising it on the ward. Also, each patient was given a free ticket at the fair to ensure her exposure to at least one of the fair activities.

On the third day, the requirement of going to the fairgrounds was eliminated. The patients exercised their choice of whether to pay one token to attend the fair while on the ward rather than at the fairgrounds.

Results. The results were analyzed separately for patients who had already been attending the fair to determine whether the sampling procedure had any effect on patients already familiar with the fair. Table 5–2 shows the results for the 10 patients who attended

Table 5–2

Reinforcer Sampling and Fair Attendance

	Standard procedure	Reinforcer sampling	Standard procedure
Total attendance	22	28	24

For 10 patients who *attended* at least once in the fair prior to reinforcer sampling.

Each cell entry is based on three opportunities to attend the fair for 10 patients.

the fair during the initial day without the reinforcer sampling procedure. These 10 patients continued to attend the fair during the subsequent two days. Their overall attendance increased from 22 to 28 attendances when the reinforcer sampling procedure was in effect and decreased again to 24 attendances when it was discontinued. Since three opportunities to attend were available each day,

28 attendances by 10 patients means that during the Reinforcer Sampling procedure, these 10 patients were attending at almost every opportunity. Thirty attendances was the maximum.

Table 5–3 shows that the reinforcer sampling procedure caused five of the six patients to attend who had not previously attended. Two of them continued to attend on the third day when the reinforcer sampling procedure was discontinued. These two attended for the maximum of three opportunities each day.

Table 5–3

Reinforcer Sampling and Fair Attendance

	Standard procedure	Reinforcer sampling	Standard procedure
Number of patients attending the fair	0	5	2
Total attendance	0	10	6

For six patients who had *no* attendance at the fair prior to Reinforcer Sampling. Each cell entry based on three opportunities to attend the fair for six patients.

These results show that this initial sampling of the fair activities caused patients who were attending the fair to attend more frequently and caused patients who had not been attending the fair to start attending it. For both types of patients some residual effect of the reinforcer sampling procedure was evident. Attendance at the fair was slightly greater after the reinforcer sampling procedure was terminated than it had been before the procedure was instituted. The sampling procedure initiated attendance for those patients who were unfamiliar with the fair and increased attendance for those who were familiar with it.

Experiment 8: Attendance at religious services and reinforcer sampling

As seen in Table A–1 in the Appendix, which lists the reinforcers used in the behavioral environment, not all of them are ordinarily considered to be recreational. One reinforcer, for example, is attendance at religious services, which is often considered desirable but not because of any inherent recreational properties that it possesses. If, however, it is useful to consider religious services as a reinforcer in the same way that the more obviously recreational events such as dances or attendances at a fair are, then the Reinforcer Sampling procedure might be expected to affect religious services in the same way as it had the other reinforcers. Yet it is the distinctively different nature of religious services compared with dances and movies which might lead one to expect that they would not react in the same way to procedures that were designed to increase the utilization of a reinforcer. Religious services are also different from many of the other reinforcers used because there usually is minimal active participation by the individual attending, in contrast with the usual active involvement in such activities as dancing and walks. In this sense attendance at religious services is more similar to attendance at a movie.

The attempt to discover means of changing attendance at religious services described below should not be construed as having had any proselytizing objective. As was also true in the study of the other reinforcing events no attempt was made to discover why the religious activity is reinforcing, but only to discover how the situation could be changed in such a way that its utilization as a reinforcer would be increased.

Procedure. Twenty-six patients participated in this experiment. As in previous experiments, the other patients were not included because they were either entirely or intermittently absent from the ward at the time scheduled for religious services. No attempt was made to exclude patients from this study because of the presence or absence of religious beliefs.

The religious service lasted for 15 minutes and was conducted by a hospital chaplain. The service was held in a separate room set aside for this purpose. The room was furnished with religious ornaments, such as a crucifix and podium especially chosen by the hospital chaplain. The chaplain started the service by distributing copies of the Bible to each churchgoer. A hymn with piano accompaniment opened and closed the meeting. The attendant announced clearly throughout the ward that a religious service was being scheduled. Then the chaplain walked through the ward greeting each patient, shaking hands with her, and inviting each patient personally to the religious service. Patients attended the religious service by depositing a token into a turnstile which was located at the entrance to the room where the services were held. This procedure was followed for seven service periods, during which the conditions associated with religious services were kept constant, such as the identity of the chaplain, the nature of his interaction with the patients, and the duration of the service. No other activities that might compete with the religious services were scheduled.

A reinforcer sampling procedure was instituted for seven services during which all the 26 patients were requested to enter a room in one part of which the religious service was to be held. None objected in any way. The turnstile separated the two areas of the room. The religious service was then started, and after five minutes, while the service was still being conducted, the attendant made the customary announcement about the availability of the religious service. Admission to the religious service, just as before, was possible by depositing one token into the turnstile. The rest of the patients left the room. A final series of seven services was held using the procedure followed during the first seven services in which attendance was not requested during the initial five minutes of the service.

Table 5–4

Reinforcement Sampling and Attendance at Religious Services

	Standard procedure	Reinforcer sampling	Standard procedure
Number of times religious services were selected	36	35	32

For the eight patients who *participated* at least once in the religious services prior to reinforcer sampling. Each cell entry is based on seven periods of religious service for eight patients.

Results. Eight of the 26 patients attended religious services when there was no requirement to attend the initial five minutes. Table 5–4 shows that for these eight patients the five-minute attendance requirement had no substantial effect. Neither the number of patients attending nor their total attendance was significantly altered. Table 5–5 shows the results for the 18 patients who did not attend even one religious service prior to the reinforcer sampling procedure. The initial period of required attendance caused five patients to attend religious services, whereas none had earlier. These

Table 5–5

Reinforcer Sampling and Attendance at Religious Services

	Standard procedure	Reinforcer sampling	Standard procedure
Number of patients participating in religious services	0	5	3
Number of times religious services were selected	0	10	8

For the 18 patients who had *no* participation in the religious services prior to Reinforcer Sampling. Each cell entry is based on seven periods of religious services for 18 patients.

five patients attended a total of 10 times. When the reinforcer sampling procedure was discontinued, the number of patients attending decreased from five to three. This drop was also accompanied by a slight reduction in the total attendance from 10 to eight.

Discussion. The results of this experiment indicate that religious services are as amenable to study as are other reinforcing activities. The patients who already had been attending the religious services simply continued to do so. What is particularly significant is that the Reinforcer Sampling procedure generated participation for those who had no record of religious attendance prior to this special procedure. Presumably, these patients were fairly unfamiliar with the services. Only through this procedure were these patients put into direct contact with an activity previously ignored by them. The increase in the number of patients attending religious services and total attendance was not caused by the simple passage of time, since there was a drop in the number of patients attending and in their total attendance when the reinforcer sampling procedure was discontinued. This was also true in the previous sampling procedure for attending the fair. Some enduring effect of the sampling procedure is seen in the continued attendance by some patients even after the procedure had been discontinued.

Experiment 9: Attendance at social evenings and reinforcer sampling

Experiment 7 demonstrated that the reinforcer sampling procedure was an effective method of increasing utilization, even when the patients had already been familiar with the nature of the reinforcer and had already used it in the specific context in which the utilization was desired. These results indicated that the reinforcer sampling procedure did much more than simply provide familiarization.

One way of evaluating this conclusion more intensively is to provide a very long period of familiarization with the reinforcer by means of the sampling technique. If one then discontinues the sampling technique, no decrease in reinforcer utilization should result if the effectiveness of the procedure is based exclusively on familiarization. If, on the other hand, the sampling procedure is doing more than providing familiarization, the reinforcer should be utilized less when the sampling procedure is discontinued. The following experiment was conducted in such a way that a very long period of familiarization with the reinforcer was provided.

Method. Thirty-eight patients participated. The other patients on the ward were unable to participate since they had other activities that competed with this one. The reinforcing event will be designated here as the "social evening." A variety of activities were possible during this social evening, including playing bingo, dancing, playing cards, and listening to a live band. The activities were scheduled off the ward in a special hospital auditorium and lasted approximately two hours. The social evening was scheduled once each week.

Procedure. For a period of four months 38 patients were taken to the hospital auditorium where they participated in the entertainment for five minutes. At the end of this five-minute sampling period, the patients were asked to choose whether to stay in the recreation hall or to return to the ward. Patients could stay for one token. The patients that elected not to attend were returned to the ward.

The five-minute period of required attendance was terminated for an eight-week period. The procedure consisted of announcing the availability of the evening entertainment throughout the ward. Patients were not required to attend, but those who wished to attend paid one token and were then escorted to the auditorium. The rest of the patients remained on the ward. No other competing activities were scheduled on the ward.

Following this eight-week period, another eight-week period was instituted during which the five-minute period of required attendance was again in force.

Results. Table 5–6 shows that fewer patients used the social evenings as a reinforcer when the reinforcer sampling period was terminated, a decrease from 22 patients to 18. Upon reinstatement of the reinforcer sampling procedure, the number of patients participating increased to 25. Overall participation similarly decreased

Table 5–6

Reinforcer Sampling and Attendance at Social Evenings

	Reinforcer sampling	Standard procedure	Reinforcer sampling
Number of patients participating in social evenings	22	18	25
Number of times social evenings were selected	123	79	125

Each cell entry is based on eight social periods for 38 patients.

from 123 to 79 when the reinforcer sampling was terminated and increased again from 79 to 125 when the procedure was reinstated.

Discussion. The principal finding of the present experiment is that the reinforcer sampling procedure was an effective method of increasing reinforcer utilization under circumstances in which familiarity with the reinforcer was not a factor. Most of the patients had been attending one or more of the social evenings over a four-month period. If the primary effect of the sampling procedure were to provide familiarization, then discontinuation of this sampling procedure should have had no effect. Instead, the number of patients attending decreased somewhat, and the average amount of attendance per patient decreased substantially. When the sampling procedure was reintroduced, participation increased.

Conclusion

Three additional experiments have been reported elsewhere (Ayllon and Azrin, 1968) in which the reinforcer sampling procedure was used for the reinforcing events of going outdoors for a 15-minute walk, attending a musical session, and attending a movie. In those experiments, as well as in the experiments reported here, the reinforcer sampling procedure was found to increase the degree of reinforcer utilization. It appears, therefore, that the effectiveness of the Reinforcer Sampling procedure does not depend greatly on the nature of the reinforcing event, since six different reinforcing events were found to be utilized more by the requirement of participation in the initial phase of the event.

In several of these experiments, it appeared that part of the effect of this required participation was that it familiarized the patient with the nature of the reinforcing event. Evidence for this interpretation is the finding that participation was usually increased most for those patients who had not recently used the reinforcer. A second line of evidence for a familiarization effect is that once the patients began using the reinforcer because of the sampling procedure, they often continued to use it even after the reinforcer sampling procedure had been discontinued. This enduring effect may be a result of the familiarization that results from the required participation.

Evidence was also obtained in most of the experiments suggesting that the increased utilization of the reinforcer was not caused solely by familiarization, since the increased utilization occurred also for those patients who had already been using it.

Other applications of the reinforcer sampling rule

The reinforcer sampling procedure was used when a given patient was first assigned to the ward in order to ensure familiarity with all reinforcers. A systematic schedule was established that required the patient to participate for a period of approximately one week in all the events and activities that were being scheduled as reinforcers. For example, she was required to go on the daily 20-minute walk and to attend movies, musical activities, dances, visits scheduled to nearby towns, and private interviews with several staff members such as the ward nurse, psychologist, and so on. Also, she was provided with a bed in the most desirable room, which contained a private cabinet, a screen, the most desirable bedspread, her own chair, etc. At commissary time she was given a wide sampling of the items available: a cold drink, a candy bar, chewing gum, a comb, and so on. She was given the best items available in the way of personal clothing. At mealtime she was scheduled to eat in the group that was considered most desirable by the other patients.

The Reinforcer Sampling procedure was used, also, for all patients and for all reinforcers as a standard and continuing procedure. As has been described all patients were required or requested to be present during the initial few minutes of each reinforcing event, at which time the opportunity to pay a token to participate in the remainder of the event was given. The only exception to this standard use of the sampling procedure was for food and drinks, which had to be consumed and for which no simple procedure was available for requiring the patient to ingest the food or drink. Even so, all patients were required to assemble in the room where the commissary was held and where the food and drinks were being dispensed. The regular use of the sampling procedure guaranteed that all of the patients would sample all of the potential reinforcers continuously during their entire stay in the motivating environment.

2. Reinforcer Exposure

The Reinforcer Sampling Rule increased the utilization of reinforcement by instructing, directing, persuading, or otherwise causing the individual to sample the reinforcer. This procedure is easily accomplished when the nature of the reinforcer is such that the individual can be made in some way to engage in this sampling. For some types of reinforcing events this is particularly easy to accomplish, since minimal activity of the individual is required in the sampling process; for example, when the reinforcing stimuli are almost totally defined by a visual and auditory change such as watching a television show or listening to a radio program or a live band. For other types of reinforcers, however, the willing and active participation of the individual is an integral aspect of the reinforcing activity; for example, eating, drinking, and wearing desired clothing. It may be difficult to force the individual to sample such reinforcers. If the individual cannot be persuaded to sample these reinforcers, then the reinforcer sampling procedure is of no avail. Some other procedure is then necessary to prime the individual into electing the reinforcer. The question raised by these considerations is, how can an individual be primed to engage in an activity when he refuses even to sample it?

Laboratory experiments

The classical conditioning experiments of Pavlov (1927) provide a suggestion on how to structure a stimulus situation so that it will prime the individual to engage in the reinforcing activity. Pavlov found that when a stimulus tone accompanied the delivery of food, the mere presentation of the tone eventually produced orienting responses toward the food and salivation. The control exerted by the particular stimuli associated with reinforcement also has been found to be very great in operant conditioning studies (Ferster and Skinner, 1957, Ch. 10).

Pavlov found in his studies of generalization that the extent to which other tones produced components of the consummatory response depended upon the degree of similarity of those tones to the one that was present during reinforcement; the greater the similarity, the greater the probability of responding. Pavlov's experiments involved a single dimension. Additional experiments using compound stimuli have confirmed the same finding: The greater the number of stimuli that are similar to those that were present during reinforcement, the greater will be the elicitation of anticipatory components of the consummatory response.

This principle regarding generalization has been extended to operant behavior. For example, Guttman and Kalish (1956) have found that when a key-pecking response of pigeons has been reinforced by food in the presence of a particular wave length, the tendency to respond for food increases as a function of the similarity of a new stimulus light to the one that was originally present during reinforcement. The Law of Generalization has been found to apply not only to food reinforcement but also to punishment (Honig and Slivka, 1964), conditioned suppression (Hoffman and Fleshler, 1964), and avoidance (Sidman, 1961). This principle of generalization suggests that if one wishes to have maximum utilization of a reinforcing event, the procedure should present all stimuli that are associated with reinforcement. This suggests including visual, auditory, olfactory, and even social stimuli associated with the reinforcing stimulus.

For purposes of an experimental analysis it is highly desirable to have a complete knowledge of the properties of a stimulus before introducing a procedure that will alter those properties. Thus, by using a pure tone or a particular wave length, the experimenter gains some assurance that the stimulus is "neutral"; that is, it has no inherent reinforcing properties prior to the experimental manipulations. From a practical point, however, it is unnecessary to use a neutral stimulus. It is more convenient and, according to the Law of Generalization, even more effective not to use neutral or arbitrary stimuli, but rather to employ existing stimuli that are ordinarily present during reinforcement. A simple way of introducing those stimuli without any special arrangements is to expose the individual in question to a situation in which other individuals are actually consuming the reinforcer. This method provides a degree of stimulus similarity that is greater than any that could be artificially contrived and appears to be as close to reproducing all the stimuli associated with reinforcement as one could achieve without actually having the individual engage in the activity in question. If the individual could be made to engage in the activity, reinforcer sampling would have been achieved.

In summary, it appears that increased utilization of a reinforcer by a given individual will result by presenting him with the sights and sounds of other individuals who are actively consuming the reinforcer. This suggestion is supported by many studies that have been conducted under the heading of social facilitation (Hake and Laws, 1967) in which it has been found that a satiated animal will be primed to eat at that moment, also, if he observes another animal eating. The inclusion of another organism utilizing the reinforcement seems to be a particularly useful way of recreating all of the stimuli associated with the delivery of reinforcement. When one individual is using a reinforcer, for example, eating food, then he is displaying to an observer not only the visual and olfactory stimuli associated with the ingestion of the food but also all the particular auditory stimuli associated with eating. These considerations suggest a general procedure for increasing the use of a known reinforcer when active sampling cannot be arranged.

Reinforcer Exposure Rule: At the moment of reinforcer availability, display all the stimuli that typically occur during reinforcer utilization; if possible, have the individual observe another individual actively utilizing the reinforcer.

Common applications

The Reinforcer Exposure Rule is concerned with maximizing the consumption of a reinforcer at the time of reinforcer availability. The general objective served by this Reinforcer Exposure Rule is similar to the sales objective of commercial organizations: They wish to increase the likelihood that their product will be purchased. It should come as no surprise, therefore, to find many examples of commercial organizations using this rule to maximize their sales. This rule, stated loosely, specifies that a potential customer should see someone else purchasing and using the product in question. In that way all of the stimuli associated with the reinforcing event will have been presented. This rule carried to its extreme is reinforcer sampling. So, for example, in selling a new car, the Reinforcer Exposure Rule naturally suggests using advertising material in which the individual sees another person driving it. To make the stimuli completely identical, of course, the situation could be changed slightly so that the potential buyer will drive the car himself. This is reinforcer sampling. The distinction is in terms of whether the individual is actively using the reinforcer.

If verbal advertising is used as the means for priming the reinforcement selection, the actual situation is not reproduced. This rule suggests that verbal material, which is only symbolically associated with the reinforcer, be minimized and that direct pictorial representation of the reinforcer be maximized unless, of course, verbal activity is an integral part of the reinforcer. If the reinforcer is an object, the pictorial representation should consist of the object in question being used by another person. Another example of the use of this rule is current architectural design in which the walls, windows, and doors are transparent and permit casual passers-by to have a full view from the outside of people engaging in the reinforcing events within. The increasing use of such architecture and its usefulness may reflect on the efficacy of the Reinforcer Exposure Rule.

Two different reinforcers, eating and drinking, were used in an effort to empirically determine the usefulness of the reinforcer exposure procedure. For neither reinforcer could active sampling by the patients be guaranteed, since both require the active participation of the individual (eating or drinking). Some patients did eat or drink the items in question when requested to do so; others did not. Since the patients were treated here in a group, the procedure was a combination of reinforcer sampling and reinforcer exposure. It was sampling for those patients that ate or drank the sample; it was exposure for the other patients who were necessarily exposed to the sight of the patient who did sample the reinforcers.

Experiment 10: Reinforcer exposure and popcorn sales

Procedure. Thirty-six patients participated. The other patients were not consistently available at the time scheduled for this activity. A special procedure was instituted in which popcorn was sold six times daily: once at the end of the three meals and once at each of the three commissary periods. The popcorn was available in one-ounce bags, each of which cost one token. There was no limit on the amount of popcorn any individual could purchase. This procedure was followed for a period of four days, during which many of the conditions on the ward which might influence sales were kept constant. For example, token payment for jobs as well as number of jobs available remained the same throughout this period. Similarly, the type of reinforcers available during this period were kept constant, and no additional reinforcers were introduced that might compete with the sale of popcorn.

A reinforcer exposure procedure was then introduced and continued for eight days. This procedure consisted of giving each patient a free bag of popcorn at each meal and commissary period. To prevent satiation, very small amounts were used, about three kernels to each patient. This small amount of popcorn provided the stimuli associated with the utilization of the reinforcer without allowing satiation. The free popcorn was distributed to each patient as she waited in line to receive her meals in the dining room, and also when she was in commissary. Some patients did not accept the free popcorn; others accepted but did not eat it; many patients ate the popcorn. Since all patients were required to attend meals and commissary, all were thereby exposed to the sights and sounds associated with consumption of the popcorn by those patients who did eat it.

For the next four days, the same procedure was followed except no free popcorn was given to the patients.

Results. Tables 5–7 and 5–8 show the results during successive four-day periods. Table 5–7 shows the results for those patients that had purchased popcorn prior to the priming procedure and were, therefore, quite familiar with the popcorn as a reinforcer. Table 5–8 is for those patients that had not. Twenty-two patients purchased popcorn prior to the reinforcement priming procedure and continued to do so during the remainder of the study. The amount of popcorn purchased by these 22 patients was relatively unchanged. The exposure procedure had little or no effect on these patients who were already purchasing popcorn.

Table 5–7

Reinforcer Exposure and Popcorn Sales

	Reinforcer exposure			
	No priming	3 Kernels	3 Kernels	No priming
Total ounces purchased	110	108	120	96

For the 22 patients who purchased popcorn *at least once* in the period prior to reinforcer exposure. Each cell entry based on four-day periods.

Table 5–8

Reinforcer Exposure and Popcorn Sales

	Reinforcer exposure			
	No priming	3 Kernels	3 Kernels	No priming
Number of patients purchasing popcorn	0	3	4	3
Total ounces purchased	0	7	9	7

For the 14 patients who did *not* purchase in the period prior to reinforcer exposure. Each cell entry based on four-day periods.

Table 5–8 shows that of the 14 patients who had not purchased any popcorn initially, three patients did purchase it during the reinforcer exposure procedure and continued to do so after the procedure was discontinued.

Discussion. The results show that popcorn was utilized more by the patients when the situation was structured such that the patients received the stimuli associated with eating popcorn. Even though the patients could not be required to eat the popcorn, the visual, auditory, olfactory, and even tactual stimuli associated with its consumption were effective in increasing its usage. This priming effect was true only of the patients who had not been purchasing popcorn. The absence of a priming effect for the others may indicate that the exposure procedure is most effective when the individual has not recently been in contact with the reinforcing stimulus.

Experiment 11: Reinforcer exposure and soda sales

Procedure. Twenty-nine patients participated in this experiment. The rest of the patients were not available on the ward at the time of this activity. The standard procedure was to sell soda pop in various flavors six times a day: once at each of the three commissary periods and once at each of the three meals. A three-ounce glass cost one token, and there was no limit on the number of glasses an individual could purchase. This procedure was followed for a period of four days, during which efforts were made to keep constant conditions known to affect sales of soda pop, such as the availability of jobs, tokens, and additional reinforcers. Beverages such as Kool-ade, lemonade, or fruit drinks were not scheduled during this period to avoid reinforcers that might compete with the sale of soda pop.

The reinforcer exposure procedure was then introduced and continued for four days. Each patient was given one ounce of soda pop free. A final four-day period consisted of reinstating the standard procedure in which no free soda was given.

Results. Table 5–9 shows the results for those patients that had purchased soda prior to the exposure procedure. The total amount of soda purchased by these 18 patients increased during the

Table 5–9

Reinforcer Exposure and Soda Sales

		Reinforcer exposure	
	No priming	1 Ounce	No priming
Total number of ounces purchased	261	354	303

For the 18 patients who purchased soda *at least once* in the period prior to reinforcer exposure. Each cell entry based on four-day periods.

Reinforcer Exposure procedure and decreased when the exposure procedure was terminated, but only partly. The priming had a residual effect after it was terminated.

Table 5–10 shows that of the 11 patients who had failed to purchase soda prior to being primed seven started doing so during the exposure procedure. The amount of soda was similarly increased. These increases were maintained even when the reinforcer exposure procedure was discontinued, again indicating an enduring effect.

Table 5–10

Reinforcer Exposure and Soda Sales

		Reinforcer exposure	
	No priming	1 Ounce	No priming
Number of patients purchasing soda	0	7	8
Total number of ounces purchased	0	60	90

For the 11 patients who did *not* purchase in the period prior to reinforcer exposure. Each cell entry based on four-day periods.

Discussion. Although the patients could not be required to drink the soda, all the stimuli associated with its consumption—visual, auditory, and olfactory—significantly influenced the number of patients utilizing a previously neglected reinforcer.

As in the procedure with popcorn, the priming with soda increased the amount of soda purchased; but unlike the priming with popcorn, the soda consumption was increased for those patients who had been utilizing it as well as for those patients who had not. The priming procedure was more effective for those who had not been purchasing the soda, confirming the suggestion in the popcorn procedure that priming is most effective for those patients who have had little contact with the reinforcer. Both experiments suggest that presentation of all of the stimuli associated with the consumption of a reinforcer will increase its utilization, even for reinforcing events that cannot be "forced" on an individual.

Increased discharge from the hospital by the reinforcer exposure rule

The Reinforcer Exposure Rule offers a method for increasing the number of patients discharged. Patients who have spent many years in a mental hospital are often opposed and even resistant to leaving the hospital. Some of these patients express fear of any changes in their living arrangements and state that they like the hospital. Some simply refuse to discuss the possibility of leaving the hospital. This general resistance to returning to the community is so widespread that hospitals have made several efforts to discourage it. The most notable of these efforts is the development of "half-way houses." These houses are intended to act as a shelter for the patient who otherwise would find the outside world overwhelming. Unfortunately, in order to place a patient in one of these half-way houses, the patient still must agree to leave the hospital, but many patients will not even accept discharge to the half-way house. If living in the half-way house is a potential reinforcer, it does not seem to be sought after eagerly. Since the Reinforcer Exposure Rule is designed to increase reinforcer utilization, it suggests itself as a means of causing the patients to seek a discharge to the half-way house. Specifically, the rule suggests that if living in the half-way house is indeed a potential reinforcer, then the patient should be required to visit the half-way house where she can observe other individuals living there. In essence the rule suggests that the patient be taken to the environment where she eventually is expected to live.

The above reasoning led to the use of the Reinforcer Exposure Rule as a means of causing two patients to seek a discharge into a half-way house.

The first patient was Donna Z, who had been hospitalized for eight years. She had been discharged under the usual procedure some time previously but had been rehospitalized within 10 days. Upon her readmission she had complained bitterly about conditions in the half-way house. The earlier discharge had taken place one year prior to the present experiment and had been conducted according to the usual hospital procedure. A physician, nurse, and social worker had evaluated her condition and had approved of her leaving the hospital. No period of acclimation to her new environment had occurred. She had gone from a full-time status in the mental hospital on one day to a full-time status in the half-way house on the next.

At the time the Reinforcer Exposure Rule was to be used with this patient, she refused to consider the possibility of discharge to the half-way house. The patient was directed by the attendant to accompany her while she was visiting the half-way house. The visit varied from a few minutes up to periods of an hour. During the visit the patient had the opportunity to observe former patients engaging in a variety of activities in the half-way house. The duration of the visits was deliberately extended to four hours so that the patient would have an opportunity to observe most of the activities that normally occur in the half-way house and to observe most of the individuals who were living there. Six of these visits were made over a period of 10 days. Some of the visits were deliberately timed to coincide with mealtime at the half-way house so that the patient could observe former patients eating their meals there. The result was that she joined the former patients for their meals since it was also mealtime for her. Two of the visits were deliberately arranged during the evening so that the patient could observe, and as it happened, participate in the evening activities. On two of these evening visits, the patient elected to stay overnight. She was returned to the hospital ward the next morning. The plan was to continue this exposure to many of the other activities in the half-way house, but it was interrupted by the patient's request that she be discharged: "It's a lot of trouble to go back and forth from here to the hospital. Why can't I stay here?" The patient's request was followed by a formal discharge. At the time of this writing she has been in the half-way house for over one year.

The same procedure was used with another patient, Janet E., who had a 12-year history of hospitalization. At no time during her stay in the hospital did she agree to be discharged. Because she was a college graduate, she was chosen for various types of "talk therapy": individual psychotherapy, group psychotherapy, remotivation therapy. None of these treatments seemed to persuade her to consider leaving the hospital. Whenever the matter was brought up, she took considerable pains to explain that she had not yet made up her mind. Often she stated that her case was "so complex" that it was best to wait until an opportune time for her to think about plans for discharge. Even after three years of working in the motivating environment she still declined any plans for discharge. It was a case of "don't call me, I'll call you." At this point it was decided to apply the Reinforcer Exposure Rule. She was taken to the half-way house ostensibly to help the staff with an errand. After the first visit, it was possible to take her for longer periods of time. Five visits within a period of 10 days were made to expose the patient to the reinforcers to be found outside. After she had stayed at the half-way house one night, she requested to be discharged from the hospital, and made this statement, "I'll be OK now because I know what to expect outside."

It would seem, therefore, that the reinforcer exposure procedure is a particularly useful method of bridging the wide gap between living in the hospital and living in the community. There seems to be no reason why the rule would not be equally effective in producing discharges to a normal home, when one is available.

E. MAGNITUDE OF REINFORCEMENT AND SATIATION

1. Magnitude of Reinforcement

Experiment 12: The effects of magnitude of reinforcement on participation

Physical exercise. The present experiment was conducted to determine whether participation in an activity was governed by the amount of reinforcement that was given for that participation. The activity selected for study was attendance at a physical exercise. The exercise period had been conducted for some time on the ward and seemed to be unattractive to the patients since only a small number attended it when it was available. During the physical exercise period, exercises were called out and the various movements were announced, much as in a school physical education class. For example, during trunk bending exercises the announcer, who was a patient, called, left, up, right, up, forward, up, etc. This physical exercise activity was programmed twice each day, during which time 34 patients were present on the ward and available for participation.

Procedure. The experimental design was to provide varying numbers of tokens for participating in the physical exercise. The number of tokens was changed every five sessions. The sequence was 0, 2, 10, 50, 2, and 0 tokens. The entire experiment extended over 30 sessions, 10 sessions being spent at 0 tokens, 10 at 2 tokens and 5 each at 10 and 50 tokens. The numbers of tokens that were to be given during each physical exercise period was announced simultaneously with the general announcement that the activity was about to start.

Results. Table 5–11 shows that participation in the physical exercise period increased directly as a function of the number of tokens given for participation. Only six patients attended when zero tokens were given, whereas 29 patients out of the 34 attended when

Table 5–11

Magnitude of Reinforcement and Participation

	Number of tokens given for attendance					
	0	2	10	50	2	0
Number of patients attending	6	16	24	29	25	14
Total attendance	15	43	90	120	96	32

Each cell entry based on five sessions for 34 patients.

50 were given. The intermediate numbers of tokens produced intermediate degrees of participation. Not only was there participation by more patients but also more overall participation. It should be noted that only 16 patients participated when two tokens were given initially; but once participation had been increased during the

50 token exchange, the same two tokens now caused 25 patients to attend.

Discussion. The results of this experiment show that not only is reinforcement of importance in maintaining a desired response but the extent of participation by patients can be controlled by varying the magnitude of the reinforcement. Almost all of the patients, that is, 29 out of 34, engaged in the activity when the number of tokens was maximal. The effect of the larger number of tokens was enduring. Once the patients had been "primed" into participation by the 50-token exchange, the two-token exchange was at least temporarily effective in maintaining that participation. The results of this study suggest that in order to increase the participation of patients in a given activity, the number of tokens that will be received for such participation should be increased. The results also have implications for analyzing an apparent lack of motivation for a given patient. Failure of an individual to participate in an activity even when he is being reinforced for so doing may indicate that the magnitude of reinforcement is simply not sufficient for that particular activity.

Of special interest, here, are the spontaneous verbal comments made by the patients during the course of the study. Initially, when participation in the activity did not produce tokens, the patients rarely participated in it and verbally stated that they disliked the activity. Later, when substantial numbers of tokens were being given for participation, the verbal statements took on quite a different flavor. The patients were overheard frequently to comment that the activity was fun, that they enjoyed participating in it, and that they felt it was giving them a good deal of physical benefit. During the last stage of the experiment, when the number of tokens given for participation was again reduced to zero, the patients again began stating that they disliked the activity, and for that reason would not participate in it.

2. Satiation

The previous experiment revealed that the greater the number of tokens given for the performance of the desired behavior, the more frequently would the behavior be performed. The obvious suggestion, it was noted, for increasing a given performance was that the number of tokens given for that performance be increased. Unfortunately, this procedure cannot be followed in that simple a manner because satiation influences the effectiveness of a reinforcer. It is known that the effectiveness of a reinforcing stimulus depends on the extent to which the individual has been previously deprived of that event. Consequently, if a very large number of tokens were to be given for a single performance, then, while it is true that performance would increase, the patient would have sufficient tokens to become satiated on all the events for which the tokens were to be exchanged. Indeed, the experimental design in the previous study provided only five opportunities to earn the 50 tokens, since a longer period of time would have allowed the patient to accumulate enough tokens so that she would no longer have any need to work. Some slight tendency in that direction was in fact noted in that on the last occasion in which the 50 tokens were given, the patients were working less on other jobs than they had been. The phenomenon of satiation, therefore, sets a practical limit on how many tokens can be given for a particular job. The total number of tokens given cannot be so great that the individual can go for extended periods of time without earning additional tokens while still using those that have been earned in the distant past.

The problem of satiation requires a second type of precaution. The same problem will arise if the delivery of the reinforcing stimulus is not controlled, that is, if the subject is able to obtain it in a nonauthorized manner or if it is freely available. In such circumstances, it can be predicted from the principle of satiation that the reinforcer will not be effective in maintaining any behavior. As a consequence, the motivating environment was arranged so that reinforcers could not be received in any manner other than by performing the desired behaviors.

Experiment 13: Satiation by a free reinforcer (popcorn)

The following experiment was conducted to ascertain whether the phenomenon of satiation, which has been so extensively investigated in animal behavior studies, also was operative in this motivating environment. The general procedure was to give each patient a specified amount of a reinforcer without attaching any response requirement or token requirement for its receipt. By varying the amount that the patients were given, one could ascertain whether the reinforcer subsequently would be utilized less, as predicted by the principle of satiation. In a sense this procedure simulates a situation in the motivating environment in which inadequate precautions might have been taken to prevent free access to a reinforcing stimulus and allows us to observe what deleterious effects might result from such unauthorized access to the reinforcer. The effectiveness of the event as a reinforcer was evaluated by determining how frequently the patients would exchange tokens for the event after having been satiated. Since these tokens were obtainable only for performing desired behaviors, it was assumed that any decrease in the frequency of token exchange would reflect a decrease in the frequency with which the patient would work for the tokens.

Method. Thirty-six patients participated in this study. The event used as a reinforcer was the purchase of popcorn. This particular event was chosen for purposes of this study since the event could be easily specified in terms of its quantity. The situation was arranged so that popcorn could be purchased at six different times during the day: once at each of the three meals and once at each of the three commissary periods. The popcorn was obtainable at a cost of one token in a pre-packaged one-ounce bag. No limit was placed on the number of bags that could be purchased at any one time. Satiation was studied by giving each of the patients a bag of popcorn free of charge immediately prior to the moment when they could purchase the one-ounce bag. During the first four days no free popcorn was given. During successive four-day periods, the amount of free popcorn given was one-fourth ounce, zero ounces, and then two ounces.

Results. Table 5–12 shows that when two ounces of popcorn were given free, only two patients purchased popcorn, in contrast with the 23 patients who had been purchasing it when none had been given free. Similarly, the number of ounces of popcorn purchased decreased to one ounce when the large amount of popcorn was given free, in contrast with the 39 ounces that had been purchased when no popcorn was freely available.

Table 5–12

Satiation by a Free Reinforcer (Popcorn)

	Ounces of free popcorn		
	0	¼	2
Number of patients purchasing popcorn/day	23	21	2
Total number of ounces purchased/day	38.8	21.2	1.0

Each cell entry based on four-day periods for 36 patients.

Discussion. The results show that satiation occurred for the reinforcing stimulus when that stimulus was obtainable without the need for token exchange. The degree of satiation was a function of how much of the reinforcing stimulus could be freely obtained. Even the relatively small amount of popcorn, one-quarter ounce, made freely available produced noticeable satiation. These findings demonstrate the great importance of arranging the motivating environment in such a way that a possible reinforcing event cannot be freely obtained if that event is to be used effectively as a reinforcer.

Experiment 14: Satiation by a free reinforcer (soda)

The present experiment was almost identical to the preceding one except that soda was used as the reinforcer rather than popcorn. A second difference was that 29 rather than 36 patients served as subjects; the other patients were not consistently available at the scheduled time for this activity.

Method. The experimental design was similar to that of the previous procedure in that the soda was available at the same location, with the same frequency, and at the same cost, differing only in that the soda was purchased in a three-ounce cup. As in the previous procedure, during the intial four-day period, no free soda was given. During the next four-day period, 10 ounces were given, and then for the next four-day period no free soda was given.

Results. Table 5–13 shows that the results obtained here were similar to those seen in the previous study in that the free reinforcer produced a substantial reduction, both in the number of patients purchasing soda and in the number of ounces purchased. Again, the amount purchased was affected to a greater extent than was the number of patients purchasing it. Under the satiation condition, in which 10 ounces were given, only 25 per cent of the previous number of patients continued to purchase the soda, but the total amount of soda purchased decreased to less than 10 per cent. Some slight residual effect of the satiation procedure is evident in that the number of patients purchasing soda and the number of ounces purchased were at a lower level immediately following the satiation procedure than prior to it.

Table 5–13

Satiation by a Free Reinforcer (Soda)

	Amount of free soda (ounces)		
	0	10	0
Number of patients purchasing soda	19	5	14
Total number of ounces purchased	288	27	192

Each cell entry based on a four-day period for 29 patients.

The results of the present experiment support the conclusion of the previous study that free access to a reinforcing stimulus will reduce or eliminate the possibility of using that stimulus as a reinforcer for desired behaviors.

Experiment 15: Satiation by a frequent reinforcer (movies)

Satiation is the result of excessive reinforcer availability. This excess should result, also, when a reinforcer is delivered too frequently. The present experiment was conducted to determine whether a very high frequency of reinforcement would produce satiation. The previous experiments on satiation used nutritive reinforcers. The present used a nonnutritive event, a movie. Satiation consists of the loss of effectiveness of a reinforcer. The measure of effectiveness of the reinforcer was the number of patients attending the movies.

Method. Thirty patients participated. First, movies were shown once weekly for 16 weeks. Each time a movie was shown, patients could attend by depositing a token in a turnstile, thereby gaining access to the room where the movie was shown. An attendant announced the movie five minutes before show-time. Next she took a record of all those patients who attended. Patients could enter any time during the showing of the film. After 16 weeks, the procedure was changed so that the number of movies shown was increased from one to 14 per week. This "satiation" period was followed by another period of 16 weeks, during which movies were again shown only once weekly.

Results. Table 5–14 shows that when a movie was shown weekly, an average of five patients attended. However, when 14 movies were shown in one week, the average number of patients attending decreased to 2.3. When the original scheduling of one movie per week was reinstated, the average number of patients returned to 4.5 per movie. These results demonstrate that when a reinforcer is used in excess, satiation sets in. These findings demonstrate that the satiation process is as applicable to nonnutritive reinforcers as to nutritive reinforcers and confirm and extend the findings of satiation in the two previous experiments.

Table 5–14

Satiation by a Very Frequent Reinforcer (Movies)

	Spaced	Satiation	Spaced
	1 per week	14 per week	1 per week
Mean number of patients attending each movie	5.0	2.3	4.5

Consider, in summary, the various experiments covered in this chapter. Later it will become evident from the experiments presented in the Appendix and summarized in Chapter 8 (Evaluation of the Reinforcement Procedure) that the desired performances of the patients were drastically reduced or completely absent when reinforcement was no longer forthcoming for those behaviors. Experiment 12 on magnitude of reinforcement showed that the high level of performance of the patients was not simply a matter of whether one reinforced, but was governed by the magnitude of the reinforcement. Experiments 13, 14, and 15 showed further that the effectiveness of reinforcement for a response required that no unauthorized or excessive access to the reinforcing stimuli be available. The substantial changes in behavior that were achieved by these manipulations of the reinforcement procedure demonstrate not only that reinforcement is a major factor but that subtle variations of the reinforcement procedure can produce varying degrees of the behavior desired. The assumption that reinforcement could be a strong tool for modifying the behavior of the mental patients seems to have been well supported by the results of these specific experiments.

The demonstration and discovery that reinforcement is such a major factor in influencing complex human behavior comes as something of a surprise when we recall that most major theories of human behavior scarcely note reinforcement as one of the possible influences. Instead, most other theories of human behavior postulate mental states as being the principal cause of complex human social behavior. A reconciliation between these two considerations is suggested by some of the results noted previously in Experiment 12 on magnitude of reinforcement. In that experiment patients stated that the reason they worked was because they liked it; and when they were not working, they said they were not working because they did not like it. Yet, the activity involved was the same at both times. What differed was the magnitude of reinforcement. When they were being reinforced with a large number of tokens, they said they liked it; they did not like it when they were being reinforced with a small number of tokens. The same kind of result was discovered in the several experiments described in the Appendix, in which an extinction procedure was imposed. It was noted in those studies that while the patients were being reinforced, they stated that they were performing the various jobs because they enjoyed it; during extinction they suddenly stopped enjoying it. These results suggest that the mental state, that is, the like or dislike, was not the cause of their working or not working, but rather one of the reactions to the reinforcement procedure. When reinforcement was being given for a job and in a large amount, the reinforcement produced two effects: one of mental satisfaction and the other of performance on the job. The mental state was not the cause of the behavior but was rather caused by the reinforcement procedure which also caused the job to be performed. Since the mental states of satisfaction were caused by the same event (reinforcement) as the job performance, it is easy to understand why previous theorists have assumed that the mental state was the cause of the job, since the two events go together. They go together because they are caused by the same third event, which is reinforcement.

Viewed in this manner, one need not come to the negative conclusion that mental states are unimportant and that verbal statements about these mental states are irrelevant. Rather, one can use the knowledge that the verbal statements are caused by the reinforcement procedure to obtain verbal statements from the patients about what aspects of the reinforcement procedure might be improved. Since the mental state seems to be caused by the reinforcement procedure, then statements of concern or unhappiness by the patients should be sensitive measures of the extent to which the reinforcement procedure is adequate. It will be recalled from Chapter 4 that verbal statements were actively solicited from patients in the motivating environment as a standard means of discovering reinforcing stimuli. Such verbal statements were eagerly attended to by the ward staff, who were constantly searching for ways to improve the reinforcement procedure.

The present approach, then, uses verbal statements as a means of discovering more effective methods of producing the desired behavior changes rather than using the verbal statements as a post-facto explanation of the behavioral changes. Viewed in this way, the patients are encouraged to respond verbally to specific aspects of the reinforcement procedure rather than to give some overall expression of satisfaction or dissatisfaction. Any such expression of dissatisfaction is, of course, the starting point for probing and questioning about specific aspects of the reinforcement procedure.

CHAPTER 6

Assuring the Response-Reinforcement Relation

A. BEHAVIOR-EFFECT

After a response has been defined descriptively, as stated in the Dimensions of Behavior Rule, the educator must devise a method of observing the behavior in such a manner that he can be assured that it has been recorded properly. The first method that comes to mind is direct and continuous observation. According to this method, the observer remains with the subject and directly views and listens to him for as long as he desires to record the behavior of interest. Needless to say, the time and expense required for such observation places severe limitations on an applied program with humans. But the problem is more than one of inconvenience and expense; the nature of the behavior may be such that it is impossible to directly and continuously observe it. Under such circumstances this problem can be restated as: Can some measurement of behavior be obtained when there is little opportunity to observe it directly and continuously?

Animal Behavior Studies

Studies of animal behavior have long been concerned with the problem of measuring behavior continuously. One solution that has been devised is to discover some distinctive environmental effect that occurs only upon the occurrence of the behavior. The environmental effect should, if possible, be an enduring one, for then the experimenter need not be present when the behavior occurs. He can at a later time and at his convenience record the enduring environmental change that has earlier resulted from the behavior.

Assume one wishes to measure the running behavior of a rat. The simple solution to this problem would seem to be to have an observer directly and continuously observe the rat and record how far or fast he has run during successive periods of time. The impracticality of such a solution has led to several devices for recording running, all of which rely upon an enduring environmental effect of a response rather than direct observation of the response itself. The question that one must ask in discovering an appropriate environmental effect is: What distinctive physical change occurs when the response is made that does not exist when the response is not made? In the case of running, the answer is simple, although perhaps not immediately obvious. The physical change is that the animal moves with respect to the surface on which it is standing. Two types of solutions then seem to follow. One is to provide a movable surface and to record the amount of movement of that surface; this is done in the running wheel. Alternatively, one can use a stationary floor and demarcate reference points on the floor, measuring only when the animal has left one reference point and arrived at another. This procedure is used in the runway, in which the start box is the initial reference and the goal box the second reference point. Photocells or other such devices may be used which automatically indicate the moment the animal has left the start box, as well as the moment the animal has entered the goal box. Similarly, in the case of the running wheel, an automatic counter can be attached to the movable wheel that automatically records the number of revolutions. The usefulness of these devices becomes apparent if one remembers that the running wheel measures a rat's running activity during several hundred consecutive hours, all without a human observer ever being present.

A second example of how studies of animal behavior have solved the problem of continuous recording is in the study of aggressive behavior. Although some naturalistic studies have attempted continuous and direct observation of animals in their natural environment, most studies have developed more practical methods of observation. The question asked here is: What distinctive environmental change occurs when the aggressive behavior is emitted? In some types of aggression, as between a special strain of rats and mice, the aggressive behavior actually leads to fatal injury of the mouse by the rat. Thus Myer and Baenninger (1966) have recorded whether the mouse has been fatally injured to obtain their measure of aggressive behavior by the aggressor rat. But what about aggressive behavior that does not have such a drastic biological outcome? Such an example is seen in the biting attack of squirrel monkeys, which is not always fatal. A physical consequence of a bite is that the object that is bitten will be compressed. Consequently, Hutchinson, Azrin, and Hake (1966) developed a special device consisting of a pneumatic tube that provided an output signal whenever the pneumatic tube was compressed as a result of bites by the monkey. In this way, they could measure biting attack by the monkey over periods of hours, days, or even months without ever being present themselves. An even more subtle form of aggression is a pecking attack on one pigeon by another pigeon, since this type of attack does not necessarily lead to puncture or physical injury to the target pigeon. Again one asks what distinctive physical change occurs during pecking attack? The answer for this behavior is that force is exerted against the target pigeon. As a consequence, experimenters have devised a method of measuring this attack using a platform on which the target is mounted and which reacts to the force exerted by the attacking pigeon, delivering an output signal that can be recorded automatically (Azrin, Hutchinson, and Hake, 1966).

Sexual behavior offers an excellent illustration of how the environmental effects principle has been used in studies of animals to record what is a very complex response. The frequency of copulations in animals is so low that continuous observation is quite impractical. An additional complication with sexual behavior is that direct visual observation by a human observer may be distracting and may consequently interfere with the occurrence of the behavior unless the observer takes special precautions. Assume that one is interested in the ejaculatory aspect of sexual behavior; one would then ask what physical change occurs distinctively with the occurrence of the ejaculatory response and not with other responses? Stated in this fashion, one obvious answer is pregnancy, and indeed the occurrence of pregnancy has often been used both with animals and man as unmistakable evidence that ejaculation has occurred. Many factors may, however, prevent the fertilization of the egg which is necessary for conception. What other physical change, then, might be available? One answer to this is the presence of sperm in the vagina. A common practice in studies of animal sexual behavior is to take a vaginal smear from the female as physical evidence of the occurrence of ejaculation. Assume, however, that one is concerned with a sexual pattern of behavior in which intromissions, that is, insertions of the penis, occur but are not necessarily accompanied by ejaculation. Again we ask what physical change is distinctively associated with this intromission? An ingenious solution based on the environmental effects principle was discovered by Pierce and Nuttal (1961) and later refined by Rubin and Azrin (1967). The physical change that occurs is contact of the moist genital organs. One distinctive physical change that will result when the moist genital organs are in contact is that electrical current can then flow between the animals. Pierce and Nuttal, therefore, put one electrode in the male and one in the female and recorded when electricity flowed between them. Using this method, Rubin and Azrin were able to record the frequency of intromissions and copulations continuously over periods of months without the necessity for direct visual observation.

It is so important in laboratory studies of animal behavior to have an enduring environmental change occur that, when possible, responses are selected which by their very nature produce a physical change. For example, in studies of learning and motivation the factors of interest are such variables as frequency of reinforcement and number of trials, and these can be studied using any response. As a consequence, studies of learning and motivation of animals have used such responses as a key-peck, lever-press, panel-push, or chain pull. In each of these instances, the response apparatus is directly linked to a switch that opens and closes as the response apparatus is manipulated by the animal, thus providing an electrical output signal to a counter or other recorder.

Response Measurement in Research with Humans

Many aspects of human behavior are difficult to measure. For example, verbal responses in general do not produce an enduring change in the physical environment. Once the speaker has made a statement, it is literally gone. No physical and enduring trace of what was said can be found in the environment. To remedy this difficulty, some investigators have used tape recorders or voice keys, both of which result in electrical changes upon occurrence of the verbal response. In this manner an enduring record of the effect of the verbal or vocal response on the environment can be obtained. In the well-known Hawthorne Electric study (Roethlisberger and Dickson, 1939) the number of items manufactured was the performance measure, rather than movements necessary to assemble them. These items constituted a physical change in the environment. The product of the employee's efforts served as the physically measurable change in the environment for determining the existence of the employee's appropriate behavior. Examples of this approach are also available from the clinical area. For example, wetting of the bed provided a natural physical change in the environment as a response measure in the study of enuresis (Mowrer, 1938). In studying the eating behavior of patients, the weight of the patient constituted a physical dimension that was a product of eating (Ayllon, 1963). Wolf, Risley, and Mees (1964) measured damage by a child to his glasses as their physical measure of a child's destructive behavior. Lovaas, Freitag, Gold, and Kassorla (1965) used the evidences of bodily harm as their physical measure of self-injury in their study of destructive behavior in schizophrenic children. In Ayllon's study (1963) of towel hoarding the number of towels in the patient's room constituted the physical measure of the hoarding behavior.

When responses such as the above naturally produce an enduring environmental change, the recording of the response is greatly simplified. In none of the instances described above was it necessary for an observer to be present when the response occurred. It is desirable, therefore, to arrange for the response to occur in such a manner that it produces some physical change in the external environment, thereby providing a convenient means of recording the occurrence of the response.

Behavior-Effect Rule: Arrange the situation so that the behavior produces some enduring change in the physical environment.

The usefulness of the Behavior-Effect Rule derives in a fairly logical and direct manner from a knowledge of the determinants of behavior. By definition, operant behavior is controlled largely by the effect that that behavior has on the environment. A skilled golfer swings at the golf ball only with those forms of the response which are most successful in moving that golf ball; a driver successfully manipulates the various controls of an automobile; the housewife uses the vacuum cleaner only if it is effective in removing the dirt; a salesman continues to speak to customers only if his conversation is generally successful in achieving a purchase by the customer. In these various examples, one might even loosely state that each of these behaviors is engaged in solely for the purpose of achieving the stated effect. Measurement of the effect alone, then, provides considerable information about whether the behavior occurred. In the example of the automobile, proper movement of the automobile can *only* occur when there is proper manipulation of the controls. In the other examples, several different types of behavior may have produced the same effect. The housewife may have cleaned the floor either with a vacuum cleaner or with a broom; the salesman may have achieved the sale not through his conversation but through some prior advertisement. In these three examples, the effect of the behavior is usually the only source of interest; the specific form of the effective behavior much less so. On the other hand, there are some instances, as illustrated by the example of the golfer, where the form of the behavior as well as the effect is of considerable interest. One would react quite differently if the golfer achieved a hole-in-one, not by striking the ball with a golf club but rather by placing it in the hole. Even in this extreme example, however, where the form of the response is of great importance, the environmental effect, that is, the ball being in the hole, is still a major consideration. The effect of a response is, then, one of the major determinants of the behavior; in some cases, the effect of the response constitutes our only interest in the behavior. For this reason it makes good psychological sense to use the effect of a response as one of the means of assuring that the response has taken place. We shall see shortly that the Behavior-Effect Rule is especially significant with regard to a change in the social rather than the physical environment.

Applications of Behavior-Effect Rule in the Motivating Environment

The Behavior-Effect Rule found extensive application in the motivating environment. Wherever possible the measurement of behavior took into account some enduring physical change that the behavior had produced in the environment. In each instance it was necessary to determine which physical effect one should select as an attribute of that behavior. Rather than deciding arbitrarily on some physical aspect to fulfill the Behavior-Effect Rule, it was very useful to decide on the physical effect after having answered the prior question posed by the Target Behavior Rule. In brief, the investigator must ask, "What is it that I want to see happen?" The answer to this question will lead to defining what constitutes the terminal or Target Behavior. For example, consider the duty of serving meals. One might ask what is it that one wants to accomplish by having this patient serve meals? Is social interaction as the meals are served desired for the server, or is the goal to develop responsibility and pride in a job well done? Or does one want all of these things and more? If the answer is yes, then it may be necessary to start all over again, because none of these features are necessarily peculiar to serving meals. An alternative answer to the original question is that it is desirable that everyone get three meals a day. This answer constitutes the target behavior (see Target Behavior Rule) and suggests directly how to fulfill the Behavior-Effect Rule. When a meal has been served, enduring environmental changes result that not only indicate whether the desired behavior has occurred but also constitute the main source of our interest in the behavior of serving it. Now it is possible to consider defining what behaviors are involved in making food available.

The job classification of the person who serves meals requires the following behaviors:

> Patient puts food into proper compartment on steam table. Assembles paper napkins and tableware on counter places at beginning of serving line; puts tablecloths, napkins, salt and sugar shakers on tables. Prepares proper beverage for each meal putting ice in glasses for cold beverages and drawing coffee from urn. Dips food; places it and beverage on trays. Gives patients their trays.

All these behaviors leave an enduring effect on the environment. The food is placed in the proper compartment; the salt and pepper shakers are on the table; each patient has her own tray, and so on.

Verbal behavior

The above is an illustration of behavior which is nonverbal. How does the Behavior-Effect Rule apply when the target behavior is verbal? Since verbal behavior is directed at another person (Skinner, 1957), the social effect of the verbal behavior, as well as its physical effect, can be used to satisfy the Behavior-Effect Rule. As indicated previously, an enduring record of vocal behavior can be made by using devices such as tape recorder. The social effects of verbal behavior, on the other hand, involve a change in the behavior of the listener. This suggests the second method of applying the Behavior-Effect Rule to verbal behavior: Measure the change in the listener's behavior which resulted from the speaker's verbal behavior.

The tour guide

Take, for example, the job of the tour guide. The tour guide had the responsibility of taking visitors through the motivating environment, showing them the facilities and describing the activities taking place. The tour guide was also instructed to answer all questions relating to the functioning of the motivating environment. She was instructed to exercise only one constraint in answering questions and that was not to discuss her own personal affairs, since these were usually irrelevant to the visitors' main objective in visiting the motivating environment. The tour guide's behavior was intended to have an effect on the visitor, namely, that he now was informed. This effect could be specified in advance in terms of specific questions asked of the visitor after the tour. What was desired was that the visitor be able to state that he had been shown every part of the ward, permitted to see all of the patients, received a description of what the patients were doing at that time, and had no further questions about the ward procedure. A standard procedure was instituted whereby each visitor was asked after the tour, "Did the tour guide answer all of your questions about activities and patients on the ward?" "Do you have any other questions?" If the visitor had unanswered questions, the tour guide's performance was known to be inadequate. Several questions were often asked as,

"Were you shown everything and everyone that you were interested in seeing?" "Has the tour guide explained to you the motivating environment and how it works?" "Has the tour guide explained to you all of the jobs and what patients receive for doing them?" Also, other questions were asked that referred to more specific information, such as, "Did the tour guide tell you about how the religious services are arranged?" or "Did the tour guide explain to you how one gets a grounds pass?" "Did the tour guide explain to you who serves the meals on the ward?" and so on. These questions were a means of determining whether the patient's behavior had the desired effect.

In another instance, the physical changes of the verbal behavior were gauged using a portable tape recorder hung about the patient's shoulder while she conducted the tour. (The patient and the visitor were both told about the tape recorder.) This was done primarily during the first few times that a patient was assigned to the job of tour guide. After the tour was concluded the ward supervisor listened to the tape, which included a recording of the comments of the tour guide as well as of the visitor. The tour guide had been given a set of topics that were to be described fully to each visitor. Some of the topics were, how many patients there were on the ward, how many staff, a description of the motivating environment system, the use of tokens in that system, the kinds of jobs available to the patients, items and events the tokens could be exchanged for, and so forth. The tape recording provided a means of measuring the patient's verbal behavior through the enduring record it left. The major effect desired of the tour, however, was the effect on the behavior of the visitor. For that reason, the questions directed to the visitor provided the principal measure.

B. TIME AND PLACE OF RESPONSE AND REINFORCER

Animal Studies

How do we arrange a situation such that a behavioral process can be studied? Take for example the learning process. There is little question that learning occurs for humans in their naturalistic environment. Yet psychologists have not used this environment extensively to study learning. Rather, attempts to study the learning process have usually modified the naturalistic environment extensively, and in such a way that learning behavior and its consequences have been restricted to a particular time and place. These modifications allow the learning responses to be more accurately recorded and the consequences of those responses to be arranged in a more standardized fashion. This is the rationale that has caused investigators of the learning process to bring the phenomenon into the laboratory, where factors extraneous to a process may be minimized and factors of special importance can be introduced. For example, in their natural environment, rats undoubtedly are continuously learning how to reach a particular area using a certain path. No basic information about this learning has resulted from studies in the naturalistic environment, however. Instead, investigators have arranged a convenient location designated as a laboratory and special situations known as mazes, in which pathway learning can be observed in a more standardized fashion. Here rewards for the learned behavior can be controlled and distractions studied or eliminated. Many advantages derive from the use of the laboratory, when compared with the free field situation. The major one with which we are concerned here is that the laboratory provides a means of direct supervision of the phenomenon in question by arranging a convenient time and place in which the phenomenon occurs.

Most behaviorist studies of animals designate a specific time and place where the animal's behavior will be observed. Experimental chambers, runways, jumping stands, and other devices constitute a location, as well as a means of observing the behavior. The experimenter, for his convenience, also selects when to observe those behaviors that are likely to be displayed in the experimental environments.

Consider, again, the example of aggressive behavior in animals previously discussed, but this time from the viewpoint of selecting an aspect of aggressive behavior that is postural or gestural in form and which does not produce an enduring environmental change. Male Siamese fighting fish are known to exhibit distinctive postural changes when they encounter another male. Some components of this aggressive display are an extension of the gill fins and movement of the tail, each of which seems to be extremely difficult to measure with an automatic apparatus. Thompson and Sturm (1965), who were interested in studying the conditioning of this aggressive display, limited their observations to a specific time and place. They placed male Siamese fighting fish in a specially devised aquarium in the laboratory where the fish could be easily observed. They further studied the fish during restricted time periods, usually less than one hour, so that the observer's attention could be concentrated on these subtle postural and gestural changes.

The importance of specifying the time and place of observation can also be seen in the study of sexual behavior, also previously discussed. If one is concerned with an aspect of the sexual behavior that is postural in character, the Behavior-Effect Rule is of little use. For example, Beach and Jordon (1956) conducted an extensive study of the postural changes that occur in the male rat during sexual activity. Rather than attempting to observe the rats in their natural habitat, awaiting the infrequent moments when the female is in estrus, they arranged to have the behavior occur at their convenience by injecting the female with a sexual hormone that would guarantee her receptivity. Having increased the likelihood that sexual behavior would occur at a time convenient to the experimenters, a convenient place of observation was also arranged by devising a special enclosure that permitted the genital organs of the rats to be viewed directly during sexual mounting, intromission, and ejaculation. We shall designate this general procedure as the Time and Place Rule. As applied to the problem of recording responses and delivering reinforcers, this procedure may be stated as follows:

Time and Place Rule: Specify the time and place of the response occurrence and the reinforcement delivery.

As indicated in the above examples, many behaviors such as facial expressions, postures, and gestures produce no easily recordable environmental effects. In such instances the Behavior-Effect Rule rarely is of use, and the Time and Place Rule becomes important. Direct observation is necessary since no environmental effect is available and the Time and Place Rule makes it more convenient for the experimenter to engage in this direct observation. By allowing the behavior in question to be emitted only at a particular time, the experimenter can maximize his concentration and recording during these preselected periods.

Table 6–1

Time and Place of On-Ward Jobs

Type of job	Place	Time
Dietary assistant		
1. Kitchen chores	Kitchen	6:45 a.m., 11:30 a.m., 4:30 p.m.
2. Coffee urn	Kitchen	2:30 p.m.
3. Ice carrier	Kitchen	9:15 a.m., 3:15 p.m.
4. Shakers	Kitchen	8:00 a.m., 12:45 p.m., 5:45 p.m.
5. Pots and pans	Kitchen	7:30 a.m., 12:15 p.m., 5:15 p.m.
6. Steam table	Kitchen	7:30 a.m., 12:15 p.m., 5:15 p.m.
7. Meal server	Kitchen	7:00 a.m., 11:45 a.m., 4:45 p.m.
8. Dishwashers	Kitchen	7:30 a.m., 12:15 p.m., 5:15 p.m.
Waitress		
1. Meals	Dining room	7:30 a.m., 12:15 p.m., 5:15 p.m.
2. Commissary	Dining room	9:45 a.m., 2:15 p.m., 8:00 p.m.
Sales clerk assistant		
1. Commissary	Kitchen	9:30 a.m., 2:00 p.m., 7:45 p.m.
Secretarial assistant		
1. Tooth brushing	Hall	12:30 p.m.
2. Exercises	Day room	9:15 a.m.
3. Commissary	Kitchen	9:30 a.m., 2:00 p.m., 7:45 p.m.
Ward Cleaning assistant		
1. Halls and rooms	Seven rooms & hall	8:00 a.m., 9:45 p.m.
2. Special	Ward	(When necessary)
3. Dormitories	Dorms 1–5	7:45 a.m.

Table 6–1 (continued)

Type of job	Place	Time
Assistant janitor		
1. Supplies	Utility room	1:20 p.m.
2. Trash	Outside building	7:45 a.m.
3. Porch	Outside building	2:00 p.m.
4. Washroom janitor	Patients' restroom	8:00 a.m.
Laundry assistant		
1. Hose	Own dorm	3:45 p.m.
2. Delivery	Outside building	7:45 p.m.
3. Folding	Own bedroom	3:45 p.m.
4. Pick up service	Hall	7:30 p.m.
Grooming assistant		
1. Clothing care	Hall	6:30 p.m.
2. Personal hygiene	Patients' restroom	6:30 a.m., 11:15 a.m., 4:15 p.m.
3. Oral hygiene	Hall	12:30 p.m.
4. Personal	Restroom	(When necessary)
5. Bath	Tub room	7:30 p.m.
6. Beauty aids	Hall	7:30 p.m.
Recreational assistant		
1. Walks	On grounds	3:00 p.m.
2. Exercise	Day room	9:15 a.m.
3. Movie projectionist	Day room	7:00 p.m.
Special services		
1. Errands	On grounds	(When necessary)
2. Tour guide	On ward	(When necessary)
3. Nursing assistant	On ward	(When necessary)

Applications of the Time and Place Rule in the Motivating Environment

One of the major objectives of the motivating environment was to train patients to perform a wide range of jobs both on and off the ward. The Time and Place Rule dictated that when the patient was to do a job and where she was to do it be specified. Application of the rule to jobs related to meals required no special arrangements, since meals are customarily restricted as to time and place. In the ward, meals were served at 6:00 A.M., 11:30 A.M., and 4:30 P.M. The place where meals were served was the ward kitchen. The rigorous adherence to this schedule allowed the performance of the meal servers, for example, to be directly observed at the time and place as specified. Similarly, the following jobs were to be done at a specific time and place: mopping at 9:15 A.M. in the hall; doing dishes at 7:30 A.M., 12:30 P.M., and 5:30 P.M. in the kitchen; assisting with baths at 7:00 P.M. in the bathroom, and so on. A detailed list of the jobs, as well as the time and place where they were performed is found in Table 6–1.

C. INDIVIDUAL RESPONSIBILITY

Another aspect of the response-reinforcement relation that should be specified in advance is the identity of the reinforcing agents. If one is to praise or correct an employee for the caliber of performance, it seems necessary to establish a procedure whereby the supervisor knows which attendant is carrying out which procedure. It is desirable, therefore, not only to specify where and when the activity is to occur but also which individual is responsible for its execution. In the absence of such specification, it has been found that no one individual can be held responsible for failure to administer the reinforcement procedure properly, since any deviation, omission, or modification is easily attributed to the behavior of some other employee. Therefore, in guaranteeing the standardized delivery of the reinforcer one and only one attendant should be designated as responsible on a given occasion, as stated in the following procedural rule:

Individual Responsibility Rule: Assign one and only one individual to act as the reinforcing agent for a given occasion.

Adherence to this rule often goes against what seems to be a commonsense principle. Intuitively, it would seem that the reinforcement procedure would be more effective with more individuals assigned to it. Our experience was, however, that the responsibility for failure or excellence could not be attached to any given individual.

The ward procedures for assuring individual responsibility were accomplished by a formal time-schedule that guaranteed that the assigned individual had no competing activities. The duties of the reinforcing agent were arranged so that no other duties were required of her at the moment that she was scheduled to carry out the reinforcer delivery. Equally important, but not so obvious, was the necessity of selecting some other individual to take responsibility for any other unexpected events which could interfere with the proper conduct of the reinforcing activity at the designated time. In the motivating environment, a schedule was posted each day which designated a specific attendant as responsible for the proper execution of a given reinforcement procedure. For example, the same attendant was not responsible for all commissary periods; but for a given commissary period, one and only one attendant was designated. Similarly, the schedule of the attendant assigned to a particular commissary period was arranged so that she was not required to engage in any other activities as part of her duties at that time. In addition, a second attendant on the ward had standard instructions to deal with any unexpected events that might occur, without enlisting the assistance of the attendant who was assigned to the commissary.

The Individual Responsibility Rule was applied also, to the activities of the patients. If the only specification was that a given job be done at a given time and place, some patients often persuaded another patient to perform the job. The tokens would then be given to a patient for a performance by another. Whenever this situation was allowed to occur, it usually did. Since the intended therapeutic value of the job was its performance, this substitution was undesirable. It was much less important that the job be done than that the patients be motivated to do it and to benefit from the social interactions specific to that job. Consequently, an attendant or a patient assistant supervised almost every job to assure that the job was performed by the specific patient designated for it. The Individual Responsibility Rule was in this way applied to the activities of both the patients and the staff. In the absence of some procedure for determining which individual engaged in an activity, it does not seem possible to bestow credit or reinforcers for appropriate performance by the individual, nor to correct inappropriate performance.

D. DIMENSIONS OF REINFORCER

To a large extent the history of psychology may be described as the development of standardized methods designed to eliminate unspecified influences by the experimenter and to allow specification of the precise event that was responsible for a behavioral change. Underlying this preoccupation with method has been the discovery that whenever a human agent is used to implement a procedure or to record the results of using that procedure, errors can be expected.

The classic example of human influence in determining behavioral change is the example of the horse, Clever Hans, that appeared to be capable of counting but only because of subtle cues that were being provided by the trainer. In this particular instance the trainer honestly believed that he was not providing any unauthorized stimuli, but was following a standardized procedure. This example illustrates that the problem is not a question of honesty. Errors and variability are introduced when humans are used to conduct and record the results of a psychological procedure. Usually one assumes that this error and variability is random; but whenever the experimenter or any other person having expectations about the outcome of the experiment is also involved in implementing it, then errors can be expected to be systematic. For example, in a very simple procedure such as a runway in which food is placed in the goal box, many sources of error exist. Among them we may list (1) the manner of handling the animal as a source of reinforcement or aversion, (2) the spacing between trials, (3) the amount of time that the animal is left in the start box, and (4) the amount and nature of the reinforcer. Random errors in performing these operations are commonly acknowledged, but even more important is the systematic error or bias by the experimenter that enters into these simple operations. This type of error or bias was recently discussed by Rosenthal and Fode (1963), who found that the results obtained by students from psychological experiments with animals were partly predictable on the basis of the students' expectations.

Errors seem to occur even more frequently when the subject and the reinforcing agent are human and the reinforcer is verbal. To minimize this danger several studies have made efforts to specify many of the dimensions of the reinforcing stimulus. For example, Thorndike (1931) restricted the reinforcer to two words, "right" or "wrong." Similarly, Verplanck (1955) attempted to specify the verbal reinforcing stimulus in physical terms by restricting the phrase used to such expressions as "I agree" or "I disagree." Rheingold, Gewirtz, and Ross (1959) in using facial expressions as the reinforcer obviously faced a problem in specifying these expressions in physical terms. Nevertheless, they attempted to specify them somewhat by limiting the distance between the subject and the experimenter and by limiting the duration of the expression. Greenspoon (1955) similarly restricted the sound that he used as a reinforcer to one or two sounds of a particular phonetic structure.

In all instances of verbal reinforcement there are undoubtedly substantial variations in the manner of intonation, the speed of execution, the immediacy, and the duration of the reinforcer. There may even be mistakes in presenting the reinforcer. For example, in a study of verbal conditioning by Azrin, Holz, Ulrich, and Goldiamond (1961), it was found that student experimenters were failing to reinforce when the schedule required it and reinforcing when the schedule specified that no reinforcer should occur. In the absence of tape recordings of the actual reinforcement procedure, one might easily have assumed that the written records submitted by the students were a valid representation of the naturalistic environment of the subject. The problem was that no independent record could be obtained of the extent to which the reinforcement procedure was being properly executed. Confidential statements by the student experimenters at a later date revealed that almost all of them had distorted the data sheets that were submitted; some had not conducted the experiments, much less delivered the previously designated number of reinforcers. The students felt they had not been lying; rather their expectations about the outcome had been so strong that when their data and expectations were in conflict, the expectations prevailed. The point cannot be stressed sufficiently that whenever a human is involved in the conduct or recording of a reinforcement procedure, then errors of a variable and systematic sort will result. The following rule helps to prevent such errors from developing.

Dimensions of Reinforcement Rule: Specify in physical terms as many dimensions of the reinforcer as possible.

The best way to eliminate the influence of a human in the recording and presentation of the reinforcer is to minimize his participation or to substitute some automated method. For example, food reinforcement in the form of a pellet has been used with rats to eliminate variability in the manner in which the food is prepared. To eliminate variability in the location of the reinforcer or the time, duration, and manner of presentation, devices for automatic food delivery have been used, such as the Anger feeder for delivering pellets, the Gerbrands grain feeder, or the many liquid delivery devices. The question of when to reinforce is automatically decided by the apparatus, not the experimenter. A record of the number of reinforcers delivered has been achieved using automatic electrical or mechanical devices which may record either the number of food reinforcers which are delivered, or, in the case of the drinkometer, the number of licking responses which are made.

Similarly, in studies of human behavior, automatic methods of delivering the reinforcer have been introduced whenever possible. Taking, again, the example of the verbal conditioning studies, Lane (1960), Lane and Shinkman (1963), Lindsley (1963), and Shearn, Sprague, and Rosenzweig (1961) have substituted automatic reinforcement delivery devices for the experimenter who is intimately involved in the specification and mode of delivery of the reinforcer. For a general discussion of the importance of this methodological consideration in verbal conditioning studies, see Holz and Azrin, in Honig (1966). These and similar investigations led to the following procedure.

Automated Reinforcement Procedure: Use automated means to deliver and record the reinforcing event whenever possible.

The ideal solution to specifying and physically controlling the dimensions of the reinforcer is to use an automated procedure. Such an automated procedure will provide a high degree of standardization of the manner in which the reinforcer is delivered.

Four types of automatic devices were used in the motivating environment. One of them was a wall-mounted cigarette dispenser which provided a single cigarette when the required number of tokens was inserted into the slot. The cigarettes could be obtained by the patients from this device at any time during the day. A device in the dispenser provided a count of the number of cigarettes delivered. The number of cigarettes obtained by the patients during each 24-hour period was also recorded by counting the number of cigarettes missing since the last count. This device provided something that no human could provide, a completely standardized mode of presentation of the reinforcing stimulus and an exact record of the number delivered.

A second automatic device used in this procedure was a wall-mounted cigarette lighter. Inserting a token into this device resulted in the heating of a coil that would light a cigarette. The duration for which the coil was heated was controlled by an internal timer. An exact count of the number of lights received by the patients was obtained every 24 hours by counting the number of tokens in the receptable or by recording the reading from the internal counter. As was the case with the cigarette dispenser, the lighter was available for operation continuously throughout the day.

A third type of automatic device was a coin-operated television set and a coin-operated radio. The token provided a duration of viewing or listening that was controlled internally by a timer. The TV and radio were available for extended periods of time, though not throughout the day since incompatibility with other reinforcers was to be avoided. (See Compatibility of Reinforcement Rule.)

The fourth type of device was a coin-operated turnstile. This turnstile was used as an automatic programming and recording device for many of the reinforcers characterized by access to a given location. It was used to gain access to the dining room, to a room where movies were shown, to religious services on the ward, to the commissary area, to various recreational activities such as musical sessions, and for all other reinforcers that required access to a given location. For each of the four devices, the manner of delivery of the reinforcement was specified by the mechanical or electrical characteristics of the apparatus. For some of the reinforcers, such as the cigarette dispenser, the cigarette lighter, and the radio, the apparatus had an advantage over a human in that it delivered the reinforcer in a standardized fashion at any moment during every 24-hour day.

Implementation of Reinforcement Procedures by Humans

The automated reinforcer procedure provides the best means of guaranteeing that the specified reinforcer will be consistently controlled in its manner of delivery. An automatic device for delivering a reinforcer can only deliver what is put into it. It is possible to know beforehand, therefore, what will be delivered by specifying what is put in. Similarly, if the nature of the reinforcer is such that it can be varied with regard to number or duration, the device can be preset to deliver a reinforcer of a given number or a given duration. When a human is used to administer the reinforcer, however, the nature, number, and duration of the reinforcing event can vary. It is necessary, therefore, to specify in objective terms as many of the dimensions of the reinforcing events as possible.

In a sense, the failure to specify a dimension of a reinforcer in physical terms is equivalent to a declaration that those aspects that are left unspecified are irrelevant and can vary widely. Even when one uses a discrete object as a reinforcer, considerable variation will occur unless rigid specifications are established beforehand. For example, if an extra serving of dessert is scheduled as a reinforcer, the attendant can be seen to exercise considerable judgment in the amount that is delivered. In this instance, the dimensions of reinforcement procedure would suggest a standardized serving spoon. Even for something as apparently standardized as candy, the attendant will exercise considerable judgment as to the number of pieces that are to be delivered unless the number is specified beforehand. Therefore, a general rule might be to specify at least the size, number, and duration of the reinforcer. For example, one can specify the size and number of sandwiches, cookies, toothpaste, articles of clothing, bottles of perfume, and so on.

The major motivational sources for patients included events and activities that were difficult to specify in the same way that one would specify a pair of sandals or a one-half ounce bar of soap. The question was, how could one specify the dimensions of reinforcers like the opportunity to go for a walk, or to attend movies, religious services, social functions, or dances? For that matter, how could one identify objectively the dimensions of private talks with the physician or nurse, or psychotherapy meetings with the chaplain, social worker, or psychologist?

Fortunately, in addition to the Time and Place Rule and the Individual Responsibility Rule, which already specified various dimensions of the reinforcer delivery, an important dimension of most of the reinforcers mentioned above was that of duration. So, for example, the religious service was scheduled at a given time and place, under the responsibility of the chaplain, and for a fixed duration, which was 10 minutes at one stage of the program. Similarly, using the Time and Place Rule, a patient could choose to talk to a social worker, but without a time limitation, the interview would have varied considerably in duration. In practice a duration was established allowing the patient to talk in private to the social worker, physician, or anyone on the staff for a fixed period of 10 minutes. Likewise, walks on the grounds were defined not only in terms of the time and place but also in terms of their duration, 15 minutes. Commissary lasted for 20 minutes. Movies lasted for approximately one and one-half to two hours. A walk to town lasted for one hour; musical activities lasted for 30 minutes, while social evenings lasted one hour. Similarly, selections of beds, furnishings, and any one of five bedrooms were available at a given time, 11:00 A.M. Here again, it was necessary to specify the time limits for use of these items. A bedroom could be secured for 24 hours; after that it was necessary to renew with tokens the option to keep the same room. Similarly, chairs and screens were available for 24 hours, after which they could be renewed. Finally, permits to go off the ward were also specified, not only with respect to the Time and Place Rule but also in terms of duration. These permits were valid for 24 hours and could be renewed at the patient's request.

E. DIRECT SUPERVISION OF RECORDING OF RESPONSE AND DELIVERY OF REINFORCEMENT

When an investigator reports results obtained with a given measuring instrument, it is assumed that he observed the results. In many types of phenomena studied in science, the scientist has little trouble making direct observations. For example, if a new type of micro-organism has been reported, the reader of the report may assume that the author himself has used the microscope through which he has discovered the new micro-organism. Similarly, for observations in astronomy, chemistry, or biology there is no problem in directly examining the operation of the measuring instrument if the measurement period is of short duration and the measuring instrument is accessible to observation. A special problem occurs, however, when the measuring instrument is somewhat inaccessible to the experimenter or its operation is of such long duration that he cannot, for practical reasons, be continuously present to supervise it. Consider the example of the change in temperature of a chemical that results from the reaction of two other chemicals that have been mixed together. If the experimenter desires measurement of the change in temperature over several days, then he may rely on an automatic recording instrument such as a polygraph, or he may assign a technician to record the visual readings from a thermometer at regular and frequent intervals. In either case, he must take additional steps to guarantee that the information provided him by the technician or by the apparatus is reliable. The apparatus may have some defects that can be detected by directly observing its performance while the phenomenon is under study. Similarly, the accuracy of the technician can be determined by providing direct observation of the manner in which the technician is recording the data. In the complete absence of any direct supervision of the measurement procedure, there is no assurance that the readings are valid. The technician may fall asleep for six hours and fill in entries that seem compatible with the data he has obtained while awake. Even with automated instrumentation, errors in recording are inevitable since no apparatus is infallible.

An alternative to direct supervision is to rely on the verbal report of the individual who performed the measurements. Yet, we have seen elsewhere, that verbal report is often unreliable. It is surprising, then, to find such heavy reliance on verbal reports in many behavioral studies that use reinforcement procedures. Even "behaviorists" whose fundamental credo would seem to be that observation of behavior is foremost often neglect to obtain direct observation of the measurement process. These very psychologists, when working with animals in the laboratory, would be constantly checking and testing their instruments. These investigators, who would not take the statement of a laboratory assistant concerning the reliability of an apparatus at face value, somehow accept at face value the verbal report of a recorder who has a vital stake in the behavior he is reporting.

The study of behavior presents a particularly troublesome phenomenon with respect to obtaining adequate supervision of the measurement procedure, since behavior is much more of a process than it is a discrete event that occurs at a given time. One general solution has been for the experimenter to restrict the occurrence of the behavior and its measurement to a fairly brief duration of time and to a convenient locale as described previously under the Time and Place Rule.

Direct Supervision Rule: Provide systematic and direct observation of the reinforcement procedure.

This procedure cannot be satisfied by merely specifying that there be some observer present during the delivery of the reinforcer. An important part of this rule is that the person who ultimately wishes to take responsibility for the validity of the data must provide the direct observation. When an automatic apparatus is used for delivery of reinforcement, this procedure states that the supervisor must make systematic and direct observation of the automatic apparatus while in actual use. It is not sufficient to obtain information about its reliability of operation prior to or subsequent to the data collection. Similarly, if a technician is being used, it is not sufficient for the supervisor to observe his behavior during a practice session prior to or subsequent to the data collection. The supervision must occur during the actual data collection if the supervisor is to make credible statements about the data.

Another aspect of the Direct Supervision Rule requires elaboration. Direct observation of a phenomenon does not mean obtaining a verbal report from someone else about its occurrence. Direct observation means obtaining as immediate sensory exposure to the phenomenon as the nature of the phenomenon permits. Thus, if one is measuring an electrical phenomenon, this means directly observing the various voltage sensing instruments, and not relying exclusively on a technician's report of the readings of those instruments. Similarly, direct observation of the reinforcement of a patient does not mean exclusive reliance on a verbal report of an assistant or technician that he delivered the reinforcer that day. It means that the supervisor obtains visual and auditory confirmation of the delivery of the reinforcer by the technician. The same rationale applies when an automatic reinforcement device is used. Direct observation is not a direct statement by an electronics technician that the reinforcing device is operating properly, but rather direct visual and auditory observation by the supervisor of the device while it is delivering the reinforcer to the patient.

Direct supervision is especially important when it is human behavior that is being observed. We have already pointed out how all disciplines, including psychology, require such supervision in order to obtain first-hand evidence that the procedures are being conducted as intended and to reveal errors or deviations. An additional factor seems to be present when supervision is applied to human behavior; the quality and quantity of the performance appears to be directly affected by the very fact that supervision is taking place. In a sense, the act of supervising an employee seems to function as a reward or a punisher. To be more specific, it is only during direct supervision that the actual performance can be known to the supervisor; consequently, only at that time can there be a true basis for rewards for appropriate performance and punishment or criticism for inappropriate performance. We viewed the supervising process as accomplishing this dual function of discovering what procedures were being followed and directly influencing those procedures.

If this view of supervision as a reinforcer or punisher is correct, then previously established principles of reinforcement should tell us about the effectiveness of different methods of supervision. This analysis states that a complete absence of supervision is analagous to a reduced level of reinforcement for desired responses and a reduced level of punishment for the undesired. Consequently, the desired responses should occur less frequently, and the undesired more frequently than if there were supervision. Given that there is validity to this minimal statement, this analysis suggests how frequent the supervision should be. It is known that the frequency of a desired response is a direct function of the frequency of reinforcement (Skinner, 1938). Similarly, the frequency of an undesired response is an inverse function of the frequency of punishment (Azrin, Holz, and Hake, 1963; Azrin and Holz, 1966c). Continuous reinforcement or punishment would constitute the highest frequency possible. The recommendation is, therefore, that supervision should be continuous. This recommendation contradicts the practice common in many mental hospitals and other organizations of having the supervisory or administrative personnel stationed at locations that are remote from the area of activity of those being supervised. For example, in mental hospitals a separate administrative building or office area out of sight and earshot of the wards where the patients spend most of their time often is used for the psychologists, social workers, psychiatrists, and physicians. Even on the ward, the attendants are often closeted in a separate attendant's office, the door of which is closed.

The present analysis dictated that this arrangement be altered in the motivating environment. The supervising psychologist and the registered nurse were given offices on the ward itself. The attendants had an office which was located at the center of the ward and which had a large opening into the ward that permitted easy visual and auditory observation of most of the ward area. The mere presence of the supervisor "on the scene" does not guarantee that supervision will occur, of course; what it does do is make it possible and certainly more probable than if the supervisor's physical location is remote from the activities to be supervised. The simple expedient of locating the supervisor's office or work station in the middle of the activity constitutes an administrative technique for increasing the likelihood of effective supervision.

Direct supervision ideally should be continuous, but this is rarely practical even if the supervisor is stationed at the scene of the supervised activity because of the supervisor's other activities and the likelihood of several activities that require supervision occurring at the same time. Fortunately, experimental evidence is available on how supervision can be scheduled intermittently and still guarantee a uniform and high level of performance. If a positive reinforcer (Ferster and Skinner, 1957) or a negative reinforcer (Azrin, 1956) is arranged at irregular periods of time, the behavior controlled by that consequence will exist at a uniform rate. The critical feature of such a variable-interval schedule is that the reinforcer's occurrence be unpredictable. Supervision at irregular, unpredictable times according to this analysis should provide a simple means of using direct supervision that is not continuous and yet will guarantee a high level of performance at all times. The experimental results obtained with variable-interval schedules of reinforcement also suggest a second method of ensuring efficiency of the supervisor. The higher the frequency of reinforcement, the higher will be the rate of response. Analogously, then, one should have very frequent supervision to maintain the highest performance. Continuous supervision would be analogous to what is designated as CRF, or continuous reinforcement. From the point of view of the individual being supervised, the direct observation by the supervisor should be frequent, but, more important, the supervised individual should have no basis for predicting in advance when the supervision will occur.

Direct Supervision of Reinforcement Procedure in the Motivating Environment

The motivating environment could provide frequent direct visual supervision of the reinforcement procedures, since they were taking place at a particular time and place (see Time and Place Rule). The ward psychologist and supervising nurse visually observed the reinforcement and did not rely solely upon the attendants' reports regarding its delivery. The supervision was not only direct; it was systematic. The supervising nurse and ward psychologist had a written schedule of the reinforcements as they were occurring during each day. A schedule was established beforehand as to which of the reinforcements were to be observed and at what time. The frequency of the supervision was a function of the results of the supervision. Whenever a deviation from the reinforcement procedure was noted, the observation schedule was revised so that the reinforcing agent could be supervised on every occasion until the procedure was conducted properly. When supervision revealed that an activity was being conducted as intended, the frequency of supervision for that activity decreased. The supervision occurred at a time unknown to the attendant. An activity could be observed at intervals of up to two months or on three or four successive occasions, thus guaranteeing the irregularity necessary for a uniform rate of responding. The location of the supervisors' offices on the ward also provided frequent opportunities to observe the patient-attendant interaction without the necessity of a specially planned supervision.

The importance of providing direct supervision was revealed in practice to be very great in this ward procedure, in spite of strong feelings that were initially to the contrary. Several incidents, described in detail, will illustrate the problems that arose when direct supervision was deficient. The following is an example of the necessity for direct supervision of reinforcement, even when the reinforcer is delivered automatically and would seem to require no direct supervision. One token was required to operate the device that provided a light for the patient's cigarette. This device was preset by a timer to provide heat for a fixed duration of time. The duration had been initially set into the timer for six seconds. All the indirect records obtained regarding this lighter indicated that it was operating satisfactorily. None of the patients complained of any malfunction. Also, a large number of tokens was found daily in the token delivery box locked within the device. This large number of tokens indicated that it was functioning properly, since the patients continued to put tokens into it. Similarly, the casual observation of the attendants during the course of their duties did not give any reason to believe there was a malfunction, since patients could be seen walking up to the lighter, depositing a token, and leaving with a lighted cigarette. As part of the Direct Supervision procedure, the cigarette lighter operation was observed for a period of several weeks; after which no supervision took place. At one of the scheduled observation periods a patient was seen to light her cigarette. The lighter worked, but its duration seemed short, since only a portion of the patient's cigarette was lit. The lighter was immediately checked, and it was found that the internal timer had somehow drifted or had been misset from six seconds to an interval of about three seconds. The duration apparently was sufficient for some of the patients to obtain a light but not all of them, as was the case with the individual observed during the period of supervision.

Another example of the necessity of direct supervision even under supposedly ideal conditions concerns the use of the token-operated television set, which remained on for 10 minutes per token.

Casual observation gave every reason to believe that it was operating as intended. Yet, direct supervision revealed that some patients were inserting a nail file into the coin slot and activating the TV picture. Only direct supervision of this reinforcer as it was being used under the usual conditions could have revealed that there was a deviation. Still another example of the necessity of direct supervision, even when using automated reinforcement devices, concerns the use of the coin-operated cigarette machine. It appeared from observation that the machine was operating properly, since patients could regularly be seen to approach the machine, insert tokens in it, and leave with a cigarette in their hands. Direct observation by the supervisor revealed that the machine functioned properly until all of the cigarettes were used. The first patient to insert tokens when it was empty did not receive a cigarette and usually informed the other patients. Here again, we see that no other method but direct supervision would have revealed that the reinforcer was not being delivered as intended.

The above examples illustrate the need for providing systematic and direct observation of the reinforcing activity by the supervisor. Deviations in the reinforcement were most likely to go unreported by the recipients and undetected by the casual observer when the deviations were (1) very infrequent, (2) inconsistent, and (3) in the direction favorable to the recipient of reinforcement.

The necessity for providing direct and systematic supervision was even more apparent for those reinforcers delivered by a human rather than by an automatic device. A consistent feature of the individuals conducting a procedure was their unshakable belief that they were not deviating. It is probably this insistence by human reinforcers in their infallibility that has made so many investigators mistakenly believe that the reinforcement administration was being carried out as intended.

Religious services

This point is illustrated in the use of religious services as a reinforcer. The patient gave a token to gain access to a room where the chaplain provided religious services for 10 minutes. The chaplain had been asked initially to use a timer to time the services, but he insisted that it was not necessary since he could approximate 10 minutes very closely, and further, that he already had a watch. The ward supervisor tried to persuade him to use the automatic timer but to no avail. After several religious services had been conducted, direct observation by the ward supervisor revealed that the services lasted for a minimum of 15 minutes and often for as long as 30 minutes. The services were never terminated except by a reminder by the ward supervisor. On each occasion that the chaplain was reminded, he insisted that the services had really been going on for only 10 minutes and that he was just "winding things up" at that instant. He thanked the ward supervisor profusely but indicated that the reminder was unnecessary. In this instance sole reliance on the estimate of the reinforcing agent would have been mistaken. In this particular example, deviation would have been extremely difficult to detect through any other means since the deviation was in the direction favorable to the patients (they wanted to hear more) and to the chaplain (he wanted to talk more). Nor would casual observation have revealed the deviation without exact timing of the duration of the services. All auxiliary indications that the reinforcing activity had taken place as intended were conspicuous; the required number of tokens was delivered to the supervising nurse, these tokens had been deposited in the automatic turnstile that controlled access to the area where the services were held, and it could be seen by even the casual observer that the chaplain was indeed holding a religious service.

The necessity for direct and systematic visual supervision is also illustrated by the following four incidents. In the first incident a deviation from the specified procedures was discovered in the beauty shop. The beauty shop procedure stated: "One token for each service; wash hair—1 token, set hair—1 token, apply makeup—1 token." Direct observation revealed that one attendant was giving two services and only charging for one. The second case involved bed making. The procedure read: "Give patient 1 token if bed is made neatly. Nothing on bed. Area under and around bed clean." Direct observation revealed that one attendant paid the patient even though she was lying on her bed. The third case involved the dishwashing duties. The procedure for dishwashers read: "Patient washes dishes, puts them away, and cleans cabinets around and under sink." Direct observation revealed that occasionally an attendant paid patients for doing a good job without entering the kitchen to observe the results of the dishwashing. The last case concerned the hours during which patients worked. Jobs were to stop at 10:00 P.M. and not start again until 6:30 A.M. Direct supervision revealed that one attendant, who was working the midnight shift, allowed a patient to help her with the duty of carrying out the trash at 5:00 A.M. because the patient was up and wanted to work.

Many additional instances could be cited, all of which point to the need for direct supervision. In some instances, it should be noted, direct supervision revealed that an employee had made improvements on a procedure on her own initiative, in which case the improvements were made a standard part of the procedure for all attendants. Also, problems in conducting a given procedure were often pointed out to the supervisor by the attendant during the period of observation; the outcome was often an improved procedure that eliminated the problem. Direct supervision should not be considered, therefore, simply as an attempt to discover errors but rather as the minimal and initial step in directing the behavior of the patient and staff toward improved procedures. The improvements are useful not only for any research endeavor but for any therapeutic program that is based on behaviors and procedures which actually took place.

F. MULTIPLE REINFORCING AGENTS

Whenever an experiment is conducted, a person is involved in some stage of it. The experiment may involve complex equipment and laboratory instruments; but in the end, it is always an individual who is responsible for the interpretation and analysis of the results. Yet, the layman is often surprised to find that published scientific experiments are written in a stark and impersonal manner. The experiment reads almost as if there were no person involved to provide direction, interpretation, analysis, or integration of the results. This impersonal mode of presentation is evident in the general prohibition against the use of the first person, "I" or "we," in the exposition. Instead, the author writes the research report in such a way that he is describing events with as little personal flavor as possible. The scientific community favors this mode of exposition because of the very objective of the scientific enterprise. The scientific endeavor attempts to discover events that are related to one another. The identification of these events and their relationship should not depend in any way upon the personal attributes of any one individual. When a great author or artist dies, usually the way in which he created his composition dies with him. When a scientist dies, however, the procedures whereby he could produce a phenomenon usually live on indefinitely. It follows from this aspect of the scientific enterprise that replication by other experimenters is a prerequisite for belief in the existence of a stated relationship. If no other investigator can replicate the experiment as described by the original discoverer, then no credence is attached to the relationship. The necessity of replication imposes a burden on the author to describe his method of observation and recording in such a way that many other investigators will be able to duplicate the conditions that resulted in the relationship or phenomenon being reported. This impersonal point of view by the investigator is a difficult one to adopt. An investigator, probably like every other person, would be pleased to receive praise for his individualistic skills. It might be a source of much pleasure to a scientist to be able to state in private that upon looking at a given microscopic slide or a cumulative record of behavior or a given chemical he can detect things in it that no one else can. Indeed, he may very well be capable of doing so, but science is not interested except to the extent that he can provide information about how other scientists can duplicate his performance. Of course, once he has notified them of the means of duplicating this performance, from one point of view, some of the "fun" is lost. The scientist is forced, then, to receive approval from his colleagues on the basis of the originality of the relationship discovered, not on the individuality or originality of his unspecifiable observation or recording methods.

The same impersonal point of view must be adopted in developing methods for delivering a reinforcer. Every reader will be able to think of specific individuals who seem daily to be unusually effective in using reinforcers to influence the behavior of others. Unfortunately, this individualistic skill is of little value in developing a general method for general usage. Instead, it is necessary for the nature of the reinforcement procedure to be specified in such objective terms that it can operate in an effective manner regardless of who uses it. It was noted above that one means of guaranteeing objective specification of the events in a scientific endeavor is to require replication. Similarly, in the case of delivery of reinforcement, one method of guaranteeing objectivity of specification is to require replication using several different individuals as the reinforcing agent. By this means, failure or difficulty by any one individual to perform the procedure as instructed constitutes a failure of replication and can be used to reveal problems of adequate specification of the procedure. This course of action provides a general procedure to be followed.

Procedure for Multiple Reinforcing Agents: Use different individuals to implement the delivery of reinforcement.

In a sense, the multiple reinforcing agent procedure goes against a common-sense rule-of-thumb in employee usage. Generally, it appears that employees are used exclusively on a particular job because they have developed exceptional skill on that job as a result of their extensive performance of it. Certainly, this rule-of-thumb seems to have merit, and it would obviously be impractical to have every employee perform every job in any situation. The multiple reinforcing agents procedure requires only that there be occasional and regular substitution by another agent. From a practical point of view, this procedure has a very substantial incidental advantage. It prevents disruption of any reinforcement delivery program when the regular reinforcing agent resigns or is absent. The individual who is substituting occasionally can then assume the responsibility with prior assurance that the reinforcer will be delivered in the usual standardized and effective manner.

Application in the Motivating Environment

In the motivating environment no single employee administered a given type of reinforcer for much more than one week without another employee serving as a substitute on at least one occasion. It is especially important that on the occasions of substitution the regular reinforcing agent *not* be present. Otherwise, of course, the delivery of the reinforcer might still be based on idiosyncratic practices of the regularly scheduled agent. In the present procedure, the use of several employees to deliver a given reinforcer was no problem administratively. Indeed, it was a necessity since the reinforcers were usually scheduled throughout the week. Since a given employee works only five days a week, the scheduling of the reinforcers seven days a week demanded the use of more than one reinforcing agent during a given week. Some of the reinforcers were scheduled very infrequently, for example, attendance at a movie period, which occurred only once per week. This movie could easily have been supervised by the same attendant each week had it been so desired. Yet, a deliberate effort was made to have a different attendant schedule a movie on different occasions. For example, a total of 32 employees (three nurses and 29 attendants) took part at different times in conducting and recording the movie reinforcement procedure.

Inadequate specification of the reinforcement procedure was discovered in several cases only by using multiple reinforcing agents. In one case, a lack of standardization was discovered in the serving of cold drinks by two different attendants at commissary period. According to the written procedure patients could buy a "glass of cold drink" upon payment of one token. It was disclosed by direct supervision that one attendant served the drinks in an eight-ounce glass, while another attendant served them in a twelve-ounce glass. This problem was solved by further specifying the procedure to give the precise number of ounces to be served, e.g., eight ounces. In a second example, the standard procedure for giving tokens for bath and shampoo stated: "Four tokens for bath and shampoo, one token for taking a bath." Nothing in the procedure was mentioned about reinforcement being contingent upon a patient being weighed. Upon close observation it was found, however, that one attendant paid a patient if she took a bath even if she refused to be weighed, while another attendant refused to give the patients their bath tokens unless they were weighed, also. This discrepancy in the payment of tokens was eliminated by restating the procedure: "One token for bath, one token for shampoo, one token for being weighed." A third example concerned the daily distribution of clean clothing. The procedure instructed the attendants to give extra clean clothing for 10 tokens. This procedure was interpreted differently by the attendants. One attendant gave the patients only one set of clean clothing upon request; another attendant gave them several sets to choose from. The solution arrived at was to specify that each patient be given two sets of clothing to choose from. In all of these examples, a lack of adequate specification of the procedure, resulting in varying interpretations by attendants, was discovered and corrected only because of the use of multiple reinforcing agents.

G. RECIPIENT OF REINFORCEMENT

Whenever there is some question in psychological experiments about whether a procedure is being adequately performed, a standard solution is to use two independent observers and to obtain a reliability coefficient. The reliability coefficient gives the extent to which the two observers agreed about the occurrence and nature of the events being recorded. The use of several individuals in succession has been described above in the multiple reinforcer procedure as one method of receiving independent observations. Another solution to this problem might be to engage a second employee in a strictly observer function whenever reinforcers are being delivered by the reinforcing agent. Ideally, the second observer should be an individual for whom there are some favorable consequences for the proper administration of the reinforcement procedure. Naturally, this solution would be very impractical, since it doubles the number of personnel required for administering the reinforcement procedure. Fortunately, by the very nature of the reinforcement interaction, there is always one other person present during the delivery of the reinforcer, namely the recipient of the reinforcer. Therefore, an alternative solution is to use this recipient of the reinforcer as the additional observer. If the recipient is verbal, it is possible for him to report on whether the reinforcer has been properly delivered. What is particularly effective about using the recipient as reporter is that he is so intimately affected by the proper execution of the reinforcement procedure.

Recipient of Reinforcement Procedure: Use the report of the recipient of the reinforcer as an additional check on the reinforcement transaction.

One limitation immediately suggests itself concerning this procedure. While it is true that the recipient may be relied on to report any deficit or omission of the reinforcer, it is also likely that he will not report any additions or other deviations in the manner of the reinforcement delivery that are favorable to him. One cannot, therefore, rely entirely on the report of recipient of the reinforcer.

A corollary to this rule is to make the reinforcement procedure public and conspicuous. In this manner other would-be recipients of the reinforcer may minimize the likelihood of a systematic error, since it may not be to their advantage to see that someone else is receiving more than he is entitled to.

Application in the Motivating Environment

The recipient of the reinforcer has a strong interest in receiving as much of the reinforcing event as possible. Take the example in which an attendant, Jones, wished to reduce her work duties by conducting a daily walk for 10 minutes instead of the scheduled 20. This deviation was brought to the attention of the supervising nurse by a patient, Sally, who complained that she had not been allowed out on her walk for as long as she was supposed to be. The problem was immediately corrected by applying the Direct Supervision Rule to detect this deviation.

In the motivating environment, patients were told orally and through posted notices what the reinforcers were. If the rules concerning the administration of the reinforcer are public, then the recipient of the reinforcer will expect not only that he will be given the reinforcer as specified by the rules but that all others will also. Then, if a recipient receives the reinforcement in a greater amount, another individual is likely to report this deviation. In following the recipient of reinforcement procedure one should obtain reports from the individual about both the proper delivery of the reinforcer to himself and its delivery to others. A formal method was used in the motivating environment to carry out this procedure. Approximately once each month the supervisor asked each of the patients the following questions: Have you received all the tokens that you earned? Were you cheated or short-changed when you exchanged your tokens for things you wanted? Have you seen anyone else short-changed when they exchanged tokens for things they wanted?

Although this procedure was designed primarily for cases of human implementation, it was found helpful even when an automatic device was used. For example, the cigarette dispensing machine usually delivered a single cigarette when a token was inserted in it. On rare occasions, however, it failed to do so. Under normal procedures when the device failed, the patients usually jostled the machine in an attempt to restore it to its proper operation. Often one of the patients reported the malfunction to a staff member. What happened was that even without a formal implementation of the recipient of reinforcement procedure, a second report of the adequacy of the reinforcement device was eventually delivered to the staff. The fact that this second report was made, even without a formal procedure for obtaining it, exemplifies the favorable consequences that exist for a recipient to make such a report upon a malfunction. In order to have maximum usefulness, however, it is desirable to establish a systematic procedure for obtaining these reports, rather than relying upon occasional and delayed reports. In the case of the automatic apparatus, the solution was a very simple and straightforward one. A sign was posted on each of the automatic machines telling the user to report any malfunction to the ward staff immediately.

The following examples illustrate deviations of the reinforcement procedure that were reported by the recipients of reinforcement, i.e., the patients. In one case patients were to be called at 4:00 P.M. to go out on their grounds passes. A deviation in procedure was pointed out to the supervising nurse by one patient, Gladys J., who complained because the attendant had not called grounds pass time until 4:05 P.M. In another case, the commissary period, which was to be held every evening, was not held on one particular evening. This failure to follow the standard procedure was brought to the attention of the supervising nurse by a patient, Martha D., when she complained, "we didn't have commissary last night." On checking, the nurse found that the attendant had decided not to have the commissary because by the time a three-hour movie was over, the standard time for commissary had passed. The procedure was then changed to make clear that commissary was to be held regardless of how late the movie ended. Thus, the deviation in procedure was discovered and corrected because of the report from a recipient of reinforcement. In a third case, the standard procedure for kitchen workers stated that they were to receive a bonus if they completed their work in 45 minutes. Lillie G. complained that she had not received her bonus tokens even though she had finished on time. The solution to this problem was to have a record kept in the kitchen on which the attendant entered the starting and finishing times of the patient.

Sometimes patients reported a procedural deviation that had been in their favor. In the first case, patient Dora C., while being paid for a job by an attendant, said, "No, dear. I only earned 10 tokens and you gave me 20 tokens. I only worked for one hour." In another case, the procedure for a grounds pass was to give the patient upon payment of tokens a slip stating the time she was to return to the ward. A specified number of tokens was to be paid for an hour off the ward. Patient Agnes I. stated when she received her pass, "Attendant, you wrote me off the ward for two hours and I paid you for only one hour."

The next example is one in which a patient reported a situation in which another patient was receiving more than she was entitled to. At one time the procedure for a patient who wanted to attend church services on the hospital grounds was to give her a pass which lasted for two hours. An anomaly in the situation was pointed out when one patient, Pamela B., came to the supervising nurse stating, "You gave Wilma W. two hours for church and her Catholic services are only 30 minutes and she can be out on the grounds one and a half hours for nothing. The rest of us get two hours, but church lasts two hours and we don't get any extra time." This problem, which was brought to the attention of the nurse because of one patient's reporting on another's receipt of reinforcement, was solved by granting a grounds pass for the duration of the service each patient was attending.

CHAPTER 7

Developing a Response

A. RESPONSE SHAPING RULE

Many of the early studies of operant reinforcement selected as the target response one which already had an existing operant level. In runway studies, food was used as a reinforcer and was located at the opposite end of a runway. The final, or target, response was that of the rat running down the runway. Even before conditioning began, the rat had walked down the runway often, sniffing and moving back and forth in a fairly continuous motion. When food reinforcement was given at the end of the runway, the speed of traversing it increased. The important point here is that the target performance had already been in existence before the first reinforcer was obtained by the animal.

Unlike the runway situation in which the target behavior existed prior to conditioning, there are other situations in which the target behavior is virtually absent. Consider, for example, the standard procedure in which it is desired that a pigeon peck at a plastic disk that is located slightly above the usual position of its head. This plastic disk is mounted on an electrical switch that will provide an output and constitutes the response mechanism for recording the final target behavior of pecking at the disk. In this situation, pecking at the key by the pigeon may have near-zero frequency. That is to say, the response might never occur spontaneously.

Fortunately, there is a laboratory technique which suggests how to begin achieving this target behavior. This technique is called response shaping by successive approximations (Ferster and Skinner, 1957). Observation of a pigeon reveals that it engages in many movements; it walks about the cage with its head usually moving in a distinct arc. Rapid sidewise movements of its head are frequently seen, in addition to the usual up-and-down bobbing movement that accompanies its locomotion. The back-and-forth movement of its head constitutes a component of the final response of the bird's pecking at the key. The first step in reaching the final performance is to select the forward movement of the bird's head for reinforcement. The experimenter focuses his attention solely on the movement of the bird's head, ignoring all other aspects of its behavior, including the flapping of its wings, locomotion, or even movements of its head in any other direction. The instant that the bird's head moves forward, whether it is a result of a specific neck movement or because of locomotion, the experimenter immediately reinforces the response. Once the forward movements of the pigeon's head are occurring at a high rate, additional movements are reinforced that are in the direction of the final performance of key-pecking. Later the experimenter withholds reinforcement until the bird moves its head over a greater distance than it had initially. Also, the experimenter reinforces the forward head movements only when the pigeon is positioned directly facing the response key. At that moment, the response will frequently result in activation of the key which constitutes the final performance and which provides automatic food delivery through the programmed circuitry.

We see from this example that we can begin with a fragmentary forward motion of the head that has only a remote component relationship to the desired performance. By reinforcing minor variations of this component behavior the target performance can be achieved.

This response shaping procedure has found extensive application both in the laboratory and in applied settings.

Response Shaping and Human Behavior

Response shaping appears to have its greatest applicability when dealing with nonverbal organisms, thereby including all animal experiments but very few human studies. In one of the few human studies which used the response shaping technique, Fuller (1949) squirted milk into the mouth of a vegetative patient whenever his arm moved. The patient was a severe mental defective who was confined to a crib and had no verbal behavior. Initially, the criterion for the milk reinforcement was the slightest movement of the arm. The criterion was gradually raised, however, so that the arm had to make larger and larger excursions before the milk was delivered. Eventually the patient was moving his arm over a large arc. Each of these movements was followed by the delivery of milk.

Another example of the application of response shaping is that of Lovaas, Berberich, Perloff, and Schaeffer (1966), who also dealt with nonverbal organisms, in this instance, autistic children. These investigators attempted to shape verbal behavior and began by reinforcing any vocal response. Indeed, the first component with which they started was the blowing of air through the child's lips when an experimenter held the lips together tightly. The experimenter gradually raised his criterion of how hard the child had to blow until the child was blowing vigorously when his lips were held together. This blowing was often accompanied by an audible sound. The experimenter then reinforced only when sounds accompanied the blowing action. The criterion for reinforcement was then progressively raised regarding the intensity of the sound. This progression was followed until finally the child was making vocal sounds that closely resembled syllables in the English language. The above background provides the basis for the Response Shaping Rule.

Response Shaping Rule: In developing a desired response chain, begin by reinforcing an existing response that has a component relation to the target behavior; then reinforce variations of the component that are in the direction of the target behavior.

This rule is useful when the individual has no verbal behavior, or when only minimal verbal behavior is possible. Lovaas' autistic children, for example, were nonverbal. Lindsley's (1956) psychotic patients were only partly verbal. Similarly, shaping was usefully employed with an autistic child (Wolf, Risley, and Mees, 1964) that had showed very little reaction to verbal instructions.

Experiment 16: The restoration of normal eating by shaping procedure

Because the population in the motivating environment was verbal, there was only one occasion in which it was necessary to utilize the Response Shaping Rule, and then only in combination with some minimal verbal behavior. The case concerned a patient, Wendy S., whose eating behavior was deficient. She subsisted on a diet drink plus vitamins for eight months. During this time she failed to go to the dining room to eat. The use of such methods as coaxing, spoonfeeding, and persuasion were avoided, since previous findings (Ayllon and Haughton, 1962) had indicated that the behavior of refusing to eat seemed to be maintained by the attention and concern given by the staff to the patient who refused to eat. Therefore, for eight months no attempt was made to coax, persuade, or verbally instruct Wendy to eat when she failed to do so. Again, it should be made clear that Wendy had a verbal repertoire that could have been utilized to prompt her to go to the dining room to eat; but verbal prompts involved giving attention to Wendy's refusal to eat and hence were avoided to prevent reinforcing this behavior. The question was how to reinstate the behavior of eating meals in the dining room when little if any verbal instructions could be utilized in generating the appropriate behavior.

Method. First, for a period of eight months Wendy received a daily drink of concentrated proteins, calories, and vitamins. This diet gave Wendy a total of 1,200 calories in addition to the vitamin supplement. Three times a day, an attendant called her, "Wendy, time to get your medication." Typically the attendant called out to Wendy from a few feet away, and Wendy cautiously approached the attendant and received the high caloric drink in addition to the tranquilizer. Wendy had received the medically prescribed tranquilizer for over a year prior to her refusal to eat.

The net effect of this extreme fast was that her weight went down from 164 to 106 pounds over a period of eight months, for a total weight loss of 58 pounds. All through this period she spent most of her time sleeping or lying down. Her rare interactions with the attendants were marked by gross psychotic verbalizations. In the ninth month an attempt was made to reinstate appropriate eating behavior by using successive approximations to the target behavior: Eating in the dining room unaided.

Procedure. The second column of Table 7–1 outlines the general procedure. To start the response shaping procedure it was necessary, first, to assess what Wendy's existing behaviors were that

Table 7–1

Procedural and Behavioral Progression During Shaping of Normal Eating

Procedure no. and date	Procedure	Behavior
7-25-65 through 2-22-66	Called to meals personally. ("Wendy, come get your medication.")	Would not enter dining room. Drank diet drink outside dining room.
#1 Procedure Dinner 2-23 through Breakfast 3-22	Called to meals personally. Given diet drink in glass. Attendant gradually increased distance had to walk to obtain the medication in the direction of the dining room. The last 40 meals the attendant called her from the dining room.	Initially walked to attendant to obtain tranquilizer. Drank diet drink. The last 40 meals she entered dining room and sat down. Drank diet drink.
#2 Procedure Dinner 3-22 through Dinner 3-23	Called to meals personally. Given diet drink plus bits of solid food in glass.	Tasted mixture but did not drink it.
#3 Procedure Supper 3-23 through Breakfast 3-30	Called to meals personally. Diet drink and *pureed food* in glass placed on tray with standard meal and served at counter.	Picked up glass but left tray on counter. Ate small portion of mixture with spoon.
Probe Dinner 3-30	Called to meal personally. Diet drink and pureed food mixture discontinued. All patients served standard *meal on trays* placed on tables, not counter.	Sat down in front of tray but did not eat.
Return to #3 Procedure Supper 3-30 through Dinner 3-31	Called to meals personally. Diet drink and pureed food in glass placed on tray with standard meal and served at counter.	Picked up glass but left tray on counter. Ate small portion of mixture with spoon.

Table 7–1 (continued)

Procedure no. and date	Procedure	Behavior
#4 Procedure Supper 3-31 through Breakfast 4-1	Called to meals personally. Diet drink and pureed food served in *cup* instead of in glass on tray.	Picked up cup. Ate contents with spoon.
#5 Procedure Dinner 4-1 through Breakfast 4-4	Called to meals personally. Diet drink discontinued. Pureed food served in cup placed on tray.	Picked up cup. Ate contents with spoon.
Probe Dinner 4-4	Called to meal personally. Pureed food served in *bowl* instead of cup.	Picked up bowl but did not eat.
Return to #5 Procedure Supper 4-4 through Dinner 4-8	Called to meals personally. Pureed food served in cup placed on tray.	Picked up cup but left tray on counter. Ate small portion at first meal. On succeeding days ate well.
#6 Procedure Supper 4-9 through Dinner 4-23	Called to meals personally. Pureed food discontinued. *Chopped food* served in cup placed on tray with standard meal.	Picked up cup, but left tray on counter. Ate contents with fork.
#7 Procedure Supper 4-23 through Breakfast 5-9	Called to meals personally. Chopped food in cup discontinued. Standard meal served on tray at counter.	Picked up tray and ate meal with fork, knife, and spoon.
#8 Procedure Dinner 5-9-66 through Dinner 5-9-67	Called to meals in the same manner as other patients instead of personally.	Put token into turnstile to enter dining room. Picked up tray and ate meal with fork, knife, and spoon.

had a component relation to the target behavior. The following behaviors were selected as meeting that criterion:

(1) Verbal behavior, as shown in her following the attendant's instructions to receive her tranquilizer.

(2) Drinking behavior, as shown in her consistent drinking of the high-caloric diet drink.

The objective of the shaping procedure was to reinforce variations of these components in the direction of the target behavior.

The first step was to develop the desired response chain: Walking to the dining room. A component of this behavior already existed in Wendy's repertoire, namely, walking to get her medication when called by the attendant. Wendy's existing verbal behavior was particularly helpful since it allowed the same stimulus, "Wendy, come and get your medication," to be used, while the distance Wendy had to walk to receive her medication gradually increased until she went into the dining room. Initially, the major objective of the strategy was simply to develop the response chain, walking to the dining room. It was expected that the stimuli associated with the sight and sound of people eating would facilitate her eating.

Another behavior in Wendy's repertoire which had a component of the target behavior was drinking the high-caloric drink. Therefore, variations of drinking, such as drinking increasingly thick soup-like drinks, were arranged, since such behavior was in the direction of one of the components of the target behavior of eating. From time to time probes were used to check whether the target behavior was already possible to Wendy, in which case the successive approximation procedure could be dispensed with. Two probes were used. Each probe involved one meal during which specific procedural changes were made to evaluate the necessity for further shaping.

At a given meal, only one attendant conducted the shaping procedures; but a total of nine different attendants participated at different times. The attendant assigned for a given meal carried out the shaping procedures and maintained written records of Wendy's behavior. Weekly records of Wendy's weight, as well as relevant nursing records, were also maintained. In addition, a behavioral record was available which indicated the amount of tokens Wendy earned and spent.

Results. The third column of Table 7–1 shows the behavioral reaction to each procedural stage of the shaping. The target behavior of eating unassisted in the dining room was achieved within two months of using the shaping procedure. By the end of those two months Wendy's weight had increased by 10 pounds. Also, she was using tokens to gain access to the dining room.

The first behavioral objective was to have Wendy enter the dining room. This objective was achieved within one month. However, the expected facilitating effect this would have on her eating behavior did not occur. Once in the dining room Wendy sat alongside others who ate the standard tray of food, but she restricted herself to the diet drink. Even after 40 meals during which she was exposed to the sight and sound of others eating their meals, she continued to drink her diet drink and made no attempt to pick up a tray of food from the cafeteria counter.

Procedure #2 introduced variations of the drink, which Wendy had never refused. Initially bits of solid food were mixed with the diet drink. Wendy tasted the mixture and proceeded to reject it for the three meals during which this procedure was in force. Wendy's rejection served to underscore the relationship of her behavior in the dining room to the shaping procedure. Had Wendy eaten this mixture of solid food and the diet drink, the arduous and slow shaping procedure would have been unnecessary.

It was the objective of Procedure #3 to accomplish gradually and more subtly what Procedure #2 could not. Therefore, the solid food was again mixed with the diet drink, but this time both were blended in a puree consistency. Wendy picked up the glass of "diet drink" from the cafeteria counter, and ate the contents with a spoon. This component was so close to the target behavior, eating unassisted in the dining room, that a probe was used to evaluate the further need for the shaping procedure. For this purpose the diet drink mixed with pureed food was discontinued for one meal. When Wendy and the rest of the patients went into the dining room, they found their dinner already served on the table. Everyone sat down and proceeded to eat. Everyone, that is, except Wendy, who after sitting down at the table stared at the meal in front of her and did not eat. The results of this probe indicated once again that the shaping procedure was necessary to reinstate the target behavior. Just being present in the dining room while others were eating and having a meal directly in front of Wendy were insufficient to ensure resumption of normal eating behavior. This probe was used for one meal only. The next procedure was a step back to Procedure #3, which once again resulted in Wendy's eating the pureed food from the glass with the aid of a spoon.

Procedure #4 attempted to use variations of the glass from which she ate and to eventually offer the food in a regular plate. A cup was used and Wendy continued to eat without any difficulty. Procedure #5 faded out the drink so that Wendy was actually eating pureed food with the aid of a spoon. At this point a probe was once again used for one meal only to evaluate the need for further shaping. The pureed food was served to Wendy, but this time in a soup bowl. She picked up the bowl from the cafeteria counter, sat down at her usual table, but did not eat. The results of this second and last probe indicated once again that Wendy's eating behavior was functionally related to the shaping procedure. To recover the previous behavior of eating pureed food from the cup, Procedure #5 was again used. By now the results were predictable; Wendy proceeded to eat the pureed food from the cup, using a spoon to do so.

Procedure #6 gradually faded out the pureed food and faded in small pieces of solid food, served still in a cup. In the last three meals of this procedure Wendy was actually eating a small serving of the regular meal, except that she did so from a cup. Up to this point, Wendy picked up the cup from the cafeteria counter when it was served on a tray of food. The tray of food, however, was never picked up. Procedure #7 discontinued the cup altogether, but when Wendy reached the counter she picked up one of the food trays, sat down, and proceeded to eat. The objective of Procedure #8 was to fade out the personal call, "Wendy, come get your medication." The general meal announcement for everyone had always been in force, and it was this call that remained as the signal for Wendy to go to the dining room. When she did so, she proceeded to put a token into the turnstile that admitted her to the cafeteria counter. She then picked up a tray of food and cutlery, sat down, and ate the meal using knife, fork, and spoon. This was the first time in ten months that she had eaten a meal in the dining room completely unassisted.

Five months from the time the shaping procedure had been initiated, Wendy was back to her previous weight level of over 160 pounds. No medical complications arose during the entire period. One year later, at the time of this writing, she was maintaining appropriate eating behavior. No other unfavorable symptom replaced her failure to eat. Although no data was obtained regarding the psychotic hallucinations, they appeared to be greatly reduced.

Her general behavior on the ward changed considerably as she progressed through the shaping procedure. Table 7–2 shows that she earned and spent less than 15 tokens during each of the three months preceding the shaping procedure. During the shaping procedure her earnings and expenditures rose to as much as 52 tokens per month. This increase continued at a high rate so that within three months from the time she had regained appropriate eating behavior, she was earning and spending over 1,000 tokens per month.

Table 7–2

Number of Tokens Earned and Spent Per Month by Wendy before, during, and after Shaping

	Before shaping			Shaping procedure			After shaping		
Months	1st	2nd	3rd	4th	5th	6th	7th	8th	9th
Tokens earned	13	13	8	24	32	52	460	1,639	1,840
Tokens spent	4	1	0	0	3	28	299	1,237	1,096

B. THE PROMPTING-SHAPING RULE

In the preceding example, the response shaping procedure was carried out using minimal verbal behavior. But, this procedure may be too time consuming and expensive and, thus, limited for general application. An alternative procedure exists that was found to be more feasible. This procedure used verbal prompts. By prompting and shaping progressively greater response units, the final target behavior could be achieved.

The Prompting-Shaping Rule: In developing a desired response chain, begin by prompting verbally and reinforcing an existing response that has a component relation to the target behavior; then prompt verbally and reinforce variations of the component that are in the direction of the target behavior.

One of the distinctive features of response shaping is that the educator waits for a desired variation of an established response to occur, and then reinforces it. When the subject possesses a verbal repertoire, however, the educator is not reduced to passively waiting for a response variation. Rather, he can prompt the desired component of the response through instructions that may also include specification of the reinforcer that will result. A very large response chain can then be established with no waiting. If the entire chain is too complex to be described by instructions, then the rule seems first to instruct the subject regarding each of the components, next to reinforce each of the components as they have been prompted, and finally to instruct the subject in the integration of the components. The Prompting-Shaping Rule is identical to the Response Shaping Rule with the important addition of prompting each of the desired response components verbally.

Learning is extremely rapid once verbal behavior is present. In the example provided by the shaping procedure of Lovaas et al. (1966) it is noteworthy that the first response to be shaped was the verbal response. In a subsequent part of the experiment, Lovaas was able to build the complex motor and social repertoires using verbal instruction. Once the child learned a few words designating foods, the experimenter then easily instructed him to eat a particular food at a particular time and not to eat others.

An important part of instruction or verbal prompting is that it can be used to describe the desired response sufficiently for the individual to make the response for the first time without ever having been reinforced for it in the past. A child who has never done so before, but who knows the meaning of chair and climb, can be told to climb upon a chair, even though reinforcement for so doing has never before been provided. A further advantage of verbal instruction is that it can also specify what reinforcements will be likely to follow a response. The child can be told not only to climb the chair but also that if he does, he will be able to reach the cookie jar. The response shaping procedure can, therefore, be greatly abbreviated.

In analyzing the reports of experiments with human subjects, one finds that virtually all experiments used instructions to prompt at least some component of the behavior. The use of instructions to develop a response sequence follows from the Prompting-Shaping Rule. The tendency of a human subject to follow verbal instructions is an existing behavior that can be used as the initial component upon which to build the entire chain.

Verbal instructions are a shortcut to developing new behavior patterns in humans. Thus, in an experimental study using children, the following type of instruction was given: "Put both sticks (styli) into all three of the holes." (This sentence was repeated until both styli had been placed in the three available holes.) "While you are in this room, some of these (the experimenter held out several jelly beans) will drop into this cup. You can eat them here if you want to or you can take them home with you." The instructions were then repeated without reply to any questions, after which the experimenter said, "I am leaving the room now; you can play any game that you want to while I am gone" (Azrin and Lindsley, 1956). Here not only the topography of the response was verbally described but also the reinforcing consequences for responding appropriately. Even in the very early stages of the Lovaas experiment cited above, where the subjects were nonverbal, the experimenters continually gave verbal instructions regarding the behavior so that the behavior of following the instructions would be associated with the delivery of the reinforcer. Similarly, even in studies with nonverbal organisms, such as Sidman and Stoddard's (1967) study with fairly nonverbal mental retardates, the subjects were instructed to press a response key even though the rest of the program was one of shaping.

In a previous study (Ayllon and Azrin, 1964) we commented on the desirability of using verbal instructions wherever possible, rather than ignoring this strong and useful existing behavior of human subjects. In that study, the desired behavior of mental patients was easily initiated by instructions but was not maintained unless reinforcement for that behavior resulted. Conversely, reinforcement was ineffective when used without instructional prompting. The combination of prompting and reinforcement for the prompted behavior was effective in maintaining the desired behavior indefinitely.

The Prompting-Shaping Rule was used routinely to teach the patients the various duties that were to be performed on the ward.

Whenever a patient selected a job that she had not performed previously, the Prompting-Shaping Rule was used. Take, for example, the job of serving meals on the ward. The patient was instructed on how to serve the entire meal. If she failed to do so, she would first be instructed (prompted) on what size portion to serve of one item, say the vegetable. Even if the patient did not perform the additional aspects of that job, for example, serving the correct portion of coffee, she was still given some tokens for serving the vegetable during this first meal. During the next meal she would be instructed again to serve the vegetable, and in addition to serve the coffee. If she served the coffee appropriately, then serving the meat might be added. Even if she was not successful in reaching the next component, she was still given some tokens. This procedure was conducted for as many meals as was necessary. The tokens were given for as many components as were performed, the full number of tokens being given when all components were performed. Oftentimes the instructions needed only to be given on the first day for the complete performance to emerge and, of course, to be reinforced with the full number of tokens. Thereafter, the instructions were omitted and the tokens simply given for the appropriate conduct of the duties in the usual fashion. Which components were prompted at a given meal depended on the extent to which the patient had successfully performed the other components. If she performed only one component, then as indicated above, some tokens were given for the successful completion of that one; and an attempt at further progress was made at the next meal. As stated previously, this procedure was followed for all on-ward jobs.

No attempt had been made initially to use the Prompting-Shaping Rule for the off-ward jobs, which occupied about six hours each day. The reason for this was the belief that once a patient could perform many duties adequately on the ward and under supervision, then and only then could she be depended on to perform the long-term jobs outside of the ward which were under minimal supervision. In spite of this earlier belief, the decision was later made to use the Prompting-Shaping Rule as a means of having more patients engage in the off-ward duties. This decision provided an excellent opportunity to evaluate experimentally the necessity and usefulness of the Prompting-Shaping Rule.

Experiment 17: Prompting-Shaping of work assignments

The general rationale in this study was to begin with a behavior that already existed in the patients' behavioral repertoire and progressively to lead to the final target behavior according to a predetermined sequence of behavioral steps.

The final target behavior was working in the hospital laundry for a six-hour period each day. This job consisted of running sheets, pillow cases, and towels through a mangle; hanging sheets on a rack; placing folded sheets in bags; sorting linen and cloths; moving the laundry cart to locations where it was needed; and assisting the laundry supervisor in related and sundry tasks. Three hours in the morning and three in the afternoon were spent in this job. The usual number of tokens was 80. Proper discharge of the responsibilities required not only performing the above duties to the satisfaction of the laundry supervisor but signing up for the position at the beginning of each day, going to the laundry unescorted, working in the laundry without the need for a ward attendant's supervision, and returning directly from the laundry to the ward at the termination of the work shift.

Five patients participated in this prompting-shaping study. None of these patients had been engaged in any off-ward job, including the laundry, for a period of at least three years prior to the time of this study. Three of the patients had been earning an average of less than eight tokens per day for on-ward duties during the four weeks preceding the study. Two of the five patients had been earning approximately 50 tokens per day for on-ward duties. All of the patients had been asked many times in the distant past whether they would perform one of the off-ward assignments; no such request had been made of the patients within the six months preceding this study. For this group of five patients, then, the successful completion of off-ward duties would represent a very substantial increase in their level of functioning and constituted, therefore, a very desirable target behavior.

Procedure. The first problem to be solved in reaching the desired behavior was selection of the first behavioral step. What was needed was a behavior that already existed as part of the patients' behavioral repertoire. One behavior that did exist for all of these patients was that they usually responded positively to a personal request or command by the attendant. For example, when the ward physician left directives to the attendants to bring the patient to the examining room, all five patients usually followed the attendant's request to "Come with me." This minimal level of behavior could be relied upon at least part of the time.

The general rationale followed in this application of the Prompting-Shaping Rule was to use as the first behavioral step having the patient follow the attendant in response to a direct request. Second, a sequence of behavioral steps was constructed, each of which could be expected to be successfully prompted and which would lead to the final target behavior of working unassisted in the laundry. This behavior sequence is given in Table 7–3. The patient was first prompted to and reinforced for accompanying the attendant to some distant point on the ward (Step 1), then for accompanying her to some location off the ward (Step 2), then for accompanying her into the laundry (Step 3). Steps 4 through 9 were concerned with extending the duration for which the patient worked. Step 4 was five minutes of work in the laundry, increasing progressively in duration to Step 10, which was six hours of work. This extension in the duration of work was accompanied, also, by an increase in the complexity of the work, since the only jobs that the patient could perform at the time she was in the laundry were those specific activities that needed doing at the time she was there. Thus, as the duration of work increased from one behavioral step to another, the diversity of the activities performed there simultaneously increased. In order to perform for six hours in the laundry, all of the different activities in the laundry had to be performed. Behavioral Steps 9 through 12 progressed along the dimension of reducing the amount of supervision needed for the performance. In behavioral Steps 1 through 8 the patient was performing under the continuous supervision of an attendant. In behavioral Steps 9 and 10 to the attendant was present only intermittently. In Step 11 the attendant was completely absent, and in Step 12 the attendant did not ask the patient whether she wished to work in the laundry that day.

Prompting-Shaping of Work Assignments for 5 Patients

Behavioral step	Day behavioral step was achieved by each patient: M.D.	M.W.	F.C.	W.S.	C.N.	Verbal prompt associated with the behavioral step	No. of Tokens given for each behavioral step
1. Walked with attendant on ward.	1		1	1		Come with me.	10
2. Walked with attendant outside ward.	1		3			Come with me outside.	10
3. Walked with attendant to laundry.	2		4	2	1	Come with me to the laundry.	10
4. Worked for 5 mins. in laundry. Attendant present.	7					Patient instructed to do whatever specific job needed.	10
5. Worked for 15 mins. in laundry. Attendant present.	9					" " "	10
6. Worked for 30 mins. in laundry. Attendant present.	10			2		" " "	10
7. Worked for 45 mins. in laundry. Attendant present.				11		" " "	10
8. Worked for 1 hr. in laundry. Attendant present.	11			16	1	" " "	20
9. Worked for 3 hrs. in laundry. Attendant occasionally absent.	12			17	8	" " "	40
10. Worked for 6 hrs. in laundry. Attendant occasionally absent.	18	1		22	12	Would you like to work 6 hrs. a day at the laundry?	80
11. Worked for 6 hrs. in laundry. Attendant absent.	20					Would you like to work 6 hrs. a day at the laundry?	80
12. Worked for 6 hrs. without being prompted individually. Attendant absent.	21	2		23	13	No prompt.	80

Each behavioral step consisted of two parts. First, a specific prompt was given to the patient to perform that specific behavioral step. Thus, Table 7–3 shows in the first behavioral step the attendant merely stated to the patient "Come with me." The second aspect of each behavioral step was the delivery of tokens when the patient had successfully followed the attendant's prompt or instruction. The number of tokens given for successfully following each of the behavioral steps is indicated in the last column on the right of Table 7–3. It can be seen that the number of tokens progressively increased as the behavioral step became more complex. The general rule that was used in deciding on how many tokens should be assigned to a given step was that any behavioral step that required less than one hour to perform earned 10 tokens; 10 additional tokens were given for each hour or fraction thereof up to a total of three hours. Three hours of successful performance earned 40 tokens, thereby providing a "bonus" of 10 tokens for performing a full three hours of work.

The experimental design required some type of control procedure that would provide information on whether this extensive behavioral training progression was indeed needed. It was possible that many of the steps in the progression could be omitted, but without some type of built-in experimental control this information would be lacking. A patient might, for example, perform for the entire six-hour day if she were simply asked to do so on the very first day of the shaping procedure. Yet, if the procedure required that she advance through each of the steps, the speed of progression would be partly limited by the experimental procedure. As a control for this possibility, a standard probe was given to each patient once each day, usually at the beginning of the day. This probe consisted of the prompt for the final behavioral step: The patient was directly asked whether she would like to work six hours at the laundry. To the extent that a negative response was given by the patient to this question, the instructor could be assured that it was necessary to follow a behavioral progression, and that the intermediate steps were not all being followed unnecessarily.

Results. Table 7–3 shows that the prompting-shaping procedure was effective in causing four of the five patients to work for the full day in the hospital laundry. The fifth patient walked with the attendant to the laundry on the fourth day, but prompts during successive days were not effective in having the patient work even for a few minutes. Two patients began working full-time and without supervision after about three weeks of the Prompting-Shaping Procedure; one patient, in 13 days. The performance of patient M. W. came as a surprise to everyone. On the very first day when she was given the probe as to whether she would work full-time in the laundry, she replied "yes"; and she successfully completed the required job performance on that very first day. By the second day she was working without supervision and without any special request by the attendant. The other three patients, who eventually reached the target behavior, did not respond affirmatively to the probe until they were in the tenth or eleventh behavioral step. These results show that for those three patients the behavioral progression was necessary.

Patient M.D. did not successfully complete the behavioral progression as it was initially programmed. As Table 7–3 shows, she reached behavioral Step 3, which was walking with the attendant to the laundry, on Day 2; but like F.C., she did not progress any further. Both patients, F.C. and M.D., refused to perform any work at the laundry, even though they would accompany the attendant to the laundry. Therefore, a second progression was established for M.D. Instead of following Steps 4 through 10, which involved progressively longer duration of work in the laundry, an attempt was made to follow the same sequence but in a different off-ward job, which was working as a laboratory assistant. On Days 5 and 6, which are not shown in Table 7–3, the patient was prompted to engage in work at the hospital laboratory. On Day 6 she was working for 15 minutes. She was then returned to the laundry and the behavioral progression of Table 7–3. On the very next day (Day 7) she achieved Step 4, which was working for about five minutes in the hospital laundry. She progressed very rapidly thereafter, such that by the twelfth day she was working for three hours, Step 9, and by the eighteenth day for the full six hours, which is Step 10. This second behavioral progression was not used for the other patient, F.C.

When the patients completed the behavioral progression, they were earning 80 tokens per day, as seen in Table 7–3. This performance was maintained by all four of these patients for as long as the laundry was made available to them as a job opportunity. In order to evaluate how long the patients would continue to perform on this job, we permitted two of the patients to continue work at the laundry rather than imposing the job rotation procedure that is described elsewhere. These two patients continued to work in the laundry for about two years, rarely missing a day of employment. For the other two patients the usual job rotation procedure was put into effect. These two patients achieved transition to other off-ward full-time jobs without difficulty. These last two patients were allowed to continue working in the laundry for a period of six months, which they did; and like the other two patients, they rarely missed a day of employment.

Discussion. The results indicate that the prompting-shaping procedure is an extremely effective method of establishing long and complex response chains in mental patients. Four of the five patients achieved the final behavioral chain of working for a full six hours each day under minimal supervision. All four did so within 23 days. The question remains as to whether this behavior would have occurred spontaneously; that is, whether the steps in the behavior progression were necessary. The results obtained with the probe demonstrate that the behavioral progression was necessary for three of the patients who completed it. The patients were all given this probe each day, being asked if they would work for a six-hour day. Three of them replied negatively until they were very advanced in the behavioral progression. The results obtained can, therefore, be attributed to the use of the behavioral progression involved in the prompting-shaping procedure.

The rapid results achieved with this prompting-shaping procedure should be contrasted with the results that had been obtained when using the reinforcement procedure alone without the systematic prompting. The conditions to which the patients had been exposed prior to this prompting-shaping procedure were roughly in accord with the shaping rule, which is to reinforce a behavior and then wait for variations of that behavior rather than prompting the variations. The shaping procedure, when used alone, may be roughly categorized as a reinforce-wait-reinforce-wait technique. Posters had been located on the ward announcing the availability of full-time employment at the laundry. All of the patients had been told verbally by the attendants that such an opportunity existed. All patients had seen other patients sign up for the laundry jobs and had heard the attendant call out each morning that it was time for those patients who had signed up for the job to leave. It is probable that these five patients had overheard the laundry workers describing their experiences at the laundry to other patients. This opportunity to work in the laundry had been available for three years prior to the present experiment. The patients had been reinforced for performing jobs on the ward, with greater numbers of tokens being given for performance of progressively longer and more difficult jobs. It had been hoped that ultimately the performance would increase both in duration and complexity and develop into the off-ward performance. This approach is in accord with this reinforce-and-wait rule. The desirability of adding a prompt to the shaping rule is evident in the patients' performing the off-ward job within three weeks of adding the prompts, after not having performed it for three years when shaping alone was used.

Evidence internal to this experiment regarding the desirability of the progressive prompts comes from the results that were obtained when the patients were asked during the procedure whether they would like to work a full six-hour day (probe). All but one of the patients responded negatively to this question.

The high level of performance reached by the patients at the end of three weeks was not a transient phenomenon; all patients continued to function at this high level after all special instructions, prompts, and probes had been removed for periods up to two years.

A useful modification of the Prompting-Shaping Rule is suggested by a detailed analysis of the individual differences among patients. Two of the five patients failed to complete the behavioral progression as it was initially established. Examination of these patients' performance on the ward showed that one of them was already earning an average of 45 tokens per day, whereas the other was averaging 52 tokens. The three patients who did complete the initial behavioral progression had been earning less than eight tokens per day. These results seem anomalous if one were to attempt to predict the speed with which the patients would progress through the behavioral sequence on the basis of their past performance. One would expect that the patients who were functioning most, that is, were earning the most tokens on the ward, would be the ones who would progress through the behavioral sequence at the greatest speed. The results were in the opposite direction. The patients who were earning the least tokens for on-ward work were the ones who went through the behavioral progression most quickly. An explanation of these individual differences can be sought in terms of the existence of competing reinforcers. For the patients who were earning about 50 tokens per day only 10 tokens could be earned by following the first behavioral step, this representing a substantial reduction in the number of tokens which could be earned immediately. These patients had more to gain by continuing to perform the on-ward jobs that they had already mastered. On the other hand, for the three patients who were earning less than eight tokens per day, the completion of the first behavioral step constituted greater earnings than was available on the ward. It may very well be, then, that the ease with which a patient goes through the behavioral progression for a new response depends on how much reinforcement is being given for other behaviors. The incompatibility here between the jobs is also a temporal one. The patients who had been earning about 50 tokens per day were occupied during a major part of the day in performing on-ward assignments. Selection by them of the first behavioral step competed in time with the performance of these on-ward assignments. On the other hand, the patients who were earning eight or fewer tokens per day were performing for such a short duration on the ward that they could easily elect the first behavioral step without any reduction in their on-ward earnings. To the extent that this interpretation is correct, the conclusion would be that when one is initiating a prompting-shaping procedure for a new response, reinforcement for all other behaviors should be temporarily discontinued or decreased.

This same point was mentioned previously in regard to the compatibility of reinforcers; in Chapter 5 it was stated that reinforcers should not be arranged simultaneously, lest one displace the other. The same appears to be true regarding responses, at least during the initial prompting and shaping of a response. Once the response is established, there seems to be little danger in having all responses simultaneously available for selection. This was the rationale of the standard job selection procedure in the motivating environment.

C. PRIMING OF RESPONSES

1. Response Exposure

The Response-Shaping Rule and the Prompting-Shaping Rule describe two general procedures for learning new behavior. In both of these procedures, the reinforcing event is delivered for progressively longer maintenance of the desired response. As was stated in the previous sections of this chapter on response-shaping and prompting-shaping, these two procedures were often necessary in developing behaviors of great length and complexity or in working with patients who had very little verbal behavior. For most behaviors and most patients, however, these considerations did not apply; most patients had verbal behavior, and most of the behaviors dealt with in this program were fairly simple and not of an extended duration. Those that were of long duration, such as the telephone operator answering the phone throughout the day, comprised a repetition of small segments of behavior, such as answering the phone, taking a message, calling the individual for whom the call was intended, etc. For most of these behaviors, other types of procedures were more practicable than response-shaping and prompting-shaping.

A convenient method of teaching new behaviors in the motivating environment was to allow the learner to observe another patient or an attendant performing the desired behavior in the appropriate manner. This procedure can be summarized as the Response Exposure Rule.

Response Exposure Rule: Have the learner observe another individual performing the desired response.

The reader will recognize this rule as being almost identical to the Reinforcer Exposure Rule. One rule is concerned with exposure to the reinforcing activity, and the other rule is concerned with exposure to the desired response.

The Response Exposure Rule is a statement of the general principle that one can learn by imitation. This principle has been described in detail by several psychological theorists (Miller and Dollard, 1941; Bandura and Walters, 1963) and need not concern us further at this time. Detailed experiments such as those by Baer and Sherman (1964) and Baer, Peterson, and Sherman (1967) have confirmed the fact that learning can occur by imitation. We may summarize some of the reasons for such learning occurring. When one observes another individual performing the desired response, there is no longer any need for a detailed description of what that response should consist of. The learner can simply closely observe these specific movements, postures, and patterns of movements of the model. This also eliminates the need for an elaborate shaping or prompting-shaping procedure. Similarly, the learner need not perform the desired behavior even once to learn what the connection is between the response and the reinforcer. By watching another individual receive three tokens for sweeping a floor he can learn that he will receive three tokens if he sweeps the floor. We need not be concerned at this point whether imitation is reinforcing in its own right, or, stated alternatively, whether the response exposure procedure will be sufficient in and of itself. The experiments described above, as well as many others, have demonstrated that imitation in combination with reinforcement of that imitation is an extremely rapid method of teaching humans new behavior.

On the basis of the above evidence, the response exposure or learning by imitation principle was routinely used in teaching patients the desired behaviors in the ward environment. For every one of the behaviors listed in the Table A–1 of the Appendix, the job was first described to the patients. Then the attendant either performed the job herself or had the patient observe another patient performing the job. The patient was then given the opportunity to perform the job herself; and if she did so successfully, she was reinforced. This method is, then, a combination of imitation and reinforcement. If the patient had any difficulty in performing the entire job sequence, as might be the case in some of the more complex jobs such as operating the dishwasher, the attendant divided the job into segments as dictated by the Response-Shaping and Prompting-Shaping Rules, concurrently providing a model that could be imitated for each of these segments. For example, the attendant, herself, demonstrated how to load the dishes, then had the patient load the dishes. Only after the patient had successfully imitated this part of the performance would the attendant demonstrate how to operate the dials on the machine, and then allow the patient to attempt the proper dial operation herself. If the patient could not progress past a certain stage of the dishwashing performance on a given day, she was nevertheless reinforced for whatever degree of progress she had reached; and the instruction continued on the next day.

The Response Exposure Rule was used for more than the initial teaching of a new behavior in the ward environment. Even after a response had been learned, and there was no question of the patient's ability to perform it, the response exposure procedure seemed to increase the frequency with which the patient performed that behavior. In terms of previous research, an analogy may be drawn to experiments in which pigeons were trained to peck a key. Hake and Laws (1967) conditioned pigeons to peck at a key to receive food. Once the birds had been conditioned, they pecked the key in the appropriate manner. Hake and Laws used a response exposure procedure in which the bird was allowed at some times to see another bird pecking a key; at other times he was working alone. It was found that the sight of another bird pecking a key caused the bird to peck much more frequently than when the sight of the other bird pecking was not present. This increase in pecking was not a matter of learning; what the response exposure procedure did was increase the frequency of a response that had already been learned.

The response exposure procedure was used in the motivating environment to increase the frequency of behaviors that had already been learned. Ideally, the Response Exposure Rule dictates that at the very time it is desired for the patient to perform a specific job, a model (i.e., another patient) be visible who is already performing the job. Unfortunately, in practice this ideal could not usually be met, since most of the jobs required only one patient at a time. As an approximation of this ideal, therefore, the job opportunities were scheduled so that many jobs were being performed by many patients at a given time during the day. This was accomplished by scheduling almost all of the jobs during very restricted parts of the day, mostly between 9:00 A.M. and 11:30 A.M. and between 1:30 P.M. to 4:00 P.M. Even though many of the jobs could have been performed by patients after 4:00 P.M. or before 9:00 A.M. and some of the patients might have slightly preferred that arrangement, this restricted period of employment was deliberately arranged so as to maximize the operation of the Response Exposure Rule. The result was that during these "working hours" many patients were working simultaneously on the ward. A given patient who was not working was, therefore, exposed to the sights and sounds of all the other patients working and being reinforced for so doing. For some types of jobs, the ideal case could be arranged in which more than one patient could perform the same job, thereby allowing each of them to be exposed to the sight of the other working. Such was the case, for example, for the job of laundry worker.

2. Reponse Sampling

The parallel between the Response Exposure Rule and the Reinforcer Exposure Rule also suggests the parallel between a Response Sampling Rule and the previously described Reinforcer Sampling Rule. With the Reinforcer Sampling Rule, reinforcer utilization was increased if one had the patient sample the reinforcing event. The series of experiments described in Chapter 5 demonstrated that this facilitation did, indeed, occur. We may formulate, then, a Response Sampling Rule that is analogous to the previous Reinforcer Sampling Rule.

Response Sampling Rule: Require the individual to perform at least the initial portions of a desired response.

The response sampling procedure was used to teach new behavior. Operant conditioning experiments have demonstrated that behavior will be increased in frequency if it is reinforced. Implicit in this statement is the fact that the behavior must first be exhibited in order to be reinforced. Some controversy exists regarding the existence of "sensory learning" or "cognitive learning" which revolves around whether one can learn simply by observing, without requiring the observer to perform the task himself. Conversely, there exists the point of view that learning is best when an active response is required. This is a basic assumption, for example, in the method of programmed instruction in which the student must make active responses by writing in the correct answers continuously as he goes through the programmed text (Skinner, 1954). Stated loosely, this point of view can be described as "learning by doing." In a sense, the controversy as to whether an active response is needed in learning is actually fairly academic since there is no opportunity to discover whether the student has learned until he has performed the active response that demonstrates his learning.

The Response Sampling Rule was used along with the Response Exposure Rule routinely in teaching new behaviors in the motivating environment. In the previous discussion of the Response Exposure Rule, it was noted that in teaching a new response the attendant first demonstrated the desired behavior and then directed the patient to perform it herself. The initial aspect of the procedure, which was to demonstrate the behavior, was dictated by the Response Exposure Rule; the directions to the patient to perform it herself were dictated in accordance with the Response Sampling Rule. In this way the attendant could observe the extent to which the patient was performing the desired behavior appropriately and could intelligently direct the patient to correct some particular portion of her performance. An alternative to using this combination of the Response Exposure and Response Sampling Rules would be simply to describe to the patient what she should do without demonstrating the behavior or without requiring her to perform it. In practice, this procedure was found to be an extremely poor method of teaching. The patient could be taught much more rapidly and efficiently if she could actually observe another person performing the job that she was being taught, and, unless she was given the opportunity to perform the behavior herself, no possibility existed of evaluating her understanding of the job.

CHAPTER 8

Evaluation of the Overall Reinforcement Procedure

A series of experiments were conducted after the motivating environment had been established to determine whether the motivating environment was effective in maintaining the desired behaviors (see Appendix). In evaluating those experiments, two questions were asked. First, was the behavior maintained at a higher level because the reinforcer was delivered for the behavior? Second, if it was maintained at a higher level, then how much higher? Only if the reinforcement for the behavior made a large difference can one say that reinforcement and extinction factors play a major causal role relative to other factors. In general, the experimental design consisted of carefully measuring the desired behaviors for a period of time during which reinforcement for responding was maximized; then the reinforcement procedure was discontinued in some manner. Careful measurements of the behavior continued to be made to see how much of a reduction of the desired behavior occurred, if any, as a result of discontinuing the reinforcement. Also, special attention was paid to how quickly such a reduction occurred. To the extent that the behavior dropped to a near zero frequency and to the extent that it decreased rapidly, one could conclude that reinforcement for that behavior was a major source of control and was more important than other sources of control. The experimental design also included a third phase, which reinstated the reinforcement procedure for the behavior. This third phase provided a measure of the degree of influence of reinforcement by examining the speed and extent to which the behavior increased once it was again being reinforced. This general plan is a counterbalanced research design often designated as a B-A-B or A-B-A design.

Since it was possible that different types of behaviors and

different types of patients might be differentially influenced by the reinforcement procedure, the experiments were done in such a way that these factors could be separately evaluated. Also, since the reinforcement procedure was so complex that it could be discontinued in many different ways, several of these different ways of terminating it were studied. It may seem that the simplest procedure would have been to discontinue entirely the delivery of tokens, as well as the possibility of exchange of the tokens for the actual reinforcer. Such a procedure would have provided information, but would not have revealed which part of the reinforcement procedure was responsible. It may have been that the tokens were irrelevant; obtaining the actual receipt of the reinforcers may have been important. Other alternatives exist; it may have been the social interaction in delivering the tokens and not the tokens themselves that was reinforcing. Or it may have been that the behavior was maintained simply because tokens were delivered, and not that they were delivered for a specific behavior. Stated otherwise, it may have been the attention that was associated with the procedure, and neither the tokens nor the reinforcer.

The outcome of Experiment I, described in the Appendix, was that the patients totally discontinued working on a previously preferred job when reinforcers were no longer forthcoming for that job. The decrease in behavior upon the termination of reinforcement was immediate for all but one of the patients. When reinforcement was reinstated, all patients immediately resumed the full-time job for which the reinforcers were being given. These results show that the reinforcement was the major and almost exclusive reason why the patients were performing their jobs. The results of this experiment are especially revealing in that the jobs used in this experiment were full-time jobs that closely approximated the type of job engaged in by normal, noninstitutionalized persons and might be considered to be especially susceptible to nonmonetary influences such as job satisfaction. Experiments II and III (see the Appendix) attempted to evaluate whether the jobs might still be intrinsically desirable and whether the reinforcement procedure in Experiment I determined which of the jobs the patients would select. The general procedure in Experiments II and III was to discontinue reinforcement for all jobs. Experiment II dealt with off-ward jobs and Experiment III, with on-ward jobs. The obvious procedure would seem to be to simply discontinue giving tokens for these jobs. As stated above, however, such a procedure would be somewhat inconclusive in that changes in behavior might result because of the termination of the patient-attendant interaction that had been associated with obtaining the tokens. The experiment was designed, therefore, so that attendant-patient interaction continued. This was done by giving each patient her usual number of tokens, but at the beginning of the day before her usual job was performed. The results showed that the performance of the on-ward patients decreased for almost all patients, and to a near zero level when reinforcement was given independently of the performance. The substantial control exerted by the reinforcement procedure manifested itself again by the immediate return to the high level of job performances on the very first day that the reinforcement procedure was reintroduced. The same effect occurred for the off-ward patients who were engaged in full-time jobs.

What would happen if the ward were conducted without tokens and with all reinforcers freely available to all patients regardless of what they did? Such a situation approximated the usual conduct of a mental hospital ward. Would the high level of performance of the patients still be maintained? The results of Experiment IV (see the Appendix) showed that it would not. The performance of the patients decreased to less than one-fourth of the previous level. If one can extrapolate these results to predict what would happen in the more usual ward procedure, one would estimate that the performance on a usual ward would be increased fourfold by instituting this motivating environment. The results of Experiment V (see the Appendix) revealed that the effects of the reinforcement procedure were not all or none, but rather depended on the amount of reinforcement that was forthcoming. In that experiment, performance of two different jobs were rewarded by two different amounts of reinforcement. All patients selected the job for which the larger amount of reinforcement was given. These results demonstrate not only that performance is determined by reinforcement but that the amount of reinforcement for the job is critical.

The results indicate that the reinforcement program was effective in maintaining the performance because the tokens were given for the specific performances desired. If the tokens were no longer given for the desired performances, then those performances decreased. If the token delivery was changed from one desired performance to another, then the performance for which the tokens were no longer being given decreased. Thus, it was not simply giving the tokens that maintained the performance but which performance it was that the tokens were given for. The results also showed that when the tokens were given was important. If the tokens were not given immediately following the performance, but rather prior to the performance, then that performance decreased.

The evidence also indicated that the tokens had to be exchangeable for the reinforcers in order for the desired behavior to be maintained by the delivery of tokens. In Experiment IV (see the Appendix) the tokens were no longer exchangeable for the reinforcers. The behavior decreased drastically in that experiment, although the results are not completely unequivocal regarding the necessity of the token exchangeability, since tokens were no longer being given upon the completion of the job in that experiment. Indirect evidence, however, comes from the extent to which the patients did indeed exchange their tokens for the reinforcers. If the tokens in and of themselves were desirable, and not because they were exchangeable for the reinforcers, then an examination of the patients' spending and earning records should have revealed that tokens were not being expended very rapidly, if at all. Analysis of the data, however, shows that (Table A–8, Appendix) the number of tokens spent during any given period of time and for any given patient was almost equal to the number that was earned. In other words, the patients were exchanging all of the tokens that they had for the reinforcers. This indirect evidence, then, strongly indicates that the reason the tokens were being earned was that they could be exchanged for the reinforcers and that the tokens would not have served as conditioned reinforcers had they not had this exchange value.

Taken together, the results show that the effect of the token reinforcer was substantial in maintaining a higher level of the desired performance than was obtainable without the token reinforcers. Performance dropped to a near zero level in five of the six experiments when the reinforcement was discontinued. In the sixth it dropped to one-fourth of its previous level. The effects of discontinuing reinforcement were immediate. In all six experiments the performance dropped substantially on the very first day that the performance was discontinued, and by the third day it had decreased to less than half of its previous level. The substantial effect of the reinforcement procedure was also evident in the return of the behavior to its previous level within one or two days when reinforcement was reinstated. These results demonstrate that the reinforcement procedure used in the motivating environment was indeed effective in maintaining the desired behaviors and that the effect of this procedure was so great that the influence of other factors in maintaining behavior seemed scarcely measurable when reinforcement was absent.

The results also show the extent to which the motivating environment was effective for given patients or types of patients. First, the results show that for all patients in all experiments behavior was maintained at a higher level when reinforcement was given for the responses than when it was not given for the responses, or given independently of them. The present reinforcement program, then, appears to have been successful in providing a procedure that will maintain a higher level of performance not for isolated individuals, but for all individuals.

Nor were patients in any particular psychiatric classification found to be unaffected by the reinforcement program. The population of patients studied included hebephrenics, mental retardates, schizophrenics, paranoids, organic psychotics, manic depressives, geriatric, etc. The patients in all of these classifications had a higher level of performance under the reinforcement program. These results suggest that a motivating environment of the type designed here would be effective for a group of individuals which was entirely composed of any one of the classifications.

The type of job for which reinforcement was being given did not appear to alter the efficacy of the reinforcement program. The reinforcement program was effective not only in maintaining the very simple performances, such as personal care and housekeeping duties, but also in maintaining the full-time job performances. These results indicate that the complexity of the job for which reinforcement is given will not alter the efficacy of the reinforcement program. The reinforcement program was also effective for all individuals regardless of individual characteristics, such as age, education, and years of hospitalization. The procedure was effective for individuals of all ages, which in this population ranged from 24 to 74 years of age. Educational level ranged from primary grades to college graduate. The number of years of hospitalization ranged from one to 37 years. The effectiveness of the motivating environment in maintaining the desired behaviors of the patients over this very wide range of individual differences indicates that the program succeeded in its attempt to design a total environment that could take advantage of the wide range of individual interests and preferences of an exceedingly heterogeneous population.

CHAPTER 9

Administrative and Therapeutic Considerations

1. PHYSICAL REQUIREMENTS

No special facilities were needed for the motivating environment, either in architectural arrangements or in physical equipment. Any ordinary physical environment should be suitable for application of this reinforcement procedure. The reason for this great flexibility is that the program is characterized by behavioral engineering (Ayllon and Michael, 1959) rather than by physical engineering. The critical features of the motivating environment are behavioral specification of the desired responses, the discovery of effective reinforcers, accurate and objective recording, and regulated access to the reinforcers. Although some types of physical architecture and equipment may simplify these objectives, almost any usual environment or facility probably could be adapted to this end.

Initial Conceptions Regarding Physical Facilities

Initially it was assumed that very special architecture and physical requirements would be needed to carry out a reinforcement program that encompassed all of the activities of the patients. To have complete control over the simuli and circumstances impinging on the patients, it was thought that a completely closed ward was indispensable. In this way patients could not leave the ward, and personnel from outside the ward would not have access to it. In order to have definitive recording of the patients' activities, continuous visual and auditory surveillance was provided. Microphones were installed in every room and at several locations in the corridor and elsewhere where patients might have any occasion to converse. At one stage even a closed circuit television camera was installed to watch selected areas. A one-way mirror was installed between the ward supervisor's office and the ward corridor to provide direct visual observation. A "walkie talkie" system was initiated briefly whereby the attendants could maintain continuous interaction with the ward supervisor with portable transceivers that they carried. Initially it was felt that strict separation had to be maintained between the activities of the patients and the activities of the ward staff to ensure privacy for the attendants. To accomplish that objective the attendant's station was fitted with a one-way mirror which permitted the attendants to watch the patients and allowed the attendants to converse with a considerable degree of privacy.

The motivating environment: An open system

All of these special changes in the ward proved to be unnecessary, and in most instances, extremely undesirable. Consider, first, the necessity for maintaining a completely closed ward to control all of the stimuli impinging on the patients. It was felt that without a closed ward there would be no control of the reinforcers that were received by the patient nor any degree of control over supervision or recording of the responses. In practice it was discovered that for many of the patients the strongest reinforcers consisted of activities that occurred outside of the ward. If the motivating environment were to be maintained as a closed system, then these off-ward reinforcers could not be utilized. One of these off-ward reinforcers was a grounds pass which gave the patient the freedom to go anywhere that she chose. Outside activities that were more specific were trips to a nearby town, movies and dances provided by the hospital, visits to a friend in some other part of the hospital, talks with the social worker, etc. Similarly, a large number of desired responses could be expected only outside the ward, such as employment in the hospital laundry, dietary kitchen, business office, laboratory, etc. It became obvious that both the reinforcers and the responses would be severely limited in terms of both quality and quantity available if a closed system were maintained. The solution was to allow availability of all these reinforcers and responses by creating an open system in which access was regulated but never prevented. Patients were given the opportunity to work at any job available outside the ward and to exchange their tokens for reinforcers available outside the ward. Access to the reinforcers were, of course, contingent upon the patient's behavior. The conclusion reached from this experience was that exit from the motivating environment itself could be used as a very strong reinforcer with no disruption of the overall objectives of the program.

Impracticality of continuous surveillance

The continuous surveillance devices consisting of the one-way mirror, the TV camera, the microphone, and the portable transceivers were found to be relatively useless in providing definitive and accurate recordings of the patient's activities. In practice, each of these devices required that a staff member be continually present attending to the device. One can imagine the difficulties in requiring a staff member to remain fixated at a one-way mirror for an eight-hour period, to listen to the microphones, to watch the TV monitor, or to listen to the transceiver. In practice, only during a small portion of the eight-hour period were relevant activities being observed, even though continuous surveillance was required. The long period of observation created such monotony and boredom that when relevant activities did occur, they often went unrecorded and undetected. The problems and inadequacies of a method that requires continuous observation of all the behavior of a number of individuals is discussed in Chapter 6. The general rule adopted, as noted in those sections, was that observation was restricted to particular times and places but was made very intensive, standardized, and specific during those times. Such intensive observation required that the supervisor be physically present at the activity, thereby avoiding the necessary distortion and selective attention that any of the mechanical devices imposed. The additional expense of surveillance devices and of staff members to supervise them was, therefore, unnecessary, and in this case, also undesirable since this additional expenditure did not provide as definitive recordings as did the simple expedient of direct-on-the-spot observation.

Usefulness of special devices for dispensing reinforcement

Although some special apparatus was used to simplify the problem of standardizing the reinforcement delivery, such standardization could be, and at times was, implemented almost as satisfactorily without these devices. The ward procedure at various times used a token-operated soda machine, a cigarette dispenser, a turnstile between two rooms, a cigarette lighter, a TV set, and a radio. The turnstile facilitated standardization of the regulated access procedure, but the same function was at times almost as reliably implemented by providing staff supervision of this access without the turnstile. Similarly, the functions provided by all of the token-operated devices for dispensing the reinforcers could also have been served by having the soda available at the commissary periods or the TV available in a separate room, access to which could have been regulated by a patient assistant or staff member. Cigarettes were made available at one time through the ward commissary procedure, and the same could have been true of the cigarette lighter. As is discussed in greater detail in Chapter 6, the automatic devices do have advantages over human implementation; however, they are not indispensable.

Privacy of staff communication

The private room for the attendants also turned out, in practice, to be unnecessary. The patients were given complete and full information as to what the ward program was all about. They were informed in many different ways about what the response requirements were, what the reinforcers were, and the relationship between them. Little or no communication occurred between attendants that the patients should not have heard. As a consequence, the construction of a specially isolated room for the staff was deemed unnecessary. A general office area where the attendants could write and keep their records seemed to be all that was necessary. No problems arose from having patients working in the office area as secretarial assistants and overhearing the staff conversations.

A scale drawing of the architecture of the ward is given in Figure 1 of the Appendix. This diagram may be of assistance in visualizing the spatial configuration in which this program was conducted, but should in no way be interpreted as a model that must be replicated. The distinctive features of the program can in no way be derived from the accidents of architecture that characterize that scheme. They are to be found in the behavioral configuration which is almost totally independent of the physical configuration.

2. METHOD OF JOB SELECTION

Information on Job Requirements and Reinforcing Consequences

A continuing source of concern among the patients on this ward, as well as on other wards, was knowledge about what the hospital staff required of them. In the absence of information clearly communicated by the staff, patients generally come to their own conclusions. They might decide that the best thing to do is to stay out of trouble by not taking too much initiative, or conversely they might decide that what is desired of them is that they interact more with other patients or with the staff. Information provided by the staff is likely to be quite different for each of the staff members who communicates it. One staff member may very well tell the patient that the trouble with her is that she is not cooperative enough. Another might tell her that her problem is that she has not yet learned to live with herself. Other types of contradictory objectives often set for a patient are that she must not form too dependent a relationship on others versus she must learn to be more dependent or relate more to others; she must not be rigid versus she must show more perseverance; she must show more diversity of action versus she must develop a better concentration on one thing; she must have a better personal appearance versus she must not be so obsessed with personal appearance; she must learn to acquiesce to authority figures versus she must show more independence of action, etc. Confronted with these varied and apparently conflicting statements of objectives for her behavior, the patient often is uncertain about what is expected of her.

The motivating environment attempted to give the patients a clear understanding of what behavior was expected of them. The statement of desired behavior consisted of the various performances for which the patient was given tokens. Several steps were taken to ensure that the patients knew what the desired behaviors were. A listing of all the desired behaviors was posted in a conspicuous place on the ward; each of the desired behaviors was further described in the poster in terms of the time and place at which the behavior would be expected to occur and the number of tokens that were being paid for its performance.

Each patient selected the jobs she wished to perform at any given time. The objective was to make the job selection as simple as possible for the patient. Also, feed-back in some form or other followed any request for a job, even if the specific job request could not be filled at that moment.

Simply posting a list of the desired performances was found to be insufficient. Some of the patients were illiterate and had no way of reacting to the posters without going through the additional step of asking another patient or staff member to read it to them. Even for those patients who were able to read, there was no assurance that they would learn about changes in the listing of the position or that they had even read it the first time. The result was that many jobs were not being selected by the patients, apparently because of lack of information concerning these positions. A general rule of thumb was to provide continuous and conspicuous information regarding the desired responses.

Each of the positions was described to each patient, giving full detail about the time, place, and number of tokens available for desired behaviors, (1) upon admission to the ward and (2) at job selection time. This procedure did not require that the patient be literate or attend to the poster.

An additional procedure that was used in the latter stages of the program which was derived from this response information rule was to assign one of the better-adjusted patients to the newly admitted one as a constant companion during the first ten days, an assignment for which the older patient received tokens. The assignment given to the better-adjusted patient was that she provide the newly-admitted patient with all the information needed regarding the response requirements as well as information about the general location and arrangement of reinforcers on the ward.

Should a job be obtained at any time? Initially, to take advantage of the patient's desire to sign up for a job at any time, the patient's request for a job could occur anywhere on the ward. The patient had only to state to any of the attendants that she wished to sign up for a position. The patient was immediately informed as to the time and place where the job would be performed and the number of tokens that were being given for that job assignment. The important consideration here was to provide immediate and continuous reinforcement for all requests for jobs. Patients could sign up for the job even during the night shift. Job requests at night were fairly infrequent, but it was considered extremely desirable to reinforce this response whenever it occurred. This procedure was found to be unsatisfactory for several reasons. First, most patients showed a fairly low frequency of initiating such requests. Second, no method was available for supervising the conscientiousness of the aides in acting immediately upon requests. Another factor was that patients, because of their long experience with institutional procedure, often believed that a job once performed by an individual became his exclusively. A characteristic reaction was, "Oh, I didn't know that I could sign up for that. I thought someone else had that." To increase the probability of job requests and to establish standardized conditions, a specific time and place was designated as the employment period. This time and place varied at different stages in the development of the ward procedure. For example, at one time it occurred during mealtime. The general procedure then was that every patient without exception was approached and asked if she cared to sign up for a job, and encouraged to be as specific as possible as to which job she wanted and when. The attendant had as complete information as possible about which jobs were available. A particular attendant was designated as the employment officer at these times, so a single individual had the responsibility for ensuring that each of the patients was approached concerning jobs. Many patients never approached the attendant with a request for a job when it was left to the patient's initiative. In fact, they would actively move away from an attendant who asked them if they wanted a job. It was partly for that reason that a set time and place were used to give each patient information on available jobs. At mealtime the patients were in a situation that made it impractical to avoid the attendant.

Should the patient do a job even if she has not formally asked for it? The job selection procedure in no way prevented the patient from performing any job that was available. The patient was free to clean her room, to assist with the dishes, to run errands for the attendant, etc. without having obtained a formal job assignment from the staff. These spontaneous activities did not result in token payment, but patients could enjoy them for their own intrinsic value. The job selection procedure guaranteed that the patient would receive token reinforcement in addition to whatever intrinsic reinforcement derived from the job. Infrequently, but consistently, patients engaged in activities which paid no tokens. An example of this (see the Appendix) was a patient who continued to perform secretarial duties for a doctor because she felt a responsibility to do it even though tokens were no longer being given. The usual feature of such spontaneous work was that the patient worked for short irregular periods if tokens were not given.

How long should the patient keep a specific job? Initially, patients were allowed to remain at a given job for as long as they kept requesting it. For example, a patient could sign up to be a kitchen assistant every day for several months. It was found that several undesirable consequences resulted from this unlimited tenure. The performance of the job became so routine and so stereotyped that almost all social interaction in the performance of the job disappeared. The patient knew exactly what was expected of her and therefore had no reason to ask questions of the staff or of other patients. All details of when to report, what to do while there, who to listen to, etc. apparently had been so well learned that the job performance became completely mechanical.

A second problem that resulted from this long-term job tenure was that the individual became overly skilled in only one activity and was not exposed to a number of others that might very well be required of her when she left the hospital. For those patients who could not be expected to leave the hospital, it was still desirable that they have experience in different jobs so that they would not become "technologically unemployed" even in the hospital. Given the objectives of most mental institutions and the vagaries of the individual's future, it was not possible to completely specify the type of job the individual should be prepared for.

Job Rotation Rule

Therefore, a general rule of thumb was that *a patient should not be allowed to hold the same job without interruption* for more than a week at a time. At the end of this period, each patient became eligible to work on jobs other than those she had performed the previous week. This job rotation procedure was useful in guaranteeing exposure of the patients to many different jobs. Although patients occasionally objected to this rotation, its benefits seemed unmistakable.

What should be done if the individual insists on keeping her initial job? Once the patient began working at a position and was reinforced for it, she often asked to keep that position indefinitely. Doing so, of course, would have been a violation of the job rotation rule. Putting to practice the Probability of Behavior rule, the efforts of the patients to continue on a given job were viewed as another potential source of reinforcement. Therefore, the privilege of keeping a job was scheduled as a reinforcer. A patient could exchange a specified number of tokens for the privilege of having a position assigned to her and not to another patient. This practice was limited only to those jobs that involved a full day's work off the ward. The jobs on the ward were sufficiently flexible as to usually allow several patients to perform them if necessary. Some off-ward jobs, on the other hand, were sufficiently limited in number and were in great demand. The general rule followed was that jobs would be assigned on a first-come, first-serve basis or on the basis of the job rotation procedure. Only when several patients requested the same job was the procedure followed of allowing guarantee of the job by payments of tokens. The more individuals requesting the job, the greater was the cost of the job guarantee. At any given time, the number of tokens required to guarantee a position was fixed; but it varied in number at different moments of supply and demand between zero and 10 tokens per day. This meant that an individual who worked a full day would receive 80 tokens for her performance on the job but may have expended as many as 10 tokens in obtaining the guarantee of that position. In practice this job guarantee did not conflict with the job rotation principle since the number of tokens required for the job guarantee was increased as long as there was more than one person requesting it. At some point a patient other than the usual one that had been working on the job would succeed in obtaining the guarantee. Thus, the jobs were still rotated among patients.

What should be done if only one patient is qualified for the job? Obviously if only one patient is qualified to perform a specific job, then the job rotation rule cannot be followed. In the initial development of the motivating environment, this situation occurred. As a result, the particular patients involved became indispensable to the job supervisor. The results were unfortunate. The attendants often began exerting a good deal of persuasion to keep the patient performing the job on a regular basis. The patients involved usually realized their indispensability and demanded unauthorized privileges, not only on the ward but on the job location. The net result was that the patient's continuation in the job became more important to the ward staff than was the general welfare of the patient. It is for this same reason that the long-standing practice of having mental patients perform all of the duties in mental institutions has been recently discontinued in the more progressive institutions. Their indispensability results in the specific job performance interfering with considerations of treatment, discharge, and general adjustment of the patient. For this reason, in the later development of the motivating environment, no patient was ever allowed to obtain a position for which she alone was qualified. A position was established only when several patients were known to be capable of filling that position.

What should be done if a patient "signs up for" a job but does not perform it? Occasionally patients did not perform a job satisfactorily or failed to start it after having signed up for it. Since all positions were of such a nature that they had to be filled in order that the ward or another unit of the hospital would function, failure to perform the job satisfactorily resulted in administrative disruption. This disruption was minimal for the on-ward positions since the attendant in charge of the ward could immediately approach other patients on the ward and obtain a substitute. The situation for the off-ward jobs was, however, quite different. A patient could request a position off the ward and instead of reporting to work she could choose to roam the hospital grounds freely. To avoid this incidental source of reinforcement, a grounds pass was made a prerequisite for a patient's selection of an off-ward position. This grounds pass, as is described in another section, was obtained only in exchange for a substantial number of tokens. Consequently, the possession of a grounds pass by a patient automatically provided some assurance that the patient was fairly well adjusted, since she had performed a number of jobs satisfactorily. Also, this grounds pass requirement for off-ward assignments guaranteed that a patient who selected such jobs would not obtain any extra reinforcement from being off the ward (she already had that privilege).

Reaction of the job supervisor to job rotation

Almost invariably the job supervisor for on-ward performance or off-ward performance objected vigorously to having a favored patient replaced by another relatively naive and perhaps strange patient. The reasons for the vigorous objection are fairly apparent: If a given patient is doing the job well, why take a chance on another patient who is unknown or who is known to perform somewhat less satisfactorily? The number of reasons given by the job supervisors for needing a given patient seemed almost infinite. It was stated that the patient really liked her job; that it would be bad for her mental health to go to work elsewhere; that she could not get used to new things; that she had made all kinds of friends, etc. A more realistic reason is, of course, that the job supervisor had to spend additional time training the new individual. In order to forestall these vigorous objections by the job supervisor, it seemed useful to state in advance the necessity of the job rotation rule in as objective terms as possible. In practice, little or no objection was raised by the job supervisors if the job rotation procedure was spelled out in advance and in detail prior to assigning the first patient. The objections by the supervisor usually disappeared and in fact led to the supervisor's satisfaction once a "pool" had been trained and was available for a given job, since the supervisor could be more objective in the ratings that he gave a patient. When there was only one patient available to do the job, the supervisor routinely judged the patient as excellent or satisfactory, probably because of fear that any other rating would lead to loss of this seemingly indispensable employee.

3. METHOD TO ESTABLISH THE PAY FOR EACH JOB

Two considerations dictated how much a given job earned for the patient. The first was the suitability of the job to the patient; the second was the supply and demand of individuals available for the job. There were two categories of performance by which patients earned tokens. One of these related to personal care, and the other, to the functioning of the ward and of the hospital.

Several opportunities to earn tokens were available which concerned personal care and hygiene, such as brushing one's teeth at least once a day, bathing at least once per week, being groomed properly each day, and following medical prescription or directions when given. The number of tokens given for each of these behaviors reflected the personal judgment of the ward staff about the great importance of this personal hygiene. It is very likely that slightly different populations and situations would not require the use of tokens to maintain these behaviors.

A more objective criteria was available for determining the earnings for jobs concerned with the functioning of the ward or of the hospital. The procedure for adjusting the earnings for each job was in terms of supply and demand. Those jobs for which many patients volunteered were assigned a smaller number of tokens. The jobs for which few patients volunteered were assigned a sufficiently large number of tokens to ensure the selection of the job by at least two patients. Periodic examination of the number of individuals who selected each job led to periodic revision of the number of tokens which was given for it. Other considerations such as the presumed difficulty or the duration of the job were not factors in assigning a given pay to a job. In fact, some jobs that were fairly demanding physically and that required about three hours through the day for completion, such as sweeping the floors, earned only about five tokens since many patients volunteered for those positions. A job that earned a large number of tokens but for which there were few patients who qualified was the job of tour guide. This job required only about 10 minutes for completion yet earned 10 tokens. This procedure minimized the dangers of personal idiosyncratic evaluation of what a given job should pay. If a particular job involved certain features that were considered highly desirable for a given individual, the earnings for that job were arbitrarily adjusted upward in order to ensure exposure of the patient to that job. The supply and demand rule, then, was the starting point for the assignment of earnings. Therapeutic and other objectives could and should be superimposed on this general rule.

How Much Can Tokens Buy?

Prices for each of the reinforcers was based primarily on supply and demand. Some kinds of reinforcers were necessarily limited because of considerations of space. Not all patients could sleep in the same well-furnished dormitory room. The opportunity to go by bus to a nearby town was necessarily limited by the size of the bus. Because of time limitations not all patients could speak to the ward psychologist or the social worker as frequently and as long as they might care to. In such instances, the cost was adjusted upward to the point where the number of patients selecting the reinforcer did not exceed the supply of the reinforcers. If the reinforcing items or activities were available in a greater quantity than was being utilized by the patients, the cost of that item was revised downward. Periodic and regular review of the number of patients requesting each item was made in order to assure the full use of all available reinforcers. Some reinforcing activities had no limitation of availability. For example, as many patients as wanted could go to the movies and dances, attend religious services, go on walks, etc. Consequently, most of these items were given a cost of only one token to provide maximum opportunity for the patients to obtain these reinforcers. Sometimes therapeutic objectives dictated that a given individual should be exposed to a reinforcer that he could not afford. In such cases, the cost to that individual was reduced to an amount that was sufficient to motivate the individual to select that reinforcer. For example, at one time to encourage a mentally defective patient to have more interaction with the supervising ward psychologist, the usual cost of 20 tokens for an interview was reduced to one token. The general rule that was followed, then, was to use the supply of, and demand for, the reinforcers as the basic rule for deciding cost, but to freely override this rule when special therapeutic considerations made it advisable to do so for a given patient.

4. MEDICAL CARE AND SUPERVISION

In order to afford the physician adequate time to examine, diagnose, and treat the physical condition of each patient, all administrative matters were turned over to the nursing staff. The administrative reorganization of the ward ensured that the physician was not interrupted, distracted, or otherwise interfered with by requests and complaints of an administrative nature and/or social interruptions caused by his presence on the ward. The attendants and nurse screened the patients' physical conditions systematically so as to call on the physician for further examination. The examination of the patient was carried out in a separate room so that the physician was not forced to go through the unit itself. In that way his time was fully under his control, and no interruptions could occur while he was performing the medical examination. This procedure also eliminated the traditional "rounds," which are a time-consuming activity involving many social and administrative matters. This does not mean that the physician had less opportunity to talk to patients on the unit; rather it meant that he could talk to one patient at a time for as long as he deemed necessary. He was in contact with the nurse daily, and she in turn screened those patients in need of a medical examination. The physician had medical nursing records available to him which made it unnecessary for him to depend on the impressionistic evaluation by a given attendant or nurse. He could also use behavioral records that gave him a much more complete picture of the effects of a given physical condition on the day-to-day behavior of the patient. The typical reaction of the physician to such a procedure was favorable. Much of the time of a physician in a mental hospital usually is spent in making decisions concerning a grounds pass for a patient, a new pair of shoes, letters to the family, privileges for each patient, etc. By turning the responsibility for these decisions and their implementation over to the nursing staff, several advantages were obtained. First of all, it allowed the physician more time to dedicate to the medical treatment of the patient. Second, it became possible for the patients to have immediate feedback on their requests for privileges or information. Because the motivating environment had systematically provided the channels for patients' requests and implementation of these requests, each of the attendants on the ward could properly meet the patients' needs and requests. Therefore, it was no longer necessary for patients to wait for a decision to come from either the physician or the nurse. When a patient was interested in obtaining a new room or additional fresh linen, it was possible for any of the attendants to immediately allow the patient these or similar items in exchange for tokens. When a patient requested to leave the ward to see a movie, it was no problem for the staff to arrange for such an exit from the ward by following the token exchange procedure. In short, when the patient made a request, the administrative procedure existed whereby the nursing staff could satisfy the request. The primary advantage of this reorganization was that the physician had more time to dedicate to the medical treatment of the patient, since he could delegate administrative matters to the nursing staff. This procedure also guaranteed that the patients would interact with the attendants. The patients now had good reason not to circumvent the attendants in favor of the physician. Decisions were made characteristically on the spot, since whatever the patient wanted could be converted into a number of tokens necessary to obtain what she wanted.

5. NURSING CARE AND SUPERVISION

Many of the duties and responsibilities that might otherwise be exercised only by the registered nurse were assigned to the attendants. The primary purpose for so doing was to allow the nurse the responsibility of supervision of the motivating environment. Whenever medical and hospital regulations permitted, the attendants provided the nursing services under the general supervision of the registered nurse. They dispensed medications, dressed injuries, prepared patients for medical examinations, etc. The usual nursing procedures such as taking temperature, pulse, respiration, and blood pressure were also performed by attendants. This freed the nurse for supervisory and training duties.

Once the attendants were no longer interrupted by activities or events not directly related to the patient's behavior, it was possible for them to keep frequent and systematic records of the patients temperature, pulse, respiration, blood pressure, etc. Although these measures are ordinarily taken in most wards, they are taken infrequently or unsystematically because of the limitation of time of the attendants. This problem becomes even greater when the registered nurse is the only one allowed to obtain these measures. By reorganizing the duties and responsibilities of the nursing staff, the present procedure freed the attendants from routine custodial activities.

An entry was made at each bath period, which was scheduled once every week, regarding (1) whether or not the patient had taken a bath and had her hair shampooed, (2) observations of the skin and identification of any rashes or bruises the patient might have had at that time, (3) a crude, but often helpful estimate by the staff of the patient's gross activity, (4) the weight of the patient undressed. This particular record is useful when working with chronic patients, since these patients rarely request the attendant or the nurse to check minor scratches or bruises that they may have sustained. By checking the patients' skin condition once weekly, it was possible to detect conditions that required prompt care.

A "vital signs" record was taken every three weeks and consisted of the temperature, pulse rate, respiration rate, and blood pressure of the patient. It was taken more often when necessary for a given patient. The record was taken at the same time every evening before the patient went to sleep, and at the patient's bedside.

Finally, there was a record that indicated the physician's visits to the unit and the patient whom he examined. This record made it possible for the nurse or the attendants to determine readily the last date on which the physician had examined a given patient. This information is often contained in other records, but they are typically either buried in a patient's file or so difficult to recover that the attendant cannot have the information for a given patient readily available. This particular record gave ready information as to whether or not the physician had changed the medication, and which staff member had taken care of the order.

All these records made it possible to monitor the physical condition of the patient systematically and allowed the staff to have continuous information on the patient's condition. In addition, when any patient appeared to require medical examination, the physician was well furnished with records that had been taken regularly over a period of months or years.

6. REORGANIZATION OF SHIFT WORK

In order to establish the motivating environment it was necessary to revamp the typically arbitrary division of labor among shifts. For this purpose, the duties and responsibilities of the nursing staff were redesigned. The primary purpose in so doing was to eliminate any procedures that did not have direct relationship to working with the patients. For example, counting clothing, "condemning" various items, filling out forms for the pharmacy, etc. were activities that, at one time, were being done during the day. These activities were changed so that they would be done only at night while the patients were asleep. During the period of time previously devoted to those functions, the attendant could now be engaged in direct interaction with the patients. The night-shift staff, on the other hand, was responsible for the performance of activities and duties that did not require the presence of the patient. (See also Ayllon and Rydman, 1961.)

7. USING BEHAVIORAL RECORDS TO IMPLEMENT NURSING PROCEDURES

The behavioral records of a patient in the motivating environment could be translated into the amount of work in terms of minutes or hours she performed daily and the amount of interactions she had in given specific activities such as attendance at movies, dances, religious services, off-ward passes, etc. The greater the number of tokens earned, the greater the amount of activity the patient had engaged in. A sudden decrease of earnings or spendings of tokens often served as a diagnostic signal for the nurse or the physician to examine the patient.

Tokens were sometimes used directly to help in maintaining a high standard of nursing care. For example, patients sometimes refused to follow the prescription of the physician. At such times the nurse could offer the patient tokens for complying with the physician's orders. Similarly, a patient might insist on going to work even though the physician's orders were that she stay in bed. For example, one day the nurse discovered that a patient, Donna V., had a temperature of 100.2°, whereupon she called for the physician. Although she directed the patient to stay in the unit until seen by the physician, the patient insisted that there was nothing wrong with her and that she wanted to go to work. To make sure she stayed to be examined by the physician, she was paid that morning the full number of tokens she would have received at work. The patient readily agreed to stay for the medical examination. The next morning her temperature had decreased to normal, and she went back to work.

8. PERSONNEL ECONOMY

The emphasis on this ward was to encourage patients to engage in functional behaviors. To a large extent, this meant that they performed activities that were normally performed by paid employees. This approach potentially offers substantial economy for an institution. The extent to which the patients assumed responsibilities normally conducted by paid employees can best be appreciated by observing what happened during a "vacation period" when the patients were given tokens without having to work. This period of time occupied several weeks and is described in some detail in Experiment III (see the Appendix). During the vacation period the patients ceased working almost entirely (Figure 4 in the Appendix). The additional work required to keep the ward functioning when the patients discontinued performing their jobs had to be made up by paid employees whose hours almost doubled. Ordinarily an average of two employees was used on each of the morning and afternoon shifts and one on the night shift. When the patients stopped working, however, two additional employees were needed during the morning shift and the afternoon shift.

Considerable savings should also result from the fact that an institution need not provide the ward with as many centralized services. Such central services often include recreational therapy, occupational therapy, rehabilitation, dietary services, laundry, janitorial services, commissary, secretaries, etc. The present ward program eliminated, or considerably reduced, the need for the ward to call upon these central hospital facilities, since their functions were an inherent feature of the motivating environment. Occupational therapists and rehabilitation workers are employed to remotivate patients to work and to provide them with job opportunities. The present ward program made little or no demands upon these departments since these functions were already being served by the ward on a continuing basis; that is, patients were continuously being remotivated to perform by means of the reinforcement procedure that has been described. Recreational therapy was already being performed by that part of the regular ward program that was concerned with arranging the many reinforcing events. Patients were taken by the attendants on walks around the hospital or to a nearby town, to movies, and on bus rides. They were given current, popular magazines, games to play, and phonograph records. The function of a beautician was served on the ward by attendants or by supervised patients, thus eliminating the demands upon the hospital beautician. Two full-time, and one part-time, dietary employees were assigned to the ward prior to the operation of the ward program; however, after its initiation only one of these workers was needed since the serving of food, the cleaning of the kitchen materials, etc. were being handled by the patients under the supervision of attendants. This one worker was necessary only because of hospital regulations which required the attendance of a dietary worker on the ward during some periods of its operation. This employee was present during less than one-half of the meals; the other half was handled entirely by the ward program. Services of a central laundry supervisor were not needed since this work, which included sorting, folding, and cleaning of the patients' clothing, was done by supervised patients. Similarly, the present ward program provided all necessary janitorial services on a continuing basis by the patients without need for a janitorial employee who is typically responsible for the cleanliness of one or more wards. A paid secretary was employed on the ward because of the large amount of work required by the research nature of the program; however, she was relieved of considerable work by patients who did all the routine secretarial work under the supervision of the attendants. Mental hospitals customarily have a centralized commissary where patients may purchase candy, cigarettes, sodas, and various sundries. The present ward program provided its own commissary services available to the patients three times each day of the week on the ward itself. Supervised patients sold and recorded the sales which occurred during the commissary period.

A constant request by treatment staff and educators is that the ratio of patients to treatment staff or ratio of pupils to educators be reduced. The ideal situation would be that of one pupil per teacher or one patient per therapist. Such an ideal is under most circumstances impossible to realize because of the great expense. The present approach makes it possible to approximate this ideal without the additional expense since each of the patients is used as part of the treatment procedure insofar as her state of progress permits. The patients assisted in the recording procedure, in reinforcing, supervising, etc. under the intermittent supervision of the paid staff member. To some extent this procedure has been followed in other applied areas of human endeavor. For example, teachers frequently use students as teachers' aides. Similarly, the same principle seems to be used in such organizations as Alcoholics Anonymous, in which each alcoholic attempts to act as a therapist for other alcoholics. The economic advantages of this procedure are obvious, but the therapeutic or educational advantages may be even greater and are the more important consideration. When the patient is used as a supervisory assistant in conducting the reinforcement procedure, she seems to benefit greatly by her increased familiarization with the many types of desired behaviors, the many types of reinforcers available, and the overall objectives of the treatment procedure. In an intuitive sense, it appears that once a patient is participating as part of the treatment staff, then the objectives of the treatment staff become her own objectives, and thereby, facilitate the changes that had been desired in her own behavior. This possible beneficial aspect of the procedure is based on a conjecture, of course, but seems to be the primary reason for its use in such organizations as Alcoholics Anonymous. At an intuitive level it seems reasonable that a patient might become more sensitive to the effects of her own behavior after having served as an assistant to an attendant, during which period she was reporting continuously on the behavior of other patients.

It is not possible to make any definitive statements concerning the extent of the economy in employees achieved in comparison to other types of ward programs, the principal reason being the lack of a standard type of ward program with which to compare this procedure. All wards, including the present one, differ considerably in their employee requirements, depending upon the nature of the patient population and the hospital regulations and resources. It seems reasonable to believe that the emphasis on the behavioral functioning of the patient in this ward program would result in a need for fewer employees than would otherwise be the case.

Aside from economic considerations, there is a considerable advantage to the patient of having various hospital services provided on the ward by the ward personnel. Mental institutions are usually so large that channels of communication and access to facilities become very difficult even under the best of circumstances. By having these services on the ward itself, they can be made available with minimal difficulty to the patients on a continuing basis. This same rationale has led to recent attempts at decentralizing the services at mental hospitals so that the professional workers will be in daily contact with the patients they serve. One such example of decentralization is the so-called "unit system" in which all of the treatment staff are located right on the ward as in the motivating environment. The overall effect seems to be more continuous and responsive treatment for the patient.

9. REACTION OF ATTENDANTS TO HAVING JOBS DONE BY PATIENTS

Only those responses were selected which had been previously or normally performed by the attendants. The use of this criterion had several desirable effects on the manner in which the attendants evaluated the patients' performances. First, the attendants viewed the general motivating environment favorably since they had to perform fewer duties. Second, the behavior appeared to be meaningful. Never was there any objection that the desired performance was unnecessary, unimportant, or useless, either by the patients or by the attendants. Third, surprisingly little ambiguity appeared to arise regarding the desired level of performance, apparently because the attendants had evolved a standard of excellence during their own previous performance of the duties. For example, attendants appeared to be quite consistent in deciding how well the floors had to be cleaned by a patient in order to earn the token. Fourth, failure of a patient to perform a duty satisfactorily often resulted in unfavorable consequences for the attendant. For example, if a patient was assigned to serve meals, failure of this patient to serve promptly and equitably led to immediate and vigorous complaints by the other patients to the attendant. This complaint required that the attendant either serve the meals herself or be inconvenienced by the urgent necessity of finding a replacement. Because of the above, no explanation was needed to justify to the attendants the desirability of the behaviors selected or to motivate the attendants to carry out any of the procedures designed to strengthen those behaviors.

10. ASSURING THE PERFORMANCE OF THE ATTENDANT

Since the reinforcement procedure was implemented by the attendants, assurance was required that they would perform their duties properly; otherwise, no possibility could exist of having the reinforcement procedure applied appropriately to the patients. The same consideration that applied in maintaining performance of the patients also applied in maintaining the desired performance of the attendants. Just as it was necessary to specify the response precisely for the patients, so was it necessary with the attendants. Each of the attendants was provided with a written and detailed description of her duties. Not only was the type of duty specified but the time and place it was to be performed and the name of the attendant who was to perform it. The duties of the attendants primarily involved supervisory functions, i.e., supervising a patient's performance and providing token exchange.

One of the requirements of response selection with the patients had been that the response produce an enduring change in the environment. The same standard was applied to the attendants' performances. The token exchange itself, of course, constituted an enduring change and provided objective evidence of the attendants' performances. Further, each attendant made a written record of all token transactions with a notation of the time, place, and patient involved in the token transaction. The requirement of a fixed time and place made it possible for the ward supervisor to observe the performance of the attendants, just as the same requirement applied to the patients made it possible for the attendants to observe the performance of the patients. In practice the written records, as well as the ward supervisor's own direct observation, assured that the ward procedure was being performed by the attendants as intended.

The discovery of reinforcers for the attendants was a vastly simpler undertaking than for the patients since all of the attendants had very complex and apparently strong behavioral repertoires that enabled them to maintain an independent existence outside of the hospital. Similarly, there was no need to institute tokens as a medium of exchange since money already existed as an established monetary exchange. The wages of the employees are an obvious reinforcer. Other reinforcers that appeared to exist on the basis of observation of the attendants were the opportunity of the attendant to state her preference for days on which to take a vacation. Another probable reinforcer was the opportunity to choose her work shift. Since not all of the attendants could have the opportunity of obtaining their preference, first choice was given to those attendants who performed best. Although the level of excellence in performance obviously cannot be evaluated precisely, the written records of the attendants' performances provided a basis for distinguishing between generally satisfactory and generally unsatisfactory performance. Periodic evaluation procedures were conducted for purposes of recommending employees for salary increase. In this way salary increases, vacations, holiday preference, and work shift preference were dependent upon the level of performance.

11. THE COMMUNITY AND THE MOTIVATING ENVIRONMENT

Patients are admitted to a mental hospital usually because of some behavioral disorder. The patient may have attempted suicide, become suddenly aggressive, engaged in periodic spells of crying, showed unusual sexual deviations, etc. These behavioral disorders may constitute a danger to the patient or to members of his community. When disorders such as the above become serious enough the community has little alternative but to have the patient committed until the disorder disappears or is sufficiently reduced that the individual will no longer be a danger to himself or to his neighbors. Very often, great concern is expressed by family members and by the individual's employer, many of whom visit the patient frequently during the initial period of commitment. As the duration of commitment increases, two noticeable changes occur. First, the interest and concern of the family, the employer, and friends diminish. Second, the behavior of the patient undergoes a progressive deterioration. Constructive behaviors that were still available at the time of the commitment are reduced because of the usually nonresponsive nature of the environment. For the patients studied here, the behavioral disorder for which each had been committed was usually absent, but in its place were a general behavioral deterioration and a lack of interest on the part of family, friends, and former employers. Any attempt to discharge the patient after many years of commitment is usually thwarted, not by the existence of the behavioral disorder for which the individual was committed, but by these other two factors of behavioral deterioration and disculturation.

The major importance of this disculturation in preventing discharge of mental patients has been recently recognized in progressive psychiatric thinking, and is especially stressed in the field of study known currently as "Community Psychiatry." The motivating environment described here provides a method of preventing the behavioral deterioration and the disculturation since the responsive environment motivates the individual to continue functional activities during the period of his commitment. By this means the disculturation can be prevented, permitting the patient to be discharged as soon as his behavioral disorder has diminished sufficiently. The role of the motivating environment in maintaining functional behavior should not be considered distinct from the objective of eliminating the behavioral disorder for which the patient was confined. As has been described earlier, the maintenance of functional behavior by the patient seems in and of itself to displace or compete with the behavioral disorder.

12. A LOOK TO THE FUTURE

The motivating environment was designed with the objective of general applicability to different types of populations and different types of situations. The extent to which this objective has been achieved can only be answered by the extent to which practitioners will successfully adapt this procedure to their own particular circumstances. Evidence that the objective has been at least partially fulfilled comes from the personal reports that we have been receiving during the past years of successful application of the motivating environment to a diversity of situations. These adaptations have occurred following personal visits to the motivating environment at Anna State Hospital or personal communication with the authors or after reading the 1965 published report on the motivating environment. Following is a list of the applications, and the environment and population in which they took place, which have come to our attention:

Mentally retarded patients in an institution for the retarded (Brierton and Garms);

The multiply disabled in a sheltered workshop (Zimmerman et al.);

Chronic psychotics in a mental hospital (Stessy et al.);

Adult psychotics in a VA Hospital (Atthowe and Krasner);

Retarded children in an institution for the retarded (Spradlin);

Adult psychotics in a mental hospital (Gericke);

Newly admitted psychotics in a mental hospital (Feingold and Migler);

Adult psychotics in a half-way house (Henderson);

Adult psychotics in a mental hospital (Hopkins);

Juvenile delinquents in a correctional institution (Cohen);

Psychotics in a mental hospital (Hughes)

Preschool boys in a nursery school (Hamblin and Bushell);

Slow learners in a private school (Gray);

The profoundly retarded with brain damage in an institution for the retarded (Rotman).

The patients in the above programs have included children as well as geriatric patients, newly admitted as well as chronic patients, totally or only partially institutionalized, males and females, retardates, psychotics, normals, criminal offenders, and so on. Similarly, the types of institutions are quite varied. The programs in some of these extensions of the present method have included formal classes or formal educational procedures as part of the target behavior, indicating the relevance of this approach to the achievement of formal educational objectives as well as for the treatment of behavioral disorders. Since quantitative data has not been forthcoming from these extensions of the present motivating environment at the time of this writing, no definitive evaluation of these extensions can be made at the present time. The evidence from the present program, as well as the initial reports of developments by others, indicates that a start has been made in developing a behaviorist approach to practical problems of therapy, rehabilitation, and learning.

Pure science does not remain pure indefinitely. Sooner or later it is apt to turn into applied science and finally into technology.

Aldous Huxley

APPENDIX: A Reprint

The Measurement and Reinforcement of Behavior of Psychotics[1]

T. AYLLON and N. H. AZRIN

An attempt was made to strengthen behaviors of psychotics by applying operant reinforcement principles in a mental hospital ward. The behaviors studied were necessary and/or useful for the patient to function in the hospital environment. Reinforcement consisted of the opportunity to engage in activities that had a high level of occurrence when freely allowed. Tokens were used as conditioned reinforcers to bridge the delay between behavior and reinforcement. Emphasis was placed on objective definition and quantification of the responses and reinforcers and upon programming and recording procedures. Standardizing the objective criteria permitted ward attendants to administer the program. The procedures were found to be effective in maintaining the desired adaptive behaviors for as long as the procedures were in effect. In a series of six experiments, reinforced behaviors were considerably reduced when the reinforcement procedure was discontinued; the adaptive behaviors increased immediately when the reinforcement procedure was re-introduced.

T. Ayllon and N.H. Azrin, "The Measurement and Reinforcement of Behavior of Psychotics," *J. exp. Anal. Behav.*, 1965, 8, 357–383.

[1] The research reported in this paper was supported in part by the Mental Health Fund and the Psychiatric Training and Research Fund of the Illinois Department of Mental Health, and Grant 4926 from the National Institute of Mental Health. A preliminary report on the social reinforcement program discussed here appeared in the SK&F Psychiatric Reporter, July 1964. The advice and cooperation of Superintendent R. C. Steck, M.D., and the staff of the Anna State Hospital was invaluable to the successful completion of this project. Grateful acknowledgment is given to Stephanie B. Stolz and D.F. Hake for critical reading of this report. Reprints may be obtained from T. Ayllon, Behavior Research Lab., Anna State Hospital, 1000 North Main Street, Anna, Illinois, 62906.

Recent research has pointed to the use of operant conditioning principles to develop voluntary behaviors of humans (Skinner, 1954; Lindsley, 1956; Holland, 1958; Long, Hammond, May, and Campbell, 1958; Ellis, Burnett, and Pryer, 1960; Bijou and Orlando, 1961; Ferster and DeMyer, 1961; Hutchinson and Azrin, 1961; Weiner, 1962; Holz, Azrin, and Ayllon, 1963). Most of the practical clinical applications have been characterized by attention to a single response, use of a single reinforcing stimulus, short and infrequent sessions, implementation by a trained psychologist, and application to a single patient at one time (Flanagan, Goldiamond, and Azrin, 1958; Ayllon and Michael, 1959; Williams, 1959; Isaacs, Thomas, and Goldiamond, 1960; Brady and Lind, 1961; Barrett, 1962; Baer, 1962; Ayllon, 1963; Wolf, Risley, and Mees, 1964). These characteristics possess inherent limitations in solving clinical problems. Limitations of time and expense are less serious than limitations of effectiveness that may result from employing only a single type of reinforcer during infrequent and brief sessions. Possibly the most important limitation for a general technology of behavior is the lack of standardization when scarce professional personnel are required to record behavior, devise procedures and interpret results, all according to criteria that may be subjective and idiosyncratic.

The present study attempted to reinforce many kinds of behavior in mental patients with many kinds of reinforcers. It used a standardized procedure requiring only nonprofessional personnel and covered a large number of patients for long periods of time. This was done in a controlled setting such as that used by Ayllon and Haughton (1962) and Ayllon and Azrin (1964).

METHODOLOGY

Selecting and Defining the Response

Responses were chosen which were necessary or useful to the patient, *e.g.*, serving meals, cleaning floors, and sorting laundry. Some of these are hard to measure objectively. For example, continuous recording of all conversation by all patients is impractical.

Behaviors that produce a fairly permanent, physically identifiable change in environment, *e.g.*, washing dishes, mopping floors, and serving meals can, however, be defined. The net result of washing dishes is obviously the cleanliness of the dishes. Conversation among patients washing dishes may be necessary to the task, but the end product of this communication would be the response to be recorded. To record the selected responses, the environment was arranged so that they could be emitted only at a designated time and place. For example, a mop would be made available only at a specified hour of the day and for a specified duration. Even though continuous recording is impractical, some responses that can be performed at any time, *e.g.*, self-grooming, should be measured continuously. According to the principle of stimulus control, a response is most likely to occur at the anticipated or usual time and place of reinforcement of that response (Ferster and Skinner, 1957). The procedure adopted for such behaviors as self-grooming was to reinforce the response at a specified time and place and to measure the response concurrently with the reinforcement procedure. In this way, if the reinforcement procedure was effective, the record of the response would be obtained at the time and place the response was most likely to occur.

Selecting and Defining the Reinforcer

Only those reinforcing stimuli which could be specified objectively and consistently were selected. An example of this type of reinforcer would be a change of sleeping quarters for the patient. Existing reinforcers were preferred over reinforcers that were not part of the naturalistic context. Effectiveness was the most important consideration in selecting reinforcers.

One of the primary characteristics of psychotic patients is the apparent absence of any effective reinforcers for them. No *a priori* decisions were made about what should be an effective reinforcer. Instead, patients' behavior was used to discover reinforcers. What the patients did, or tried to do, was observed throughout the day when no outside pressures were present. For example, patients might continuously hoard various items under their mattresses, stay at the exit to the ward and try to leave, frequently request special interviews with the social worker or ward psychologist, or push their way into the cafeteria in order to eat before the others.

The general principle expressed by Premack (1959) that any behavior with a high frequency of occurrence can be used as a reinforcer has been verified in almost all operant conditioning studies, especially those involving chained schedules (Kelleher and Gollub, 1962). In accordance with this, behaviors of high natural frequency were arranged as reinforcers by allowing the patients to engage in them at a scheduled time.

The procedure for recording delivery of reinforcers was similar to that for recording responses. Reinforcers were delivered only at specified times and places, and only those that produced enduring changes in the environment were selected, *e.g.*, the opportunity to leave the ward for a walk. The occurrence of such a reinforcer could be easily measured in terms of the presence or absence of the patient on the ward.

Programming

Operant conditioning methodology requires delivery of the reinforcing stimulus immediately after the response. If the response is operating a dishwasher, and the reinforcer is a special interview with the psychologist, delivery of the reinforcer after the response would require that the psychologist be continuously available, a clearly impractical requirement. A conditioned reinforcer was therefore used to bridge the delay between response and reinforcement. It has already been demonstrated, *e.g.*, Kelleher (1957), that a conditioned stimulus can be used to reinforce behavior when it follows the response. The reinforcing stimulus need only be exchangeable later for the conditioned reinforcer. Special metal tokens were used as conditioned reinforcers. Their unique physical characteristics guaranteed that they could not be obtained outside the ward. When the selected response was performed, the attendant gave the token to the patient. The token could be exchanged later during the day or even on subsequent days or weeks for the reinforcing events. Credits, points, merits, money, *etc.*, could have fulfilled the same function.

EXPERIMENTAL EVALUATION

A. Experimental Design

After 18 months of preliminary development, six experiments were conducted to determine the effectiveness of the reinforcement procedure in maintaining the desired behavior. The behavior studied was the performance of work which patients could select from a posted list of jobs.

The first experiment studied the influence of the reinforcement procedure on the patient's choice of jobs from among those within the hospital but outside the ward. The second experiment studied the absolute level of performance on these jobs. The third was similar to the second, but studied performance of jobs on the ward. In Exp. IV, the relationship between the token reinforcers and the other reinforcers was discontinued. The fifth experiment studied the choice of on-ward jobs. Experiment VI studied the effect of the reinforcement procedure and of staff interaction on choice of off-ward jobs.

All experiments followed the A-B-A experimental design in which each subject served as its own control. This eliminated the need to compare patients, and made it possible to take any spontaneous changes into account. During each experiment, the regular incidental activities of the ward were maintained. No change in medication, especially tranquilizers, was initiated, no patients were added or discharged, and no change was made in the ward staff.

This type of research holds several potential sources of variability. One is the interaction between patients and general hospital staff. These influences were minimized because the chronic nature of the patients' illness discouraged various hospital services from including them in activities. Another source of variability is the interaction between patients and their relatives or friends. This was of little or no consequence in this study because such visits averaged fewer than three per year for each patient.

Possible influence of the investigators was minimized by

implementing the reinforcement procedure through attendants who functioned in a standardized manner. Direct interaction between patients and investigators was held to a minimum and consisted primarily of observation.

Preliminary Experiments

Procedures were first tested and revised during a period of 18 months. Definitive evaluation of the method was provided in the six experiments after this period.

Ward Setting. As shown in Figure 1, the ward contained five dormitories, a dining room, a recreation room or day room which adjoined the dining room, a nurse's station, ward offices for the registered nurse and the psychologist, and an examining room.

Special Equipment. To enable the staff to observe activities in the dining room, day room, corridors, and in one of the dormitories, one-way mirrors were placed in three of the rooms. Microphones at several locations permitted monitoring by the staff. They were used only during the first 18 months. Two movable turnstiles (Super Kompak Coinpassor Model #67) regulated entrance and exit into specified areas. The turnstiles were operated by the previously described tokens. The recreation room had a token-operated TV set. Insertion of one token turned the set on for 15 min.

Staff. The ward staff included a physician, a nurse, a psychologist, and the attendants. In addition to her medical duties, the nurse supervised implementation and administration of the behavioral procedures. The attendants carried out the behavioral procedures under

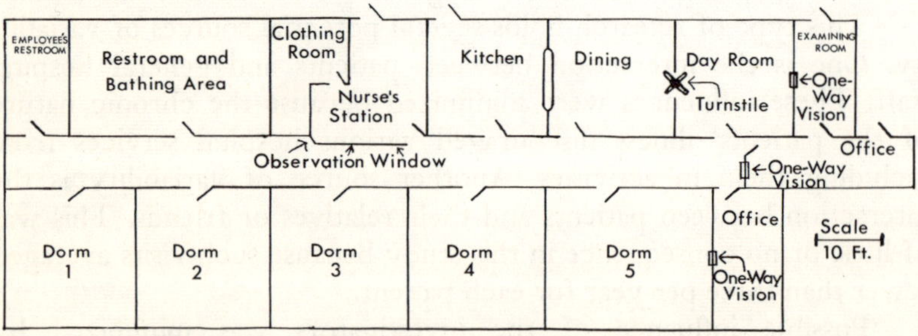

Figure 1 Experimental Ward Floor Plan

the direction of the psychologist and nurse in accordance with verbal and written instructions. An average of two attendants worked the day shift (6:30 a.m.–3:00 p.m.) and afternoon shift (2:30 p.m.–11:00 p.m.). One attendant served the night shift (11:00 p.m.–7:00 a.m.).

Patients. Ward population varied from 43 to 45 female mental patients. Patients not receiving therapy (except for tranquilizers) and who did not have hospital work assignments were selected. Therapy is meant to comprise individual, group, occupational, counseling, rehabilitation, recreational, industrial, shock, insulin, and metrazol therapy. These restrictions resulted in the selection of patients that had been hospitalized for long durations. A secondary criterion excluded any debilitating medical condition which might require periodic confinement to the medical wards.

B. Reinforcement Procedure

Table A–1 describes the types of reinforcers and the number of tokens required for each. The available reinforcers are grouped in six main categories: privacy, leave from the ward, social interaction with staff, devotional opportunities, recreational opportunities, and commissary items.

The privacy reinforcers included five types of items or events that increase or restrict contact with other patients. (1) *Choice of bedroom.* Approximately 7–11 patients were in each of the bedrooms at different times. Each patient could daily choose a bedroom, and, indirectly, her roommates, by exchanging the appropriate number of tokens. The requirement was four tokens for one room, eight for another, 15 for a third, and 30 for still another. The fifth bedroom did not require tokens. Typically, patients who did not select bedrooms were placed in the free room. (2) *Choice of eating group.* The four eating groups for each meal had 5–15 patients in each at different times. All patients who did not select an eating group ate in the last group. (3) *Choice of a personal cabinet.* Each patient could secure daily a locked cabinet in which to store her belongings. (4) *Choice of a personal chair.* In securing a chair and keeping it in her bedroom, each patient avoided sharing the chair or having it appropriated by other patients. (5) *Choice of a*

Table A–1

List of Reinforcers Available for Tokens

	No. of tokens daily
I. Privacy	
Selection of room 1	0
Selection of room 2	4
Selection of room 3	8
Selection of room 4	15
Selection of room 5	30
Personal chair	1
Choice of eating group	1
Screen (room divider)	1
Choice of bedspreads	1
Coat rack	1
Personal cabinet	2
Placebo	1-2
	Tokens
II. Leave from the ward	
20-min walk on hospital grounds (with escort)	2
30-min grounds pass (3 tokens for each additional 30 min)	10
Trip to town (with escort)	100
III. Social interaction with staff	
Private audience with chaplain, nurse	5 min free
Private audience with ward staff, ward physician (for additional time—1 token per min)	5 min free
Private audience with ward psychologist	20
Private audience with social worker	100
	Tokens
IV. Devotional opportunities	
Extra religious services on ward	1
Extra religious services off ward	10
V. Recreational opportunities	
Movie on ward	1
Opportunity to listen to a live band	1
Exclusive use of a radio	1
Television (choice of program)	3
VI. Commissary items	
Consumable items such as candy, milk, cigarettes, coffee, and sandwich	1-5
Toilet articles such as Kleenex, toothpaste, comb, lipstick, and talcum powder	1-10
Clothing and accessories such as gloves, headscarf, house slippers, handbag, and skirt	12-400
Reading and writing materials such as stationery, pen, greeting card, newspaper, and magazine	2-5
Miscellaneous items such as ashtray, throw rug, potted plant, picture holder, and stuffed animal	1-50

room divider. A screen or room divider was typically used to shield the patient's bed and immediate space from view of other patients.

Reinforcers in the second category gave the patient the opportunity to leave the ward with or without an escort. When the patient chose to leave the ward with an escort, her stay was limited. When she chose to leave unescorted, she could extend her stay by exchanging tokens for a corresponding number of minutes. A greater number of tokens permitted visiting the neighboring town with an escort for approximately 1 hr.

Reinforcers in the third category enabled the patient to secure a private audience with a member of the hospital staff. A 10-min private meeting could be extended by exchanging tokens for any additional time desired. No tokens were required for the first 5 min of social interaction with the ward physician, nurse, and hospital chaplain. This unrestricted access was designed to safeguard patient health and well-being.

The fourth category allowed the patient to take active part in religious services of her choice. Access to the weekly religious service, conducted on the ward by the hospital chaplain, was gained through a token-operated turnstile. Religious services off the ward were also available to patients through token exchange.

The fifth category included events and items which allowed the patient to relax in leisure, such as the opportunity to attend movies shown on the ward, to listen to a live band, and to have the exclusive use of a radio or a television set. Hospital-wide activities, such as dances, were also available through the exchange of tokens.

The sixth category of reinforcers consisted of personal belongings, including consumable items, extra clothing and grooming accessories, reading and writing materials, and a choice of items by special request. Among the items requested were stuffed animals, potted plants, a bird cage, a parakeet, and a watch.

C. Token Exchange

Patients could exchange tokens to secure the reinforcement at the commissary and at the nurse's station. Most of the token exchange took place at the commissary. Three times each day (9:30 a.m., 2:00 p.m., 8:30 p.m.), a commissary period was held in the ward dining room. Transactions could be made only during these periods of approximately 45 min. The morning commissary provided only edible and consumable items such as coffee, milk, cigarettes, and newspapers and magazines. The afternoon and evening commissary provided the entire range of items.

To obtain items from the commissary, a patient deposited a token in the turnstile, waited her turn in line, and requested desired items. Under the immediate supervision of an attendant, two patients operated the commissary. One patient made the proper exchanges of tokens and goods, the other recorded the transaction. Patients could obtain as many items as they had tokens for and could make as many trips to the exchange counter as they wished. At the end of the commissary period, the patients who operated the commissary tabulated the number and types of items dispensed and the number of tokens exchanged by each patient. This record was presented to the attendant, who in turn checked it against her own record. Both records were filed to allow cross-checking.

Transactions at the nurse's station concerned renewal of all those items classified as privacy and leave from the ward, and appointments were made to engage in social interaction. An attendant recorded the transaction and the time and name of the individual involved.

EXPERIMENT I

This studied the relationship of the ward reinforcement procedure to the performance of patients on off-ward assignments. In any mental hospital, patients do accept job assignments without any apparent extrinsic reinforcement other than that deriving from some intangible job satisfaction. It is thus unwarranted to conclude that the reinforcement procedure was responsible for maintaining the patients' performance solely from the evidence that the performance occurred and was followed by reinforcement with tokens. For example, when asked why they were working at a particular assignment, patients frequently respond in terms of the attractiveness of the job location, the "nice" people with whom they worked, the satisfying nature of the work itself, or the personal satisfaction derived from being of general benefit to the hospital. It seems reasonable to assume that these uncontrolled reinforcers were acting on the patient. This experiment sought to determine if the uncontrolled reinforcers were responsible for job selection. If the ward reinforcement procedure exerted no greater control than the uncontrolled reinforcers, eliminating the reinforcement should make little difference to job selection. On the other hand, if the ward reinforcement procedure was important, removing the reinforcement should be expected to change job selection. The speed and extent to which patients changed jobs when the reinforcement procedure was changed should provide an index of the strength of the controlled reinforcement relative to the uncontrolled.

Patients

Age, duration of hospitalization, diagnosis, and medication of the eight patients studied are presented in Table A–2. Five were classified as schizophrenic, and three as mental defective. Their mean age was 47 with a range of 33 to 72. The mean duration of continuous hospitalization was nine years. Five were receiving no tranquilizers and three were on a maintenance dosage of phenothiazine derivatives.

Response

The response consisted of the performance of off-ward work assignments. Table A–3 shows the types and numbers of jobs as well as the approximate duration of each and the tokens available per job. Patients were eligible for these jobs upon request. Each job typically required 6 hr of work daily, five days a week, under conditions similar to regular outside employment. Each had a definite starting and quitting time, was performed under supervision, and involved duties that were indispensable for the day-to-day functioning of the hospital. Equivalent duties were being performed by paid hospital personnel with whom the patient worked.

Table A–2

Age, Years of Hospitalization, Diagnosis and Drugs for the Eight Patients Studied in Experiment I

Subject	Age	Years of hospital-ization	Diagnosis	Tranquilizing drugs
S-1	60	5	schizophrenic reaction, hebephrenic type	none
S-2	33	6	mental defective, moderate	phenothiazine derivative
S-3	42	2	mental defective, moderate	none
S-4	37	6	schizophrenic reaction, chronic undifferentiated type	phenothiazine derivative
S-5	72	8	schizophrenic reaction, paranoid type	phenothiazine derivative
S-6	37	8	schizophrenic reaction, chronic undifferentiated type	none
S-7	44	12	mental defective, moderate	none
S-8	55	29	schizophrenic reaction, hebephrenic type	none

Mean Age: 47 Range: 33–72 years
Mean years of hospitalization: 9 Range: 2–29

A printed list of jobs containing a work description and the tokens available at its completion was shown to patients each week. At that time the patient selected a job by contacting the nurse and volunteering for the desired job. The final assignment of jobs was regulated by the supply and demand of volunteers for specific positions. During the initial period of preliminary development, it was found helpful to rotate jobs weekly so that each patient had the opportunity to become familiar with the different jobs.

Table A–3

Types and Number of Off-Ward Jobs

Types of jobs	Number of jobs	Duration	Tokens paid for each job
Dietary worker Helps serve meals for 85 patients and cleans tables after meals.	1	6 hr daily	70
Clerical Types and answers the telephone. Calls hospital personnel to the telephone.	2	6 hr daily	70
Laboratory Cleans cage pans, fills water bottles and cleans floor in laboratory.	2	6 hr daily	70
Laundry Helps to run sheets, pillow cases and towels through mangle at hospital laundry. Also folds linens.	3	6 hr daily	70

Procedure

The automatic job rotation was discontinued for the duration of Exp. I. The patient could engage in a preferred job in contrast to a non-preferred job. Reinforcement was withdrawn from the preferred job and scheduled for the non-preferred job. The basic design was as follows:

	Preferred job	*Non-preferred job*
Phase I	reinforcement	extinction
Phase II	extinction	reinforcement
Phase III	reinforcement	extinction

Each phase consisted of 10 consecutive days. Each patient was given verbal instructions daily by an attendant as follows:

We want you to know that the people you are working for are very pleased with your job and would like you to continue working there. We have a problem though. Other patients want to work there also, but we can't pay them because we have a limited number of tokens for the jobs in the laundry (lab., dietary, office). So to be fair to everyone, we're going to give you a choice: you can continue working in the laundry but you won't get any tokens for it, or you can volunteer for another job where we have tokens available for work. One job that is still open is the dietary (lab., office). Anyone working there gets 70 tokens daily. Now, remember the choice is all yours. Do you want to choose now?

During Phase III, the patient was told by a ward attendant that her current (non-preferred) job no longer paid tokens but that her previous (preferred) job was available for token reinforcement.

Results

Figure 2, for seven of the eight patients, shows that when the reinforcement was shifted from the preferred job to the non-preferred, the shift in performance from the preferred to the non-

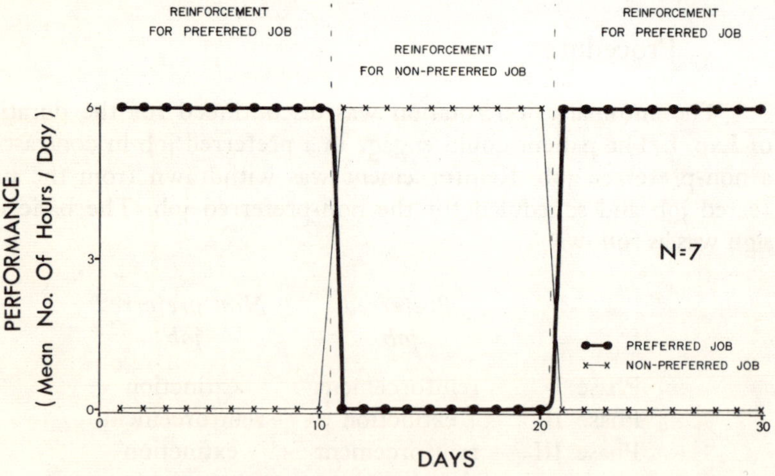

Figure 2 Mean Number of Hours of Performance by Seven of Eight Patients

preferred job was immediate and complete and endured for the entire 10-day period of Phase II. The return to the preferred assignment was equally abrupt and complete when the token reinforcement was reinstated for the preferred assignment on the 20th day.

The results for the eighth patient, S-5, are presented separately in Figure 3, since the experimental design was altered for her. Unlike the other seven patients, S-5 did not shift her job assignment upon the shift in reinforcement. The patient was allowed to remain in the preferred but unreinforced job for an additional time. She did change her choice of job assignment on the 21st day and continued on the non-preferred job to the 30th day. When on the 31st day the reinforcement was changed back to the preferred response, she immediately selected the preferred job.

Initially, several patients had explained their choice of the preferred job assignment on the basis of job satisfaction and social contact. When the non-preferred assignment was reinforced on the 11th day, however, the statements indicated that these uncontrolled reinforcers were not playing an important role. One patient commented: "No, honey, I can't work at the laundry for nothing, I'll work at the lab. I just couldn't make it to pay my rent, if I didn't get paid." Another commented: "You mean if I work at the lab, I won't get paid? I need tokens to buy cigarettes for my boy friend and to buy new clothes so I'll look nice like the other girls." Other

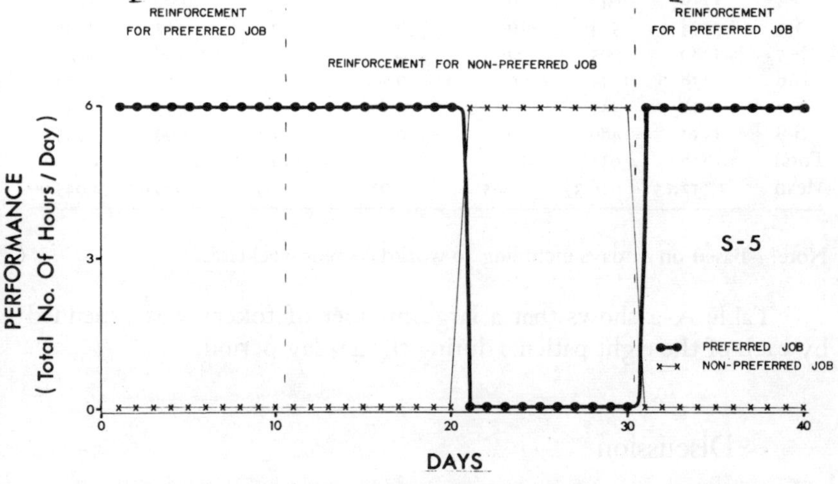

Figure 3 Number of Hours of Performance by One Patient, S-5

comments showed the strength of the token reinforcement relative to any uncontrolled reinforcement.

S-5 said to the attendant: "Doctor ——— needs me and I told him I'd do his typing next week, so I'll keep my work. I can live without tokens." This indication of the strength of the uncontrolled reinforcement was followed by a verbal indication of the ultimately greater strength of the token reinforcement on the 21st day when the patient selected the reinforced job assignment and simultaneously stated to the attendant: "I have finished the work that I promised to do for Doctor ———. I need the tokens and I don't mind working for you, but when I make a promise, I keep it."

Table A–4

Amount of Tokens Exchanged by the Eight Patients Who Worked in Off-Ward Jobs (Experiment I)

Subject	Privacy	Leave from ward	Social inter-action with staff	Devotional opportu-nities	Recrea-tional opportu-nities	Com-missary	Total
S-1	1824	617	20	0	8	691	3160
S-2	842	558	0	0	3	3196	4599
S-3	1716	642	0	0	0	1069	3427
S-4	1794	524	0	0	0	417	2735
S-5	1789	303	0	4	0	108	2204
S-6	278	1253	0	0	0	522	2053
S-7	1021	545	10	1	5	1055	2637
S-8	1554	489	0	0	3	699	2745
Total	10,818	4,931	30	5	19	7,757	23,560
Mean	1,352.25	616.37	3.75	.62	2.37	969.62	2,945.00

Note:—Based on 42 days including 30 workdays plus weekends.

Table A–4 shows that a large number of tokens was expended by each of the eight patients during the 42-day period.

Discussion

The off-ward jobs were performed consistently. All eight patients reported promptly each day for 30 days. Their performance produced no complaints from the supervising employees. No requests were made for a day off or for time off for any reason. This contrasts markedly with the usually erratic and inconsistent performance of patients who voluntarily engage in hospital duties. The patients' verbal statements gave no indication that they were operating under coercion. They appeared to value their job assignments. Although the patients could at any time be free of their job assignment simply by not requesting it at the beginning of the day, no patient did so. The tokens fulfilled their intended function as mediator between the response and the reinforcement.

Preferences for one type of reinforcement over another were highly personal. A large number of events proved to be reinforcing.

The critical test of whether the tokens were conditioned reinforcers occurred when they were no longer provided for the preferred job but were for the non-preferred job. The immediate shift in performance of seven of the eight patients to the non-preferred job is dramatic evidence of the reinforcing properties of the tokens. The return to the preferred job when tokens were again available for it further confirms their effectiveness. The uncontrolled reinforcers provided by the preferred job assignment played a very slight role relative to the token reinforcers. Only one patient failed to change jobs immediately when the token reinforcement was changed from the preferred to the non-preferred job. For this patient, some uncontrolled reinforcement in the job assignment seemed to be evident. The verbal reactions of the patients paralleled their choice of assignment in indicating the strength of the token reinforcement. The results indicate, therefore, that the effect of token reinforcement was greater and more enduring than any uncontrolled reinforcement provided by a particular job assignment.

EXPERIMENT II

Experiment I demonstrated that the token reinforcement procedure determined patients' job choices and overcame any uncontrolled reinforcement inherent in a particular job. The possibility still existed that work was intrinsically reinforcing *per se* and that the reinforcement procedure affected only the selection of jobs.

Patients' statements that they are working because they like to keep active, that they like to contribute something to the hospital, or that "It's not good to be doing nothing" support this possibility. This experiment examined whether patients would cease working when the token reinforcement was discontinued for that work.

Discontinuing the token reinforcement for the job would, however, also terminate the patient-attendant interaction associated with obtaining the token. The experimental design selected, therefore, continued the attendant-patient interaction. The patients were given the usual number of tokens each day by the same attendant. The major difference was that tokens were given at the beginning of the day, before the job, rather than at the end of the day when the job was completed. Thus, the procedure involved non-contingent reinforcement rather than extinction.

Controlled laboratory studies (Skinner, 1938) have demonstrated that behavior that has been immediately reinforced will decline to a near zero level when the reinforcement is delivered on a non-contingent basis. This alters only the temporal dimensions of the response-reinforcement relationship while keeping constant the magnitude and frequency of reinforcement. It made it possible to evaluate the efficacy of the reinforcement without altering the complex patterns of behavior developed by the patients in utilizing the tokens.

Patients

The same eight patients used in Exp I (see Table A–2) were studied.

Response

The response was the same as in Exp I: choice of off-ward job assignment. After Exp I, the automatic job rotation procedure was reinstated for approximately one and one-half months. For the duration of Exp II, only a single job opportunity was made available to each of the eight patients: the job spontaneously selected by the patient during Exp I, *i.e.*, the preferred job.

Procedure

Experiment II lasted 15 days. For the first five days, Phase I, 70 tokens were presented to the patient by the attendant when each day's job assignment was satisfactorily completed. For the next five days, Phase II, the same number of tokens was presented to the patient by the same attendant but before the patient left the ward for the job assignment. On the first day of Phase II, the attendant gave each patient the following instructions:

> This week you are going to receive the usual 70 tokens before you go to work. In a sense, you will be getting a vacation with pay. You'll get your tokens daily even if you don't work. Of course, we're pleased with your work and would like you to continue working.

During this first day, several patients asked if they would receive extra tokens if they did work. Consequently, the instructions on subsequent days of Phase II contained the added statement that "you will not get extra tokens for working." On Days 11–15, the procedure of Phase I was reinstated. On each day of Phase III, the attendant stated to the patient:

> The vacation with pay is over. From now on, you'll receive the usual 70 tokens after you've completed the job.

Results

During Phase I, when reinforcement was contingent upon performance, each patient completed the required 6 hr of work per day without lost time. On the sixth day, when reinforcement was no longer contingent upon performance, all patients stopped working. No work was done during the five days of Phase II.

The patients' comments when the non-contingent reinforcement started were : S-1: "You think I'm crazy to work without extra pay!" S-3: "I'll take the vacation. I can rest and get paid too. How nice." S-6: "Oh boy! Now I can go out on my grounds pass every day."

When reinforcement was again made contingent upon performance (Phase III), the patients immediately began to work the full 6-hr day. The number of hours per day for each patient changed abruptly from 0.0 hr on Day 10 to 6.0 hr on Days 11–15. Some of the comments of the patients on Day 11 were: S-5: "Well, I enjoyed my vacation, but I'm ready to go back to work. I like to keep busy." S-6: "The vacation was nice, but I'll go to work. I need the tokens. I can go out on my grounds pass after work." S-7: "Will we get another vacation next year?"

Discussion

Little or no intrinsic reinforcement for work *per se* existed in the absence of the token reinforcement. Even for the one patient who stated that she liked to keep busy, this subjective tendency did not show in any performance during non-contingent reinforcement. It must be concluded, therefore, that the token reinforcement exerted almost complete control over whether a patient worked.

The absence of performance during non-contingent reinforcement appears to be attributable to the change in the response-reinforcement relationship: the ward procedure remained the same in all essential aspects. The absolute level of patients' performance can be drastically modified by arranging the token reinforcement procedure contingent upon performance.

EXPERIMENT III

Experiments I and II revealed that token reinforcement determined both the selection and performance of off-ward assignments. This experiment attempted to evaluate the effect of the token reinforcement in maintaining the on-ward activities of patients.

Several factors might have made off-ward assignments more sensitive to token reinforcement, *e.g.*, the magnitude of the response requirement. The off-ward assignments consisted of 6 hr of work per day; on-ward assignments were usually less than 1 hr. Further, the small number of tokens (usually fewer than 10) earned for any given on-ward assignment might not have had as much effect as the 70 tokens paid for off-ward assignments. A third factor is the apparently greater adjustment of the patients engaging in off-ward assignments. These patients, on gross observation, appeared to be more verbal, in greater social contact with their environment, and more adaptive to changing circumstances. On the other hand, even casual contact with most of the other patients usually revealed extensive behavioral deficits in both verbal performance and social adjustment. These less-adjusted patients might, therefore, be much less sensitive to the presence or absence of reinforcement than the apparently more-adjusted patients on off-ward assignments. In particular, the reduced level of patients' verbal behavior suggests that they might be less amenable to verbal instructions when the reinforcement contingencies were being altered.

The experimental design was similar to that used in Exp II in that the response-reinforcement relationship was maintained for a time, then removed, then reinstated. The effect of the reinforcement could be evaluated by comparing the on-ward work behavior of the patients when the response-reinforcement relationship was maintained with the time during which the response-reinforcement relationship was eliminated. As in Exp II, reinforcement was maintained but was delivered before instead of after job assignments were performed.

Subjects

The entire ward population of 44 patients served, including the eight patients from Exp I who were eligible for on-ward work on weekends and evenings. As shown in Table A-5, the last diagnosis entered in the hospital records showed 37 schizophrenics, six mental defectives, and one patient suffering from chronic brain syndrome. The mean age was 51 years, with a range of 24–74. The mean length for continuous hospitalization was 16 years, with a range of 1–37. No tranquilizers were given to 27 of the 44 subjects during the investigation. A maintenance dosage of phenothiazine derivatives were administered to the other 17.

Table A–5

Age, Years of Hospitalization, Diagnosis and Drugs for the 44 Patients Studied in Experiment III

Subject	Age	Years of hospitalization	Diagnosis	Tranquilizing drugs
S-1	60	5	schizophrenic reaction, hebephrenic type	none
S-2	33	6	mental defective, moderate	phenothiazine derivative
S-3	42	2	mental defective, moderate	none
S-4	37	6	schizophrenic reaction, chronic undifferentiated type	phenothiazine derivative
S-5	72	8	schizophrenic reaction, paranoid type	phenothiazine derivative
S-6	37	8	schizophrenic reaction, chronic undifferentiated type	none
S-7	44	12	mental defective, moderate	none
S-8	55	29	schizophrenic reaction, hebephrenic type	none
S-9	65	22	schizophrenic reaction, paranoid type	none
S-10	48	27	schizophrenic reaction, catatonic type	phenothiazine derivative
S-11	71	18	schizophrenic reaction, paranoid type	none
S-12	36	13	manic depressive psychosis, mixed type	phenothiazine derivative
S-13	56	1	schizophrenic reaction, paranoid type	none
S-14	58	7	schizophrenic reaction, mixed type	none
S-15	71	27	schizophrenic reaction, hebephrenic type	none
S-16	35	11	schizophrenic reaction, chronic undifferentiated type	none

Table A-5 (continued)

Subject	Age	Years of hospital-ization	Diagnosis	Tranquilizing drugs
S-17	45	10	mental defective, severe with psychotic reaction	none
S-18	55	25	schizophrenic reaction, paranoid type	none
S-19	50	13	schizophrenic reaction, paranoid type	none
S-20	74	37	schizophrenic reaction, chronic undifferentiated type	none
S-21	31	9	schizophrenic reaction, chronic undifferentiated type	phenothiazine derivative
S-22	59	4	schizophrenic reaction, chronic undifferentiated type	none
S-23	41	22	schizophrenic reaction, hebephrenic type	phenothiazine derivative
S-24	24	10	schizophrenic reaction, chronic undifferentiated type	phenothiazine derivative
S-25	37	19	schizophrenic reaction, hebephrenic type	phenothiazine derivative
S-26	61	13	schizophrenic reaction, paranoid type	none
S-27	44	8	schizophrenic reaction, chronic undifferentiated type	phenothiazine derivative
S-28	58	12	schizophrenic reaction, paranoid type	phenothiazine derivative
S-29	59	19	psychosis with syphilitic meningo encephalitis	none
S-30	42	15	schizophrenic reaction, mixed type	phenothiazine derivative

Table A–5 (continued)

Age, Years of Hospitalization, Diagnosis and Drugs for the 44 Patients Studied in Experiment III

Subject	Age	Years of hospitalization	Diagnosis	Tranquilizing drugs
S-31	35	13	schizophrenic reaction, chronic undifferentiated type	phenothiazine derivative
S-32	46	16	schizophrenic reaction, paranoid type	phenothiazine derivative
S-33	39	20	schizophrenic reaction, hebephrenic type	phenothiazine derivative
S-34	47	8	schizophrenic reaction, paranoid type	phenothiazine derivative
S-35	62	29	schizophrenic reaction, catatonic type	none
S-36	61	27	schizophrenic reaction, mixed type	none
S-37	72	11	psychosis with cerebral arteriosclerosis	none
S-38	61	11	mental defective, severe	none
S-39	45	22	schizophrenic reaction, catatonic type	none
S-40	58	33	schizophrenic reaction, hebephrenic type	none
S-41	49	23	schizophrenic reaction, hebephrenic type	none
S-42	55	13	mental defective with psychotic reaction	none
S-43	47	22	schizophrenic reaction, hebephrenic type	phenothiazine derivative
S-44	64	30	schizophrenic reaction, catatonic type	none

Mean age: 51 Range: 24–74 years
Mean years of hospitalization: 16 Range: 1–37 years

Procedure

Experiment III started 30 days after the end of Exp II. During the preliminary period, jobs were rotated as much as possible among the patients. During the experiment, once a patient had signed up for a job, she could not change.

The experiment lasted 60 days. During the first 20 days (Phase I) the patients worked at the job assignments selected. During the next 20 days (Phase II) verbal instructions were read from a printed card by the attendant every day as follows:

> For the next few days you are going to receive your tokens for this work before you go to work. In a sense, you'll be getting a vacation with pay. You'll get your tokens each day whether or not you work. Of course, we are very pleased with your work and would like you to continue working; there will be no extra tokens for work.

Each patient was given the same number of tokens as she had earned during the first 20 days. During Phase III, the tokens were again made contingent upon performance of the on-ward assignment. The instructions read to the patient by the ward attendant were:

> The vacation with pay is over. From now on you will receive the tokens for this job after you have completed the job.

On-Ward Responses

The on-ward jobs available to patients upon request involved duties required for the day-to-day functioning of the ward. Equivalent duties were typically performed by paid hospital personnel (attendants) on other wards. Table A–6 describes the jobs and shows the approximate duration and number of tokens available for each. All jobs were supervised by an attendant, in some cases to make sure that the token transactions at the commissary were appropriate and to provide an independent record of transactions, and in other cases, to make sure a job was properly done. The available jobs were grouped in 11 major categories.

Table A–6

Types and Number of On-Ward Jobs

Types of jobs	Number of jobs	Duration	Tokens paid
Dietary assistant			
1. Kitchen Chores Patient assembles necessary supplies on table. Puts one (1) pat of butter between two (2) slices of bread for all patients. Squeezes juice from fruit left over from meals. Puts supplies away. Cleans table used.	3	10 min	1
2. Coffee Urn Patient assembles cleaning compound and implements. Washes five (5) gallon coffee urn using brush and cleaning compound. Rinses inside, washes and dries outside. Puts implements away.	1	10 min	2
3. Ice Carrier Patient goes with attendant to area adjacent to ward where ice machine is located taking along ten (10) gallon ice container. Scoops flaked ice from machine into container and carries it to the kitchen.	1	10 min	2
4. Shakers Patient assembles salt, sugar and empty shakers on table, fills shakers and puts supplies away.	2	10 min	2
5. Pots and Pans Patient runs water into sink, adds soap, washes and rinses all pans used for each meal. Stacks pans and leaves them to be put through automatic dishwasher.	3	10 min	6
6. Steam Table Patient assembles cleaning supplies. Washes and dries all compartments used for food. Cleans and dries outside of table. Places all pans in proper place on steam table.	3	10 min	5

Table A–6 (continued)

Types of jobs	Number of jobs	Duration	Tokens paid
7. Meal Server [a] Patient puts food into proper compartments on steam table. Assembles paper napkins and silver on counter placed at beginning of serving line, puts tablecloths, napkins, salt and sugar shakers on tables. Prepares proper beverage for each meal putting ice in glasses for cold beverages and drawing coffee from urn. Prepares proper utensils for dirty dishes and garbage. Dips food, places food and beverage on trays. Gives patients their trays. After the meal is over Dietary workers empty all leftover food and garbage, places all trays, glasses and silver used on cabinets ready for the dishwasher.	6	60 min	10
8. Dishwasher [a] Patient prepares dishwater, fills automatic dishwasher. Washes dishes, silver and glasses. Operates automatic dishwasher, washes cabinets, sinks and tables and puts everything away. Patient counts silver (knives, forks and spoons) for all patients and places them in containers ready for next meal.	9	45 min	17
Waitress			
1. Meals Empties trays left on tables and washes tables between each of four (4) meal groups.	6	10 min	2
2. Commissary Cleans tables, washes cups and glasses used at commissary. Places cups and glasses in rack ready for automatic dishwasher.	3	10 min	5

Table A–6 (continued)

Types and Number of On-Ward Jobs

Types of jobs	Number of jobs	Duration	Tokens paid
Sales clerk assistant			
1. Commissary [a] Assembles commissary items. Displays candy, cigarettes, tobacco, cosmetics, dresses and other variety store items so that they can be seen by all. Prepares ice, glasses and cups for hot and cold beverages. Asks patient what she wishes to buy. Collects the tokens from patient and tells the secretary the name of the patient and the amount spent. Puts commissary supplies away.	3	30 min	3
Secretarial assistant			
1. Tooth Brushing [a] Assists with oral hygiene. Writes names of patients brushing teeth.	1	30 min	3
2. Exercises [a] Assists recreational assistant with exercises. Writes names of patients participating in exercises.	2	30 min	3
3. Commissary [a] Assists sales clerk assistant. Writes names of patients at commissary, records number of tokens patient spent. Totals all tokens spent.	3	30 min	5
Ward cleaning assistant			
1. Halls and Rooms Sweep and mop floors, dust furniture and walls in seven rooms and hall.	24	30 min	3
2. Special Cleans after incontinent patients.	1	30 min	4
3. Dormitories [a] Supplies each of five dormitories with the necessary cleaning implements.	1	180 min	8

Table A–6 (continued)

Types of jobs	Number of jobs	Duration	Tokens paid
Fills buckets with cleaning water and delivers bucket of water, broom, mop and dust pan to each dormitory at a designated time. Picks up cleaning supplies and implements after a 30-min interval.			
Assistant janitor			
1. Supplies	1	10 min	1
Places ward supplies in supply cabinets and drawers.			
2. Trash	3	5 min	2
Carries empty soft drink bottles to storage area, empties waste paper baskets throughout the ward and carries paper to container adjacent to building. Carries mops used during the day outside to dry.			
3. Porch [a]	2	10 min	2
Sweeps and washes walk adjacent to building. Washes garbage cans with soap and water.			
4. Washroom Janitor	1	20 min	3
Obtains necessary cleaning supplies and implements from utility room. Cleans four wash basins and four toilet bowls with cleanser and brush. Returns cleaning supplies and implements to utility room.			
Laundry assistant			
1. Hose	1	15 min	1
Match and fold clean anklets and stockings.			
2. Delivery	1	10 min	2
Carries bags of dirty clothing and linens from ward to outside linen house adjacent to building.			
3. Folding [a]	2	30 min	3
Folds and stacks clean linens in neat			

Table A-6 (continued)

Types and Number of On-Ward Jobs

Types of jobs	Number of jobs	Duration	Tokens paid
stacks and takes it to the clothing room.			
4. Pick Up Service [a] Sorts dirty clothing and linens and puts items into bags marked for each item.	1	60 min	8
Grooming assistant			
1. Clothing Care Patient sets up ironing board and iron. Irons clothing that belongs to patients other than self. Folds clothing neatly. Returns ironed clothing, iron and ironing board to nurses station.	1	15 min	1
2. Personal Hygiene [a] Patient takes basket with grooming aids, gargle, paper cups, lipstick, comb, hairbrush and powder into patients' washroom. Patient stays with grooming basket and assists any who need help with their grooming before each meal. Returns grooming basket after the meal has ended.	3	60 min	3
3. Oral Hygiene [a] Assembles toothpaste, toothbrushes, gargle solution and paper cups. Pours gargle into cups and dispenses toothpaste or gargle to all patients.	1	20 min	3
4. Personal [a] Patient assists selected patients who need extra aid with personal grooming.	1	30 min	3
5. Bath [a] Patient assists with baths, washing,	2	45 min	4

Table A–6 (continued)

Types of jobs	Number of jobs	Duration	Tokens paid
shampooing and drying. Cleans tub after each bath.			
6. Beauty Aids [a] Assists in shampooing, setting and combing hair for patients who desire special service.	1	30 min	4
Recreational assistant			
1. Walks [a] Assists ward staff when taking group of patients on walks. Walks in front of group.	1	20 min	3
2. Exercise [a] Operates record player and leads patients in exercises.	1	20 min	3
3. Movie Projectionist Sets up movie projector and shows movie to patients. Changes reels and rewinds tape.	1	90 min	10
Special services			
1. Errands Leaves the ward on official errands throughout the hospital grounds, delivering messages and picking up supplies and records pertaining to the ward.	1	20 min	6
2. Tour Guide Gives visitors a 15-min tour of the ward explaining about the activities and token system. Answers visitors' questions about the ward.	1	15 min	10
3. Nursing Assistant [a] Assists staff with the preparation of patients to be seen by the medical doctor. Assists staff with the control of undesired interaction between patients.	1	10 min	10

Table A–6 (continued)

Types and Number of On-Ward Jobs

Types of jobs	Number of jobs	Duration	Tokens paid
Self-care activities			
1. Grooming Combs hair, wears: dress, slip, panties, bra, stockings and shoes (three times daily).			1
2. Bathing Takes a bath at time designated for bath. (once weekly)			1
3. Tooth Brushing Brushes teeth or gargles at the time designated for tooth brushing. (once daily)			1
4. Exercises Participates in exercises conducted by the exercise assistant. (twice daily)			1
5. Bed Making Makes own bed and cleans area around and under bed.			1

[a] Job requires two or more patients for its completion.

Dietary assistant. Patients helped distribute food, clean and maintain the ward kitchen, usually interacting socially with other patients.

Waitress. Patients washed dishes, cups, and glasses, and cleaned dining room tables after meals and commissary.

Sales clerk. Patients organized and arranged all the necessary items for exchange at commissary. This required considerable social skills since the clerk had to wait on patients, count the tokens received from each and interact appropriately with the commissary assistant to complete the job properly.

Secretarial assistant. Patients recorded the names of all patients attending a scheduled activity. This required skills such as following instructions, reading, writing, and sometimes, addition and subtraction. Patients performing these jobs had to know every patient by their last name. These jobs took place at a designated time and place under the continuous supervision of an attendant.

Ward cleaning assistant. Patients supplied each dormitory with mops, buckets, and brooms so that others could use them to clean their own rooms. They also swept and cleaned the ward and helped to care for a few patients who were incontinent.

Assistant janitor. The patient cleaned and maintained the ward and adjacent area, using ordinary housekeeping skills.

Laundry assistant. The patient helped collect soiled laundry and supply and distribute clean laundry. Skills in counting, folding linen, and clothing in general are necessary for these jobs.

Grooming assistant. Patients helped to wash, dress and groom other patients.

Recreational assistant. Patients helped to supervise scheduled leisure activities. Social interaction with patients and skill in operating a movie projector and record player are necessary for the satisfactory performance of these jobs.

Special services. Patients went on errands, conducted tours for visitors, and helped to prepare other patients for nursing care.

Self-care. The patient improved and maintained her own appearance and hygiene, wore clothing appropriately, washed and combed her hair, bathed, brushed her teeth, took part in light physical exercises, and made her bed, cleaning the area adjacent to it. The patients who helped in this were reinforced for helping. All patients could obtain tokens for self-care.

Approximately half the jobs could be performed by one person; the other half required cooperation among two or more persons. Tokens available for each job depended on supply and demand. For example, the janitor work took 180 min each day, but received only eight tokens, since many patients were interested in this job. On the other hand, the dishwasher worked 45 min but earned 17 tokens, since fewer patients wanted this job.

Results

Figure 4 presents the total hours of work performed by the 44 patients during each of the 60 days, based upon the approximate

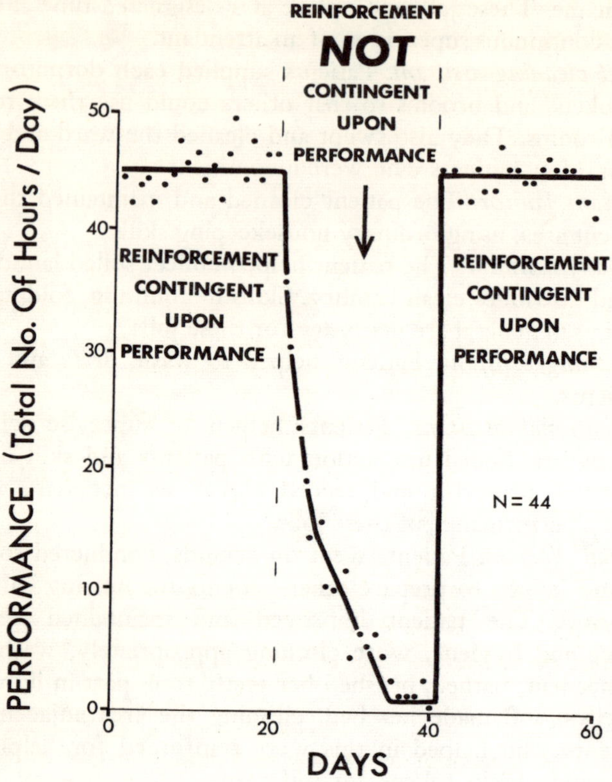

Figure 4 The Total Number of Hours of the On-Ward Performance by a Group of 44 Patients, Exp III

duration of each job assignment as specified in Table 6, excluding self-care.

During Days 1–20, about 45 hr were spent each day performing job assignments. On the first day that the tokens were not contingent upon performance, the amount of work decreased to about 35 hr. On the third day, it decreased to about 20 hr, and by Day 36, had dropped to only 1 hr per day. When the tokens were again made contingent upon performance on Day 41, the time spent on job assignments increased immediately to 45 hr, approximating the level during the first 20 days. Performance was maintained at about 45 hr for the next 20 days (Days 41–60).

Table A–7 shows that the responding of each patient decreased substantially when the reinforcement was not contingent on the responses, and increased substantially when reinforcement was again contingent. This was not true for those patients who began with a zero level of performance. A near-zero level of performance of

Table A–7

Performance of the Patients After Response-Reinforcement Relations Were Altered (Exp III)

	From contingent to non-contingent reinforcement	From non-contingent to contingent reinforcement
Number of patients showing an increase in performance.	0	36
Number of patients showing a decrease in performance.	36	0
Number of patients showing zero minutes of performance.	8	8
Total number of patients.	44	44

Note:—Based on the terminal five days for each phase.

eight patients was not altered by the changes in the reinforcement contingency. The remaining 36 patients showed reduced performance during the noncontingent reinforcement, and a substantial increase when the reinforcement was again made contingent.

Table A–8 shows the number of tokens earned and spent during the first 20 days of Exp III. The number received during Days 21–40 and Days 41–60 was very similar and is not shown. During the 20-day period about 21,000 tokens were earned and spent, averaging about 500 per patient. The number earned within the 20-day period was rarely equal to the number spent for any given patient. Patients often accumulated large numbers of tokens to make a desired exchange, and also would often lend or borrow tokens.

All patients earned and spent tokens. Of the 44 patients, 36 earned tokens from on-ward or off-ward assignments and for self-

Table A–8

Number of Tokens Earned and Spent by the 44 Patients Studied in Experiment III

Subject	Tokens earned for: Off-ward jobs	On-ward jobs	Self-care	Total tokens earned	Tokens spent
S-7	1015	789	90	1894	1873
S-2	805	730	84	1619	2351
S-5	910	369	117	1396	999
S-3	1190	44	39	1273	1794
S-8	980	120	92	1192	2127
S-1	910	191	81	1182	1424
S-9	00	1032	142	1174	1189
S-6	1050	00	66	1116	938
S-22	00	954	88	1042	753
S-4	875	00	95	970	1165
S-34	00	763	89	852	741
S-35	00	770	73	843	325
S-26	455	269	93	817	995
S-32	00	577	63	640	553
S-14	00	409	113	522	227
S-21	00	392	24	416	269
S-30	00	196	123	319	221
S-19	00	231	83	314	310
S-13	00	263	9	272	166
S-33	00	232	19	251	118
S-36	00	167	74	241	170
S-40	00	126	90	216	673
S-17	00	108	96	204	237
S-39	00	141	43	184	221
S-38	00	68	115	183	82
S-27	00	91	90	181	337
S-44	00	29	143	172	205
S-20	00	162	7	169	70
S-15	00	71	91	162	39
S-24	00	38	111	149	176
S-18	00	30	115	145	152
S-12	00	91	49	140	86
S-16	00	40	67	107	74
S-11	00	00	89	89	87

Table A–8 (continued)

Subject	Tokens earned for: Off-ward jobs	On-ward jobs	Self-care	Total tokens earned	Tokens spent
S-43	00	48	39	87	121
S-31	00	00	85	85	1
S-37	00	00	85	85	47
S-25	00	4	69	73	37
S-10	00	00	44	44	3
S-42	00	15	23	38	32
S-29	00	00	36	36	5
S-23	00	00	30	30	23
S-28	00	00	28	28	2
S-41	00	00	15	15	1
Total	8,190	9,560	3,217	20,967	21,419
Mean	186.14	217.36	73.11	476.61	486.79
Range:	0-1,190	0-1,032	7-143	15-1,894	1-2,351

Note:—Based on the first period of 20 days of contingent reinforcement.

care. Of these 36 patients, 18 earned more than 300 tokens, the other 18 more than 80. Eight patients earned tokens only for self-care. They were relatively unaffected by the reinforcement program in terms of job assignments.

Earnings for off-ward assignments accounted for almost half of total earnings, whereas earnings for self-care accounted for only about 15 per cent of the total. Although the reinforcement for self-care was initiated to maintain a minimum standard of cleanliness and personal hygiene, changes in the reinforcement contingencies produced no appreciable difference in self-care practices. The reduction in self-care during the non-contingent reinforcement procedure was no more than 10 per cent.

The patients' comments paralleled the change in their work performance. Several patients continued working during the first few days of non-contingent reinforcement and made statements such as: "I think I'll work even if it is a vacation," or: "I want to help out here; there aren't enough people to do the work." Yet during the successive deliveries of the token reinforcement before each job with no extra tokens upon completion of the job, each patient gradually stopped performing the job assignments. A frequent comment during the latter stages of the non-contingent reinforcement was: "I'm not going to do any work if I don't get anything for it." When an attendant encouraged one patient to work, the patient replied: "Not if I don't get any extras, I won't."

Discussion

The on-ward work was not maintained without contingent token reinforcement. Patients were sensitive to the response-reinforcement relationship in spite of the fact that many had extremely low IQ's, a severe state of psychosis, and often a minimal level of verbal comprehension. The changes in verbal behavior paralleled those in Exp I and II. Although the patients frequently indicated that they had some intrinsic interest in their work, they showed a fairly strong lack of interest if no additional tokens were to be provided.

The change in the response-reinforcement relationship was effective in decreasing or terminating the patients' previously reinforced behavior. The need to maintain the response-reinforcement relationship was, therefore, general and not idiosyncratic to particular patients. For the eight patients who began with no behavior, no decrease in performance could result from the non-contingent reinforcement. Their only reinforced performances were in the self-care category. However, the self-care behaviors for all patients did not change appreciably when the tokens were made non-contingent. The reason for this is not known.

The present experiment, together with Exp II, demonstrated that reinforcement must be contingent upon desired performance, on-ward or off-ward, if the strength of that performance is to be maintained.

EXPERIMENT IV

The previous experiments attempted to ascertain the effect of the token reinforcement procedure by delivering tokens for an alternative non-preferred response or by delivering them independently of behavior. In this experiment, the tokens were removed from circulation while the events hitherto used for reinforcement were made freely available to the patients. The absence of tokens, combined with the free availability of reinforcers, approximates the usual manner in which mental hospital wards are managed.

After Exp III, the usual token reinforcement procedure was reinstated for approximately 45 days. Patients signed up for on-ward job assignments, and tokens were given immediately after the assignments were successfully completed.

Patients

Forty one of the 44 patients studied had also participated in Exp III. Of the remaining three patients in Exp III, two had been discharged from the hospital, and one had been transferred off the ward because of a chronic physical illness. Three new patients were added to the ward at least 21 days before Exp IV, sufficient time for them to function under the token reinforcement procedure. Their

Table A–9

Age, Years of Hospitalization, Diagnosis and Drugs for the Three Patients Who Replaced S-3, S-7 and S-29 During Experiment IV

Subject	Age	Years of hospitalization	Diagnosis	Tranquilizing drugs
S-45	31	2	schizophrenic reaction, chronic undifferentiated type	phenothiazine derivative
S-46	55	31	schizophrenic reaction, catatonic type	phenothiazine derivative
S-47	37	17	schizophrenic reaction, mixed type	phenothiazine derivative

Note:—See Table 8 for information on the number of tokens received and spent by S-3, S-7 and S-29.

diagnosis, medication, and years of hospitalization are presented in Table A–9. It can be seen from this and Table A–5 that the characteristics of the three new patients did not differ considerably from many of the other 41 patients.

Procedure

The present study was concerned with performance of the on-ward jobs described in Table A–6. As in the previous experiments, the automatic job rotation procedure was discontinued for the duration.

The experiment lasted 45 days. During the first 15 days, the token reinforcement was given immediately upon satisfactory completion of the performance, and the tokens could be exchanged for the various reinforcers. From Day 16 to 30, all tokens were removed from the ward, except for those in the personal possession of the patients. Upon completion of any job assignment no tokens were given to the patient. The various reinforcing events were made freely available to all patients, and tokens could not be used to obtain any of the reinforcers. All patients could go on a walk, have private talks with the staff, go to the dances and have their choice of the various commissary items. On the first day that the tokens were discontinued, the attendants gave the following instructions to each patient:

> For the next couple of weeks or so, we are going to have an inventory of all the tokens on the ward. This means that we are going to spend a lot of our time counting all of the tokens that we have in our office. During this time we will not be giving tokens for work on the ward, and also, there won't be any need for you to exchange tokens. Everyone will stay in the same sleeping rooms and the same eating groups that they are in right now. If you have a grounds pass, you can keep using it without having to exchange tokens for it. Commissary items will be available free; so you won't need any tokens for that either. Now, it is up to you if you want to continue working. We won't have any tokens to give you for it.

On Day 31, the standard token reinforcement procedure was reinstated, and the following instructions were given to each patient by the ward attendant.

The inventory period is over. We have finished counting the tokens that we had in our office. From now on you'll receive the usual tokens as soon as you have completed your jobs.

The job made available to each patient was the one she had before the tokens were discontinued.

Results

Figure 5 shows the number of hours of work per day during the 45-day experimental period. For the first 15 days, under the usual token reinforcement, about 45 hr of work was performed each day. While the token reinforcement was discontinued (Days 16–

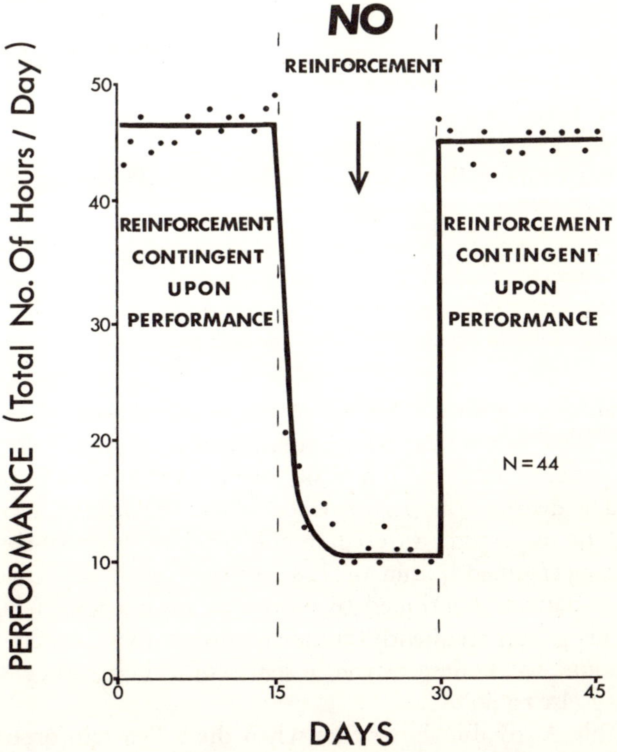

Figure 5 The Total Number of Hours of On-ward Performance by a Group of 44 Patients, Exp IV

30), the hours of performance dropped rapidly to less than one-fourth the previous level, apparently stabilizing at about 10 or 11 hr per day. On the 31st day, when the token reinforcement procedure was reinstated, performance increased immediately to its previous level of approximately 45 hr per day.

Table A–10

Performance of the Patients After Response-Reinforcement Relations Were Altered (Exp IV)

	No token reinforcement	Reinstatement of token reinforcement
Number of patients showing an increase in performance.	0	36
Number of patients showing a decrease in performance.	36	0
Number of patients showing zero minutes of performance.	8	8
Total number of patients.	44	44

Note:—Based on the terminal five days for each phase.

Table A–10 shows that all 36 patients who had job assignments worked less when the token reinforcements were discontinued. Eight patients had no job assignment. Although all 36 patients showed a decrease in performance when the tokens were discontinued, the magnitude differed among patients. Twenty-six of the 36 patients performed 5 min or less of work each day. Each of the other 10 patients continued to work for an average of 60 min per day. This group frequently commented that they preferred to perform some work despite the absence of tokens, since there was "nothing else to do".

Table A–10 also shows that when the token reinforcement procedure was reinstated, all 36 patients who had been working increased their performance.

Discussion

The virtually complete elimination of the tokens from the ward reduced performance of all patients. These results, together with the findings of Exp I, II, and III, show that the token reinforcement procedure was indeed effective in maintaining performance as compared with either reinforcement for an alternative response, token reinforcement independent of responses, or no token reinforcement.

One puzzling aspect of the results was that performance did not reach the near-zero level in the complete absence of tokens as it had in Exp III, when tokens were delivered independently of behavior. Ten patients out of 36 continued working in the absence of tokens, albeit at a reduced level. The patients' comments suggested that staff-patient interaction during the exchange of tokens might have been an important consideration. In Exp III, patients may have been receiving some type of social reinforcement when the ward attendant gave them the tokens. In the present experiment, however, no such reinforcement could take place because the procedure eliminated token transactions. It is possible that the absence of social interaction with the attendants during token transaction deprived the patients of social reinforcement. In an attempt to obtain it they performed their job assignments. The job assignments were supervised by an attendant and always involved some patient-attendant interaction. Whatever the nature of the reinforcement, there did seem to exist some level of uncontrolled reinforcement for these 10 patients to continue to perform their job assignments. This continued performance in the absence of token reinforcement provided an excellent opportunity to ascertain the strength of this uncontrolled reinforcement.

EXPERIMENT V

Ten patients from Exp IV had been freely selecting job assignments each day without interruption for a period of 45 days. This experiment examined whether the token reinforcement procedure would be strong enough to cause the patients to discontinue their long-standing preferred job assignment and to select a non-preferred job. The general procedure was similar to that used in Exp I, which was concerned with the off-ward rather than on-ward job assignments. The patient was given a choice between the preferred job, which provided few tokens, and a non-preferred job that provided a large number of tokens.

Patients

The 10 patients from Exp IV who had continued with their preferred job assignment in the absence of token reinforcement were used. Table A–11 shows their psychiatric classification, age, years of hospitalization, and tranquilizing medication. Nine were classified as schizophrenic and one as mental defective. The average age was 56 and the average duration of continuous hospitalization was 15 years. Seven of the patients received no tranquilizers; the other three received phenothiazine derivatives on a maintenance dosage.

Procedure

Immediately after Exp IV, the token reinforcement procedure was reinstated for all 44 patients for the job assignment each patient had been performing at the start of Exp IV. For the 10 patients considered here, a choice was offered between this preferred job and a second, non-preferred job that required an equivalent amount of time. One token was provided for performing the non-preferred job whereas an average of 83 tokens was provided for the preferred job. On the seventh day the token contingencies were reversed. On the 13th day the token contingencies were returned to the original status. The total experimental period was 18 days. The patients were told the number of tokens each day as they signed up for their job assignments and were offered a choice of one or the other job assignment, never both. The ward attendants informed patients verbally of the changing number of tokens for the two assignments.

Table A–11

Age, Years of Hospitalization, Diagnosis and Drugs for the 10 Patients Studied in Experiment V

Subject	Age	Years of hospital-ization	Diagnosis	Tranquilizing drugs
S-5	72	8	schizophrenic reaction, paranoid type	phenothiazine derivative
S-9	65	22	schizophrenic reaction, paranoid type	none
S-13	56	1	schizophrenic reaction, paranoid type	none
S-14	58	7	schizophrenic reaction, mixed type	none
S-17	45	10	mental defective, severe with psychotic reaction	none
S-22	59	4	schizophrenic reaction, chronic undifferentiated type	none
S-32	46	16	schizophrenic reaction, paranoid type	phenothiazine derivative
S-33	39	20	schizophrenic reaction, hebephrenic type	phenothiazine derivative
S-35	62	29	schizophrenic reaction, catatonic type	none
S-40	58	33	schizophrenic reaction, hebephrenic type	none

Mean age: 56 Range: 39–72 years
Mean years of hospitalization: 15 Range: 1–33 years

During Phase I the instructions given to each of the patients, individually, were:

As you know we have patients who would like to change jobs from time to time. This week we have several people who are interested in the same job you're doing. Since we want to be fair, we would like to give you the choice to keep your job or to get another job. Now you should know that your present job will pay 80 tokens. We have a second job which is ________, and that pays one token. Which do you want?

During Phase II, the instructions given to each patient were modified as follows to indicate the change in the number of tokens offered:

. . . your present job will pay one token. We have a second job which is ________ that pays 80 tokens. Which one do you want?

During Phase III, the procedure reinstated the greater token reinforcement for the preferred job and the smaller one for the non-preferred job.

Results

Figure 6 shows the duration of performance on the preferred and non-preferred job assignments for nine of the 10 patients. The tenth patient is considered separately. For the first six days these nine patients worked exclusively on the preferred job, which earned

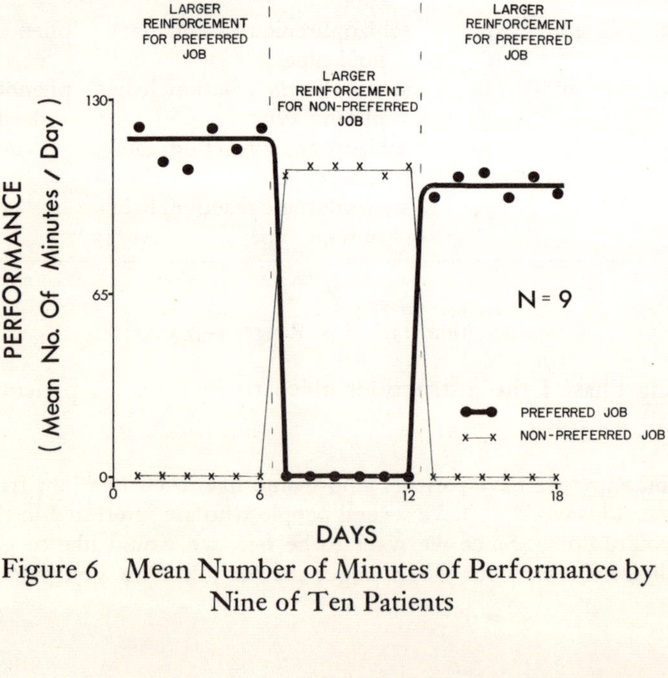

Figure 6 Mean Number of Minutes of Performance by Nine of Ten Patients

the larger number of tokens. On Day 7, when the larger number of tokens was earned on the non-preferred job assignment, the nine patients worked exclusively on the non-preferred job for Days 7–12. On Day 13, when the larger number of tokens was again earned by the preferred assignment, these patients immediately selected the preferred jobs and continued on them for the duration of the experiment.

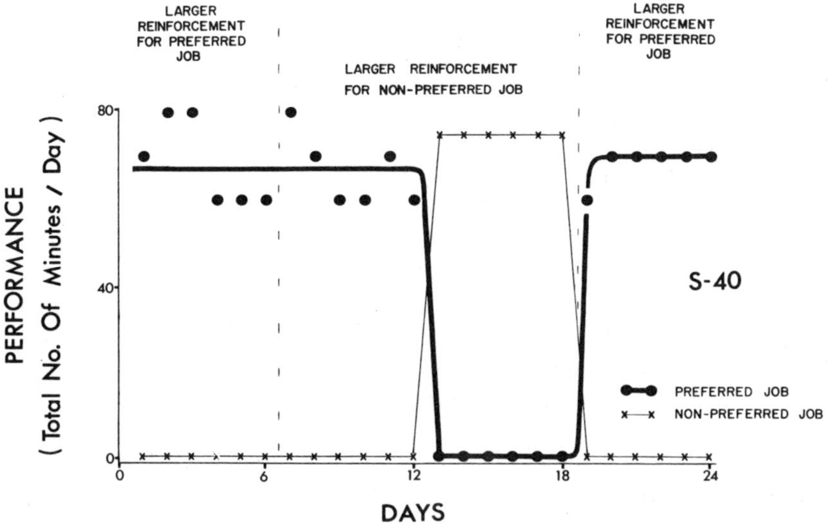

Figure 7 Total Number of Minutes of Performance by One Patient, S-40

The tenth patient continued working on the preferred job with the smaller number of tokens from Day 7–12. (See Figure 7) On Day 13, she changed to the non-preferred job. During an additional five days in which the preferred job earned fewer tokens, this patient continued to select the non-preferred job with its larger number of tokens. On Day 19, the contingency was reversed. The patient immediately selected the preferred job assignment and continued with it for the duration of the experiment.

Discussion

All patients discontinued their preferred job despite a long-standing preference. Both jobs were of the same duration, and both provided the opportunity for social reinforcement associated with the token exchange. The choice of jobs was determined by the relative number of tokens, and not by any reinforcement intrinsic to the job.

EXPERIMENT VI

Experiments I–V found that performance was reduced or eliminated when the response-reinforcement relationship was changed, and returned when the response-reinforcement was reinstated. In each case, the change in the response-reinforcement relationship was indicated by the attendant's spoken instructions to the patients. Orally conveyed instructions are difficult to standardize. They may convey some unintended cue. The attendant's intonation or facial expression may lead the patient to believe that she should stop or start working. The present experiment attempted to replicate the procedure of Exp I with a similar number of patients, using written, rather than spoken, communication.

Patients

The five patients in this experiment had participated in Exp I. Of the other three patients in Exp I, one had a heart condition that precluded a full day's work, and the other two had been discharged from the hospital.

Procedure

The present experiment was conducted two months after Exp V and lasted 15 days. Each patient was given a choice of job assignments typed on the assignment sheet, which she carried when reporting to her assignment each morning. The assignment sheet told the patient where to report and the number of tokens that would be earned for that job. One of the assignments was the preferred job as ascertained by the patient's selection during the preceding two-week period. The second job was of equivalent duration but had not been selected by the patient during the preceding two weeks. For Days 1–5, 70 tokens could be earned for the preferred job assignment and none for the non-preferred job assignment. For Days 6–10, no tokens were listed for the preferred, 70 for the non-preferred job. On days 11–15, the numbers were again reversed. At the time each patient picked up her assignment sheet from the nurse's station in the morning, she notified the attendant of her selection; the attendant recorded the information but did not reply in any way. When the patient asked the attendant what the change in numbers meant, the attendant replied, "Whatever it says on the assignment sheet."

Results

The results were almost identical to those of Exp I. All five patients discontinued the preferred job when tokens were reduced from 70 to 0. All resumed working at the preferred job when the number of tokens for that job was returned to 70. The shift in performance was immediate for four of the five patients. The fifth patient did not notice that the number of tokens had changed, and on the sixth day completed a full day's work. After she discovered that no tokens were scheduled for that job, she selected the non-preferred job assignment. On the 11th day, all patients immediately shifted to the job assignment that earned 70 tokens.

Discussion

Oral instructions played no major role in determining the choice of job assignment. Even when the change in the number of tokens was indicated only in written numerical form, the change in performance was immediate and complete. It must be concluded, therefore, that the choice of jobs as well as the degree of performance was governed by the token reinforcement procedure and not by the oral instructions of the attendants. This finding agrees with previous results (Ayllon and Azrin, 1964) which showed that instructions had no enduring or consistent effect in modifying adaptive behavior of chronic mental patients unless the instructions were accompanied by favorable consequences for following them. Yet it would be incorrect to assume that verbal instructions were unnecessary. The same study showed that instructions provided important discriminative stimuli for initiating behavior: "By utilizing the existing verbal repertoire of humans, the instructions elminate the necessity of arduous and impractical shaping procedures such as must be used with animals" (Ayllon and Azrin, p. 330). For this reason the present reinforcement program used verbal instructions wherever possible to initiate behavior that could then be reinforced.

CONCLUSION

The results of the six experiments demonstrate that the reinforcement procedure was effective in maintaining desired performance. In each experiment, the performance fell to a near-zero level when the established response-reinforcement relation was discontinued. On the other hand, reintroduction of the reinforcement procedure restored performance almost immediately and maintained it at a high level for as long as the reinforcement procedure was in effect. The reinforcement procedure effectively maintained performance both on and off the experimental ward. The standard procedure for reinforcement had been to provide tokens contingent upon the desired performance and to allow exchange of the tokens for a variety of reinforcers. Performance decreased when this response-reinforcement relation was disrupted (1) by delivering tokens independently of the response while still allowing exchange of tokens for the reinforcers (Exp II and III), (2) by discontinuing the token system entirely but providing continuing access to the reinforcers (Exp IV), or (3) by discontinuing the delivery of tokens for a previously reinforced response while simultaneously providing tokens for a different, alternative response (Exp I and VI). Further, the effectiveness of the reinforcement procedure did not appear to be limited to an all-or-none basis. Patients selected and performed the assignment that provided the larger number of tokens when reinforcement was available for more than one assignment (Exp V).

A major problem in designing the reinforcement procedure was to discover reinforcers for chronic mental patients. The principle adopted was to use as reinforcers the opportunity to engage in behaviors that already existed in high strength. This allowed wide differences in personal preferences and changing interests. Such diverse events as leave from the ward, a personal screen for privacy, an extra opportunity to speak with the chaplain, choice of chair, etc., have never before been systematically utilized in patient treatment. Yet the frequency of usage of these events indicates that they constitute a relatively strong, albeit untapped, source of motivation for mental patients.

Since the reinforcers were based on existing behavior, the number of reinforcing events for a given patient depended on that patient's level of existing behavior. For the great majority of these patients, behaviors of some sort could be identified and programmed as a reinforcer. Table A–8 shows that half of the patients expended more than 200 tokens and as many as 2400 tokens within 20 days. For these patients, the reinforcers were being actively and continually used as a means of motivation. Eight patients, who expended fewer than 50 tokens within 20 days, all earned by self-care rather than from job assignments, were relatively unaffected by the reinforcement procedure. Statistical comparison of them with the other patients revealed no difference in diagnosis or age. It appears that their failure to modify behavior appreciably stemmed from the relative absence of any strong behavior patterns that could be used as reinforcers. The only two behaviors that existed in strength were sleeping and eating. The present program did not attempt to control the availability of food. This action may have to be considered in future research in order to rehabilitate patients with such an extreme loss of behavior. Such patients appear to be a rarity under current methods of hospital treatment. The long-term hospitalization of these patients (10–20 years) may have extinguished many behavior patterns that existed at the time of initial hospitalization, a loss that has been described elsewhere as disculturation (Goffman, 1961; Sommer and Osmond, 1961). The favorable results obtained with the other patients suggest that adjustive behavior might have been created with these behaviorally debilitated patients if the present type of procedure had been initiated earlier when some behavior patterns were still intact.

The primary function of the tokens was to bridge the delay

between the response and the delivery of the reinforcement. The tokens also provided an objective record of reinforcement delivery and permitted an objective check by the supervising personnel on the appropriate occurrence of the conditioned reinforcement procedure. Also, the attendants did not have to be concerned about voice tone or facial expression as they would if they were delivering a social or verbal type of reinforcement. From the patient's point of view, the token provided an unambiguous indication of approval independent of the attendant's particular mood or whim at the time of delivery. Further, the token procedure eliminated the need to discover what reinforced the patient when the response occurred. It was necessary only to deliver the tokens and allow the patient complete self-expression of her individual preferences at a later time when the token could be exchanged for a wide variety of different reinforcers (Ferster, 1961). Most important, the objectivity of the procedure guaranteed that the patient would be reinforced even for minimally useful responses, thereby freeing the attendants and the staff from the need to define what was "normal" or worthy of being rewarded.

The effectiveness of the reinforcement program was not restricted by any identifiable trait or characteristic of the patients. The primary limitation was the patient who had lost almost all behavior. Age had no discernible limit on effectiveness. Subjects' ages ranged from 24–74 years. Nor was IQ a limitation. Three mental defectives were treated (including one Mongoloid) as well as many high school graduates and one college graduate. No particular type of diagnosis proved to be especially restrictive; the diagnosis included manic-depression, paranoid schizophrenia, and one diagnosis of brain disorder attributable to syphilitic encephalitis. Length of hospitalization of the patients was as little as one year and as long as 37 years.

A fundamental objective of the present research was to develop methods that enable mental patients to function independently and effectively. The degree of success achieved raises practical questions of how this type of treatment program relates to therapeutic objectives, administrative feasibility, cost, etc. A discussion of administrative implications will be presented elsewhere. The present report is primarily concerned with theoretical rationale, methodological principles, and experimental findings.

There is growing evidence of the general applicability of this social reinforcement program. It has been adopted with almost no change by Spradlin (personal communication) at Parsons State Hospital for use with mentally retarded children. Similarly, this program has been adopted with slight changes by L. Krasner (personal communication) at a VA mental hospital for use with male adult psychotics and with more extensive changes by H. Cohen (personal communication) for use with juvenile delinquents at the National Training School for Boys.

REFERENCES

Ayllon, T. Intensive treatment of psychotic behavior by stimulus satiation and food reinforcement. *Behav. Res. Ther.*, 1963, **1**, 53–61.

Ayllon, T. & Azrin, N. H. Reinforcement and instructions with mental patients. *J. exp. Anal. Behav.*, 1964, **7**, 327–331.

Ayllon, T. & Haughton, E. Control of the behavior of schizophrenic patients by food. *J. exp. Anal. Behav.*, 1962, **5**, 343–352.

Ayllon, T. & Michael, J. The psychiatric nurse as a behavioral engineer. *J. exp. Anal. Behav.*, 1959, **2**, 323–334.

Baer, D. M. Laboratory control of thumbsucking by withdrawal and representation of reinforcement. *J. exp. Anal. Behav.*, 1962, **5**, 525–528.

Barrett, B. H. Reduction in rate of multiple tics by free operant conditioning methods. *J. nerv. ment. Dis.*, 1962, **135**, 187–195.

Bijou, S. & Orlando, R. Rapid development of multiple-schedule performances with retarded children. *J. exp. Anal. Behav.*, 1961, **4**, 7–16.

Brady, J. P. and Lind, D. L. Experimental analysis of hysterical blindness. *Arch. gen. Psychiat.*, 1961, **4**, 331–339.

Ellis, N. R., Barnett, C. D., & Pryer, M. W. Operant behavior in mental defectives: Exploratory studies. *J. exp. Anal. Behav.*, 1960, **3**, 63–69.

Ferster, C. B. Positive reinforcement and behavioral deficits of autistic children. *Child Develpm.*, 1961, **32**, 437–456.

Ferster, C. & DeMyer, M. The development of performance in autistic children in an automatically controlled environment. *J. chron. Dis.*, 1961, **13**, 312–345.

Ferster, C. B. & Skinner, B. F. *Schedules of reinforcement.* New York: Appleton-Century-Crofts, 1957.

Flanagan, B., Goldiamond, I., & Azrin, N. H. Operant stuttering: The control of stuttering behavior through response-contingent consequences. *J. exp. Anal. Behav.*, 1958, **1**, 173–177.

Goffman, E. *Asylums.* New York: Doubleday, 1961.

Holland, J. G. Human Vigilance. *Science*, 1958, **128**, 61–67.

Holz, W. C., Azrin, N. H., & Ayllon, T. Elimination of behavior of mental patients by response-produced extinction. *J. exp. Anal. Behav.*, 1963, **6**, 407–412.

Hutchinson, R. R. & Azrin, N. H. Conditioning of mental hospital patients to fixed-ratio schedules of reinforcement. *J. exp. Anal. Behav.*, 1961, **4**, 87–95.

Isaacs, W., Thomas, J., & Goldiamond, I. Application of operant conditioning to reinstate verbal behavior in psychotics. *J. speech hear. Disord.*, 1960, **25**, 8–12.

Kelleher, R. T. Conditioned reinforcement in chimpanzees. *J. comp. physiol. Psychol.*, 1957, **50**, 571–575.

Kelleher, R. T. & Gollub, L. R. A review of positive conditioned reinforcement. *J. exp. Anal. Behav.*, 1962, **5**: Suppl. 543–597.

Lindsley, O. R. Operant conditioning methods applied to research in chronic schizophrenics. *Psychiat. res. Repts.*, 1956, **5**, 118–139.

Long, E. R., Hommack, J. T., May, F., & Campbell, B. J. Intermittent reinforcement of operant behavior in children. *J. exp. Anal. Behav.*, 1958, **1**, 315–339.

Premack, D. Toward empirical behavior laws: I. Positive reinforcement. *Psychol. Rev.*, 1959, **66**, 219–233.

Skinner, B. F. *The behavior of organisms: An experimental analysis.* New York: Appleton-Century-Crofts, Inc., 1938.

Skinner, B. F. The science of learning and the art of teaching. *Harvard Educational Review*, 1954, **24**, 86–97.

Sommer, R. & Osmond, H. Symptoms of institutional care. *Social Problems*, 1961, **8**, 254–262.

Weiner, H. Some effects of response cost upon human operant behavior. *J. exp. Anal. Behav.*, 1962, **5**, 201–208.

Williams, C. The elimination of tantrum behaviors by extinction procedures. *J. abnorm. soc. Psychol.*, 1959, **59**, 269.

Wolf, M., Risley, T., & Mees, H. Application of operant conditioning procedures to the behavior problems of an autistic child. *Behav. Res. Ther.*, 1964, **1**, 305–312.

REFERENCES

Ayllon, T. Intensive treatment of psychotic behavior by stimulus satiation and food reinforcement. *Behav. Res. Ther.*, 1963, **1**, 53–61.

Ayllon, T. & Azrin, N. H. Reinforcement and instructions with mental patients. *J. exp. Anal. Behav.*, 1964, **7**, 327–331.

Ayllon, T. & Azrin, N. H. The measurement and reinforcement of behavior of psychotics. *J. exp. Anal. Behav.*, 1965, **8**, 357–383.

Ayllon, T. & Azrin, N. H. Punishment as a discriminative stimulus and conditioned reinforcer with humans. *J. exp. Anal. Behav.*, 1966, **9**, 411–419.

Ayllon, T. & Azrin, N. H. Reinforcer sampling: A technique for increasing the behavior of mental patients. *J. Appl. Behav. Anal.*, in press.

Ayllon, T. & Haughton, E. Control of the behavior of schizophrenic patients by food. *J. exp. Anal. Behav.*, 1962, **5**, 343–352.

Ayllon, T., Haughton, E., & Hughes, H. B. Interpretation of symptoms: Fact or fiction? *Behav. Res. Ther.*, 1965, **3**, 1–7.

Ayllon, T. & Hughes, H. Behavioral engineering. *Sci. J.*, 1965, **1**, 69–73.

Ayllon, T. & Michael, J. The psychiatric nurse as a behavioral engineer. *J. exp. Anal. Behav.*, 1959, **2**, 323–334.

Azrin, N. H. Some effects of two intermittent schedules of immediate and nonimmediate punishment. *J. of Psychol.*, 1956, **42**, 3–21.

Azrin, N. H. Use of rests as reinforcers. *Psychol. Rep.*, 1960, **7**, 240.

Azrin, N. H. & Holz, W. C. Punishment. In W. K. Honig (Ed.), *Operant behavior: Areas of research and application.* New York: Appleton-Century-Crofts, 1966.

Azrin, N. H., Holz, W. C., & Hake, D. F. Fixed-ratio punishment. *J. exp. Anal. Behav.*, 1963, **6**, 141–148.

Azrin, N. H., Holz, W. C., Ulrich, R., & Goldiamond, I. The control of the content of conversation through reinforcement. *J. exp. Anal. Behav.*, 1961, **4**, 25–30.

Azrin, N. H., Hutchinson, R. R., & Hake, D. F. Extinction-induced aggression. *J. exp. Anal. Behav.*, 1966, **9**, 191–204.

Azrin, N. H. & Lindsley, O. R. The reinforcement of cooperation between children. *J. of abnor. Soc. Psychol.*, 1956, **52**, 100–102.

Azzi, R., Fix, Dora S. R., Keller, F. S. Silva, Rocha, E., & Ignez, M. Exteroceptive control of response under delayed reinforcement. *J. exp. Anal. Behav.*, 1964, **7**, 159–162.

Baer, D. M. Laboratory control of thumbsucking by withdrawal and representation of reinforcement. *J. exp. Anal. Behav.*, 1962, **5**, 525–528.

Baer, D. M., Peterson, R. F., & Sherman, J. A. The development of imitation by reinforcing behavioral similarity to a model. *J. exp. Anal. Behav.*, 1967, **10**, 405–416.

Baer, D. M. & Sherman, J. A. Reinforcement control of generalized imitation in young children. *J. exp. Child Psychol.*, 1964, **1**, 37–49.

Bandura, A. & Walters, R. H. *Social learning and personality development.* New York: Holt, Rinehart and Winston, 1963.

Barrett, B. H. Reduction in rate of multiple tics by free operant conditioning methods. *J. nerv. ment. Dis.*, 1962, **135**, 187–195.

Beach, F. A. & Jordan, L. Sexual exhaustion and recovery in the male rat. *Quart. J. exp. Psychol.*, 1956, **8**, 121–133.

Bijou, S. W. & Orlando, R. Rapid development of multiple-schedule performances with retarded children. *J. exp. Anal. Behav.*, 1961, **4**, 7–16.

Bijou, S. W. & Sturges, P. T. Positive reinforcers for experimental studies with children—consumables and manipulatables. *Child Develpm.*, 1959, **30**, 151–170.

Bolles, R. C. *Theory of motivation.* New York: Harper & Row, 1967.

Bullock, D. H. Repeated conditioning-extinction sessions as a function of the reinforcement schedule. *J. exp. Anal. Behav.*, 1960, **3**, 241–243.

Butler, R. A. The effect of a deprivation of visual incentives on visual exploration motivation in monkeys. *J. comp. physiol. Psychol.*, 1957, **50**, 177–179.

Chapple, E. D. The interaction chronograph: Its evolution and present application. *Personnel*, 1949, **25**, 295–307.

Cofer, C. N. & Appley, M. H. *Motivation: theory and research.* New York: Wiley, 1964.

Collier, G. Some properties of saccharin as a reinforcer. *J. exp. Psychol.*, 1962, **64**, 184–191.

Collier, G. & Willis, F. N. Deprivation and reinforcement. *J. exp. Psychol.*, 1961, **62**, 377–384.

Cowan, P. A. & Walters, R. H. Studies of reinforcement of aggression: I. Effects of scheduling. *Child Develpm.*, 1961, **34**, 543–551.

Cowles, J. T. Food-tokens as incentives for learning by chimpanzees. *Comp. psychol. Monogr.*, 1937, **14**, No. 71.

Daniel, W. J. An experimental note on the O'Kelly-Steckle reactions. *J. comp. Psychol.*, 1943, **35**, 267–268.

Davis, R. C. Modification of the galvanic reflex by daily repetition of a stimulus. *J. exp. Psychol.*, 1934, **17**, 504–535.

Ellison, G. D. Differential salivary conditioning to traces. *J. comp. physiol. Psychol.*, 1964, **146**, 373–380.

Ferster, C. B. Positive reinforcement and behavioral deficits of autistic children. *Child Develpm.*, 1961, **32**, 437–456.

Ferster, C. B. & DeMyer, M. K. A method for the experimental analysis of the behavior of autistic children. *Amer. Journal of Orthopsychiatry*, 1962, **32**, 89–98.

Ferster, C. B. & Skinner, B. F. *Schedules of reinforcement.* New York: Appleton-Century-Crofts, 1957.

Festinger, L. *A theory of cognitive dissonance.* New York: Harper & Row, 1957.

Fuller, P. R. Operant conditioning of a vegetative human organism. *Amer. J. Psychol.*, 1949, **62**, 587–590.

Greenspoon, J. The reinforcing effect of two spoken sounds on the frequency of two responses. *Amer. J. Psychol.*, 1955, **68**, 409–416.

Grice, G. R. The relationship of secondary reinforcement to delayed reward in visual discrimination learning. *J. exp. Psychol.*, 1948, **38**, 1–16.

Guthrie, E. R. *The psychology of learning.* New York: Harper & Row, 1935.

Guttman, N. & Kalish, H. I. Discriminability and stimulus generalization. *J. exp. Psychol.*, 1956, **51**, 79–88.

Hake, D. F. & Laws, D. R. Social facilitation of responses during a stimulus paired with electric shock. *J. exp. Anal. Behav.*, 1967, **10**, 387–392.

Harlow, H. F. The formation of learning sets. *Psychol. Rev.*, 1949, **56**, 51–65.

Herman, R. L. & Azrin, N. H. Punishment by noise in an alternative response situation. *J. exp. Anal. Behav.*, 1964, **7**, 185–188.

Hoffman, H. S. & Fleshler, M. Stimulus aspects of aversive controls: Stimulus generalization of conditioned suppression following discrimination training. *J. exp. Anal. Behav.*, 1964, **7**, 233–239.

Holland, J. G. Technique for the behavioral analysis of human observing. *Science*, 1957, **125**, 348–350.

Holland, J. & Skinner, B. F. *Analysis of behavior.* New York: McGraw-Hill, 1961.

Holz, W. C. & Azrin, N. H. Conditioning human verbal behavior. In W. K. Honig (Ed.), *Operant behavior: Areas of research and application.* New York: Appleton-Century-Crofts, 1966.

Holz, W. C., Azrin, N. H., & Ayllon, T. Elimination of behavior of mental patients by response-produced extinction. *J. exp. Anal. Behav.*, 1963, **6**, 407–412.

Honig, W. K. & Slivka, R. M. Stimulus generalization of the effects of punishment. *J. exp. Anal. Behav.*, 1964, **7**, 21–25.

Hull, C. L. *Principles of behavior.* New York: Appleton-Century-Crofts, 1943.

Hutchinson, R. R. & Azrin, N. H. Conditioning of mental-hospital patients to fixed-ratio schedules of reinforcement. *J. exp. Anal. Behav.*, 1961, **4**, 87–95.

Hutchinson, R. R., Azrin, N. H., & Hake D. F. An automatic method for the study of aggression in squirrel monkeys. *J. exp. Anal. Behav.*, 1966, **9**, 233–237.

Isaacs, W., Thomas, J., & Goldiamond, I. Application of operant conditioning to reinstate verbal behavior in psychotics. *J. Speech and Hearing Disorders*, 1960, **25**, 8–12.

Kelleher, R. T. A comparison of conditioned and food reinforcement on a fixed-ratio schedule in chimpanzees. *Psychol. Newsletter*, 1957, **8**, 88–93.

Kelleher, R. T. & Gollub, L. R. A review of positive conditioned reinforcement. *J. exp. Anal. Behav.*, 1962, **5**, 543–597.

Kimble, G. A. *Hilgard and Marquis' conditioning and learning* (2nd ed.). New York: Appleton-Century-Crofts, 1961.

Krechevsky, I. "Hypothesis" in rats. *Psychol. Rev.*, 1932, **39**, 516–532.

Lane, H. L. Temporal and intensive properties of human vocal responding under a schedule of reinforcement. *J. exp. Anal. Behav.*, 1960, **3**, 183–192.

Lane, H. L. & Shinkman, P. G. Methods and findings in an analysis of a vocal operant. *J. exp. Anal. Behav.*, 1963, **6**, 179–188.

Leavitt, H. J. The effects of certain communication patterns on group performance. *J. abnorm. soc. Psychol.*, 1951, **46**, 38–50.

Lewin, K. *A dynamic theory of personality*. Translated by D. K. Adams & K. E. Zener. New York: McGraw-Hill, 1935.

Lindsley, O. R. Operant conditioning methods applied to research in chronic schizophrenia. *Psychiat. res. Rep.*, 1956, **5**, 118–139.

Lindsley, O. R. Direct measurement and functional definition of vocal hallucinatory symptoms. *J. nerv. ment. Dis.*, 1963, **136**, 293–297.

Long, E. R., Hammack, J. T., May, F., & Campbell, B. J. Intermittent reinforcement of operant behavior in children. *J. exp. Anal. Behav.*, 1958, **1**, 315–339.

Lorenz, K. Z. *Evolution and modification of behavior*. Chicago: University of Chicago Press, 1965.

Lovaas, O. I., Berberich, J. P., Perloff, B. F., & Schaeffer, B. Acquisition of imitative speech by schizophrenic children. *Science*, 1966, **151**, 705–707.

Lovaas, O. I., Frietag, G., Gold, V. J., & Kassorla, I. C. Experimental studies in childhood schizophrenia: Analysis of self-destructive behavior. *J. exp. child Psychol.*, 1965, **2**, 67–84.

Lovaas, O. I., Schaeffer, B., & Simmons, J. Q. Building social behavior in autistic children by use of electric shock. *J. exp. res. in Personal.*, 1965, **1**, 99–109.

McClelland, D. C., Atkinson, J. W., Clark, R. A., & Lowell, E. L. *The achievement motive.* New York: Appleton-Century-Crofts, 1953.

Miller, N. E. Learnable drives and rewards. In S. S. Stevens (Ed.), *Handbook of experimental psychology.* New York: Wiley, 1951.

Miller, N. E. & Dollard, J. *Social learning and imitation.* New Haven: Yale University Press, 1941.

Moreno, J. L. & Jennings, H. H. *Sociometric measurement of social configurations, based on deviation from chance.* New York: Beacon House, 1945.

Mowrer, O. H. Enuresis—a method for its study and treatment. *Amer. J. Orthopsychiat.*, 1938, **8**, 436–459.

Mowrer, O. H. *Learning theory and personality dynamics.* New York: Ronald, 1950.

Myer, J. S. & Baenninger, R. Some effects of punishment and stress on mouse killing by rats. *J. comp. physiol. Psychol.*, 1966, **62**, 292–297.

Nathan P. E., Schneller, P., & Lindsley, O. R. Direct measurement of communication during psychiatric admission interviews. *Behav. res. Ther.*, 1964, **2**, 49–57.

O'Kelly, L. E. & Steckle, L. C. A note on long-enduring emotional responses in the rat. *J. Psychol.*, 1939, **8**, 125–131.

Orlando, R. & Bijou, S. W. Single and multiple schedules of reinforcement in developmentally retarded children. *J. exp. Anal. Behav.*, 1960, **3**, 339–348.

Pavlov, I. P. *Conditioned reflexes.* Translated by G. V. Anrep. New York: Dover, 1927.

Peirce, J. T. & Nuttall, R. Durations of sexual contact in the rat. *J. comp. physiol. Psychol.*, 1961, **54**, 584–587.

Premack, D. Reversibility of the reinforcement relation. *Science*, 1962, **136**, 255–257.

Rheingold, H. L., Gewirtz, J. L., & Ross, H. W. Social conditioning of vocalizations in the infant. *J. comp. physiol. Psychol.*, 1959, **52**, 68–73.

Roethlisberger, F. & Dickson, D. J. *Management and the worker.* Cambridge: Harvard University Press, 1939.

Rogers, C. R. *Client-centered therapy: Its current practice, implication, and theory.* Boston: Houghton Mifflin, 1951.

Rosenthal, R. & Fode, K. L. The effect of experimenter bias on the performance of the albino rat. *Behav. Sci.*, 1963, **8**, 183–189.

Rosenthal, R. & Lawson, R. A longitudinal study of the effects of experimenter bias on the operant learning of laboratory rats. *J. Psychiatric Research*, 1964, **2**, 61–72.

Rubin, H. B. & Azrin, N. H. Temporal patterns of sexual behavior in rabbits as determined by an automatic recording technique. *J. exp. Anal. Behav.*, 1967, **10**, 219–231.

Rydman, L. & Ayllon, T. Nursing routines: Masters or servants? *Ment. Hosp.*, September 1961, 36–37.

Salzinger, K. & Pisoni, S. Reinforcement of affect responses of schizophrenics during the clinical interview. *J. abnorm. soc. Psychol.*, 1958 **57**, 84–90.

Shearn, D., Sprague, R., & Rosenzweig, S. A method for the analysis and control of speech rate. *J. exp. Anal. Behav.*, 1961, **4**, 197–201.

Sidman, M. Stimulus generalization in an avoidance situation. *J. exp. Anal. Behav.*, 1961, **4**, 157–169.

Sidman, M. & Stoddard, L. T. The effectiveness of fading in programming a simultaneous form discrimination for retarded children. *J. exp. Anal. Behav.*, 1967, **10**, 3–15.

Skinner, B. F. *The behavior of organisms: An experimental analysis.* New York: Appleton-Century-Crofts, 1938.

Skinner, B. F. The science of learning and the art of teaching. *Harvard Educational Review*, 1954, **24**, 86–97.

Skinner, B. F. *Verbal behavior.* New York: Appleton-Century-Crofts, 1957.

Sommer, R. & Ayllon, T. Perception and monetary reinforcement: The effects of rewards in the tactual modality. *J. Psychol.*, 1956, **42**, 137–141.

Sparks, B. W. & Niess, O. K. Psychiatric screening of combat pilots. *U.S. Armed Forces Med. J.*, 1956, **7**, 811–816.

Spence, K. W. *Behavior theory and conditioning.* New Haven: Yale University Press, 1956.

Staats, A. W., Staats, C. K., Schutz, R. E., & Wolf, M. The conditioning of textual responses using "extrinsic" reinforcers. *J. exp. Anal. Behav.*, 1962, **5**, 33–40.

Thompson, T. I. & Sturm, T. Classical conditioning of aggressive display in Siamese fighting fish. *J. exp. Anal. Behav.*, 1965, **8**, 397–403.

Thorndike, E. L. *Human learning.* New York: Appleton-Century-Crofts, 1931.

Thorndike, E. L. *The psychology of wants, interests, and attitudes.* New York: Appleton-Century-Crofts, 1935.

Tinklepaugh, O. L. An experimental study of representative factors in monkeys. *J. comp. Psychol.*, 1928, **8**, 197–236.

Ulrich, R. E. & Azrin, N. H. Reflexive fighting in response to aversive stimulation. *J. exp. Anal. Behav.*, 1962, **5**, 511–520.

Verplanck, W. S. The control of the content of conversation: Reinforcement of statements of opinion. *J. abnorm. soc. Psychol.*, 1955, **55**, 668–676.

Watson, J. B. The effect of delayed feeding upon learning. *Psychobiol.*, 1917, **1**, 51–60.

Weiner, H. Some effects of response cost upon human operant behavior. *J. exp. Anal. Behav.*, 1962, **5**, 201–208.

Wolf, M., Risley, T., & Mees, H. Application of operant conditioning procedures to the behavior problems of an autistic child. *Behav. res. Ther.*, 1964, **1**, 305–312.

Wolfe, J. B. Effectiveness of token-rewards for chimpanzees. *Comp. psychol. Monogr.*, 1936, **12**, No. 60.

Wolpe, J. *Psychotherapy by reciprocal inhibition.* Stanford, Calif.: Stanford University Press, 1958.

Index